SHAPES OF SANITY

By the Same Author —

HOW DISTANT THE STARS
- Case Notes and Other Poems.
F. W. Cheshire, Melbourne.

THE MEDICAL INTERVIEW
- A Study of Clinically Significant Interpersonal Reactions.
Charles C Thomas, Publisher, Springfield, Illinois.

HYPNOGRAPHY
- A Study in the Therapeutic Use of Hypnotic Painting.
Charles C Thomas, Publisher, Springfield, Illinois.

THE DOOR OF SERENITY
- A Study in the Use of Spontaneous Painting in Psychotherapy.
Faber and Faber, Publisher, London.

MARRIAGE AND PERSONALITY
- A Psychiatric Study of Interpersonal Reactions for Student and Layman.
Charles C Thomas, Publisher, Springfield, Illinois.

THE INTROVERT
- A Psychiatric Study of the Introvert and His Social Adjustment for Student and Layman.
Charles C Thomas, Publisher, Springfield, Illinois.

A SYSTEM OF MEDICAL HYPNOSIS
- A Study in the Clinical Application of Psychodynamic Theory.
- In preparation.

Shapes Of Sanity

A Study in The
Therapeutic Use of
Modelling in the
Waking and Hypnotic State

By

AINSLIE MEARES

M.D., B.Agr.Sc., D.P.M.

CHARLES C THOMAS • PUBLISHER
Springfield • Illinois • U.S.A.

CHARLES C THOMAS • PUBLISHER

BANNERSTONE HOUSE

301-327 East Lawrence Avenue, Springfield, Illinois, U.S.A.

Published simultaneously in the British Commonwealth of Nations by

BLACKWELL SCIENTIFIC PUBLICATIONS, LTD., OXFORD, ENGLAND

Published simultaneously in Canada by

THE RYERSON PRESS, TORONTO

With THOMAS BOOKS careful attention is given to all details of manu-
facturing and design. It is the Publisher's desire to present books that are
satisfactory as to their physical qualities and artistic possibilities and appropriate for their particular use. THOMAS BOOKS will be true to those laws
of quality that assure a good name and good will.

Printed in the United States of America

PREFACE

This work on the use of modelling in psychiatry comes in response to the call, which is so often made, for shorter methods of psychotherapy. It follows work which has been done, with the same object in view, in regard to the psychodynamic use of painting in both the waking and the hypnotic state. Some of these results have been described in the two books — *The Door of Serenity* and *Hypnography*.

The present volume in no way claims to be a final authoritative account of the use of modelling with psychiatric patients. It is felt that the sum total of our experience in this area of psychiatry is as yet too limited for any such book to be written. There is need for further investigation of the psychodynamics concerned in the plastic, as opposed to the verbal expression of conflict. This work is offered as an account of the author's own experiences in this field. In his hands, the techniques described as plastotherapy and hypnoplasty have significantly shortened the time of psychotherapy. It is believed that others using these methods will achieve similar results.

The approach is primarily descriptive, but where it has seemed possible, some attempt has been made to discuss probable psychodynamic implications of the observed facts.

AINSLIE MEARES

45 Spring Street
Melbourne, Australia

CONTENTS

PART III. MODELLING AS AN ADJUVANT TO PSYCHIATRIC TREATMENT

SHAPES OF SANITY

I

GENERAL INTRODUCTION

THIS WORK is not the result of a research project in the ordinary meaning of the word. It comes from experience with patients actually undergoing treatment.

The initial experience with modelling came in an effort to communicate with a psychotic patient. As this was rewarding, the modelling was continued with other patients, both psychotic and neurotic, both in the waking state and in hypnotic trance. It seemed that useful results were being obtained, particularly in the way of reducing the time of treatment. So it has come about that modelling has been used by the author more and more with patients in psychotherapy.

It gradually became clear that other psychological mechanisms were operating besides those encountered in ordinary psychotherapy. So, in order to investigate these mechanisms, the models for the last six years have been preserved, and the patients' associations to them have all been recorded verbatim. The present study is an attempt to present this material in some kind of organized fashion, so that others may further investigate the method as a possible routine technique to shorten the time of psychotherapy.

It must be made clear from the outset that modelling can be used to help the psychiatric patient in a number of quite different ways. For effective treatment, it is essential that the therapist is clear in his own mind as to which particular way he is going to use the modelling with any particular patient on any particular occasion. Furthermore, any description of various techniques and psychodynamic processes must make it quite clear as to which way the modelling is being used. So, in order to avoid endless circumloquation, two terms have been coined for two important varieties of the therapeutic use of modelling.

"Plastotherapy" is a technique in psychotherapy in which modelling is used to give plastic expression to suppressed or repressed material; it is also used as a means to control the doctor-patient relationship according to the needs of the therapeutic situation. Plastotherapy is thus clearly distinguished from modelling in occupational therapy or recreational therapy. It is essentially a part of psychotherapy, and as such, is a highly dynamic procedure.

"Hypnoplasty" is a technique in hypnoanalysis in which modelling is used to allow the hypnotized patient to give plastic expression to suppressed or repressed material.

There is one further difficulty in the use of words which must be clarified. In this text, modelling is referred to as "Art Therapy" only when the modelling is used in such a way that the aesthetic elements in the process become a significant therapeutic mechanism. This, of course, is a much more restricted use of the term than is often found in present-day psychiatric literature, in which the term Art Therapy may be used to refer to any form of graphic or plastic expression by psychiatric patients.

PART I

PLASTOTHERAPY

Modelling as a Vehicle for
PSYCHOTHERAPY

II

SOME THEORETICAL ASPECTS
OF PLASTOTHERAPY

INTRODUCTION

T HE METHOD OF using modelling as a vehicle for psychotherapy is conveniently described as plastotherapy. It is merely a technique in psychotherapy, and is in no way a form of treatment in its own right. All the principles of ordinary psychotherapy apply to plastotherapy. In one case the conflict is expressed in verbal symbols; in the other it is expressed in plastic symbols. While the same principles still operate, different psychological mechanisms are called into play. So that many defences, which operate against the expression of a conflict in words, are either inapplicable to the expression of the same conflict in modelling, or can function only in a modified way. As a result of this, plastotherapy becomes a useful adjunct to psychotherapy.

The essence of this technique is that the patient models something with clay. His associations to the shape which he has made are then obtained. It is found that the object made with the clay is almost always connected in some way with significant conflicts in the patient's mind. It comes about that, when talking about the model, or giving associations to it, the patient discloses significant material more quickly than is the case in simple verbal psychotherapy. The material obtained in this way is then integrated with the general programme of treatment.

It is found that this technique can be effectively used to reduce the time of psychotherapy. It also has some value in diagnosis, particularly as regards pre-psychotic conditions; and it throws light on some interesting aspects of the process of symbolism.

Perhaps we should commence with a word of warning. The reader who has had no experience of this form of therapy may easily be surprised at the gross disorganization shown in the illustrations of the models made by patients in the waking state. Many of the models are so disordered that they are likely to give the impression that the patient who made the model must have been much more disturbed in the clinical sense, and in his social adjustment, than was actually the case. This disorganization of the models is largely brought about by the way in which plastotherapy disturbs the patient through the disclosure of suppressed and repressed material.

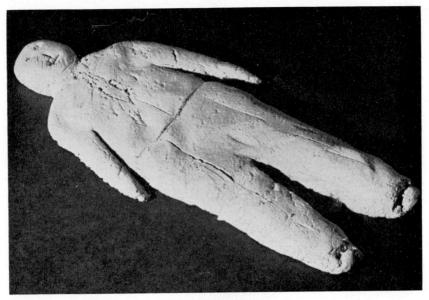

Figure No. 1

This is plastotherapy in its simplest form. A girl makes a model of a human figure. She says it is a corpse. Then she explains that, when she was on holiday recently, a man had died in a nearby room. She abreacts her emotion. She had contemplated becoming a nurse, but this experience had made her feel that she was unsuited to nursing, as she felt that she could never bring herself to look upon death.

This represents the expression of a conflict which was obviously in her clear consciousness. However, the modelling has the effect of bringing her face to face with her problem in a much more direct way than mere verbal expression. In fact, she is brought to look upon the model of a corpse, a symbol of death, which she herself has created. A procedure such as this has a deconditioning effect. The conflict ceases to be so disturbing to the patient. For her, death loses some of its horror.

Figure No. 2

Many of the models give the impression that the person who made them must have been in a very disturbed state of mind when the model was made.

This model was made by a patient suffering from a purely psychosomatic condition. She complained of difficulty in swallowing, which was subsequently proved to be of psychological origin. There was no question of psychosis or incipient psychosis. Her thought, mood and behaviour were perfectly normal, and she had no symptoms other than her dysphagia.

The model rather gives the impression of quite a disturbed state of mind. There are tooth marks, and the whole piece is twisted in the centre. It is the patient's individual symbol of the blocking in her throat.

REDUCTION OF TIME

Plastotherapy aims to reduce the time of psychotherapy.

The evidence indicating that this aim is in fact achieved is presented in the following text, in the illustrations of the models, and in the excerpts from case histories. This material becomes more meaningful if it is considered on a background of some of the theoretical aspects of the processes involved. These concern the initiation, intensification and acceleration of the effective psychodynamic processes of treatment.

The modelling of psychiatric patients is dominated by the action of two opposing forces. On the one hand, there is the psychic energy associated with the repressed or suppressed conflicts, which is continually working to give these conflicts expression. On the other hand, there are the patient's conscious and unconscious defenses which work to save him the hurt which the expression of these conflicts would bring to him.

The models made in plastotherapy, and the patient's associations to them, give clear evidence of the dynamic way in which repressed or suppressed conflicts seek expression. It is not just a question of the patient discussing something which is worrying to him. This view would credit the ego with a degree of power and control which in these circumstances it does not possess. Experience with modelling would confirm the idea that the repressed or suppressed conflicts achieve psychic energy of their own; and that this energy works for the expression of the conflict, independent of the integrated control of the individual's personality. Evidence of the operation of such forces is seen in those cases where the patient has deliberately gone out of his way to avoid expressing some conflict, yet he finishes by making a model which unconsciously discloses the very idea which he had deliberately set out to conceal.

The reduction in time of treatment is largely achieved through the more rapid ventilation of the significant conflicts. The patient may be aware of conflicts, but he still may not express them. He evades them; he tries to deny them even to himself. The shame, the humiliation is such that he will not, perhaps cannot, bring himself to face it. In formal psychoanalytically orientated psychotherapy,

11

such material is eventually brought out, but it may be a long and costly business. On the other hand, such a patient may express himself in plastotherapy with surprising ease and directness. The patient wants to express himself; at the same time, he will go to great lengths to avoid expressing himself. In his modelling, he is not using words, and it would seem that he does not feel that he is disclosing himself. In this way, his defences are circumvented. He expresses the idea in the model; but without his associations, the real meaning is usually still not clear to the therapist. In reality, he has expressed himself, but as yet he has not fully communicated the idea. One would expect such a patient to halt at this point; but in actual practice, this is not so. The patient looks at the model. In it he sees the expression of the ideas which are so disturbing to him. The fact that he sees them expressed in this way seems to lead him on to express the ideas in words. It is only at this stage that the full meaning becomes clear to the therapist.

Figure No. 3

This model demonstrates the way in which plastotherapy allows the direct expression of ideas which the patient would not contemplate expressing verbally.

The patient is an introvert young woman of twenty-eight years. She seeks help because she panics when any boyfriend comes near to the point of asking her to marry him. She is a rather prudish girl, and is so inhibited that any discussion of her sexual problems is a matter of utmost difficulty for her. On the second visit, she is given the clay. She promptly makes a phallus. It seems almost incredible that a girl who is neither psychotic nor pre-psychotic actually makes the physical likeness of something which she is quite unable to bring herself to mention in words.

> *I was going to make a baby.*
> *Could not get John out of my mind.*
> *John's sex organ.*
> *Could not get it out of my mind.*
> *Was going to change it, then thought I should leave it.*

The effect of this on the patient is twofold. In the first place, the awful thought is ventilated; and secondly, she is really confronted with it. She is literally brought face to face with the idea which she was in fact unable even to whisper. She thus comes to tolerate the idea, so that it ceases to have the same disturbing effect on her.

13

Figure No. 4

A young woman suffers from depression and anxiety symptoms. She makes this shape.

It seems to be connected (with her symptoms)
Woman's uterus.

She has recently learned that her husband is sterile. The empty womb thus gives pathetic expression to the psychogenesis of her illness.

THE INITIATION OF PSYCHODYNAMIC PROCESSES

In formal psychotherapy, there is often a good deal of time spent in getting the therapeutic process started. Some patients, driven by their inner disquiet, will ventilate suppressed conflicts without much difficulty; but there are many others who from shame, or fear of hurt to their self esteem, withhold such material. The traditional psychoanalytical attitude is one of patience and waiting, in the belief that relevant conflicts will be disclosed all in good time. In ordinary formal psychotherapy, many hours may be spent in verbal skirmishing between patient and therapist. It is essentially a matter of communication by words. The patient has years of experience in the use of psychological defences in this type of situation. These are the very circumstances in which he is most apt at defending himself. In fact, we meet him at his strongest point. Hence much time is needed to break down these defences. In plastotherapy, however, the situation is different. The patient is confronted with an unfamiliar situation; ideas are expressed in plastic as well as in verbal symbols; and the greater ease of non-verbal communication allows more effective manipulation of the interpersonal relationship between patient and therapist.

The actual mechanisms of plastotherapy which bring about the more rapid disclosure of the relevant conflicts differ according to whether the significant material is really repressed or is consciously withheld.

In the latter case, the use of clay modelling facilitates the ventilation of suppressed material in a number of ways. In the formal interview, the patient may be relatively secure. His normal defensive facade protects him. He is comfortable in himself. He is in charge of himself, and of what he says. He answers the therapist's probing truthfully, although perhaps evasively. Everyone who has experience in psychotherapy is only too familiar with this state of affairs. The patient is now given the clay. This places him in an unfamiliar situation. His everyday attitudes, mannerisms, and behaviour patterns, by which he habitually defends himself, are less effective in this new situation in which he now finds himself. As a result, there is an immediate increase in the patient's subjective experience of anxiety. The therapist is now in the position of being able to use this mobilized anxiety in therapy. He can control the anxiety in such a way as to aid the ventilation of the suppressed material.

When the significant conflict is unconsciously repressed, or more firmly denied and withheld, plastotherapy may initiate the ventilation of the material through the actual model itself, or more commonly, through the patient's associations to the model. In the formal interview, or in ordinary free-association, the patient may produce almost endless trains of irrelevant ideas. This type of defence comes so easily that, once it is established, much time may be needed to break it down. But it is found that the model is usually related in some way to the significant conflict. The result is that the patient's associations to the model lead more quickly to the expression of the repressed material than do free associations, or the ordinary techniques of interviewing.

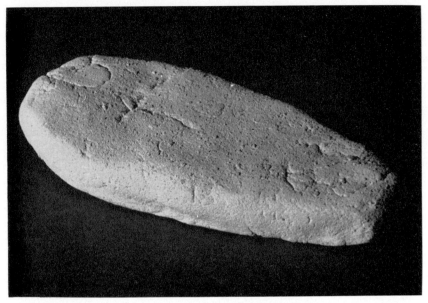

Figure No. 5

A schizoid youth was brought to consultation with the complaint that he was unable to get on with his family, and unable to hold a job.

In two formal interviews, he was vague and evasive. He defended himself by inconsequential generalizations, and when brought to face specific problems, he would deny any conflict whatsoever.

He was then given the clay, and asked to model. He made a coffin. His associations give evidence of the way in which the psychotherapeutic process was initiated.

> *Don't know what it is.*
> (Patient rather distressed)
> *Don't know what it signifies, or anything.*
> Therapist: *What does it look like?*
> *Shape of some description.*
> *Don't know what it resembles.*
> *The only thing I can think of is peace of mind.*
> *Settling down doing something*
> *Living a normal life.*
> *Fulfill one's ambitions.*
> (Pause)

17

Therapist: *"What does it look like?*
Looks like a coffin.
Could be going to kill myself.
(Patient is quite distressed.)

At first the patient defends himself by denial. This defence is ineffective because he has made the coffin which is there before him. It is seen how his associations quickly lead to the significant idea.

The patient was quite disturbed by this disclosure, and reacted by being very resistive to modelling on the next two or three occasions.

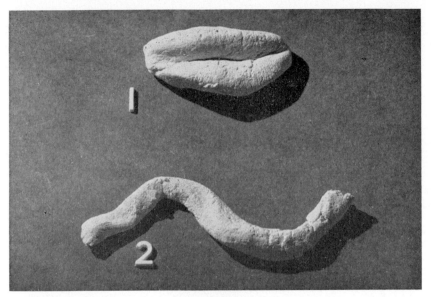

Figure No. 6

The therapeutically effective psychodynamic processes may be started off by the patient shaping symbols which have no meaning to him at the time he is making them.

A woman patient was suffering from anxiety symptoms as a result of domestic conflict. The two models are typically female and male symbols respectively. However, her associations make it clear that she was not aware of the sexual significance of the shapes when she was doing the modelling.

1. *Did not look at what I was doing — just relaxed and let my fingers do anything.*
   Was looking out of the window.
   Would not have any idea.
   A sick banana.
   Something split in half.
   Not entirely in half.
   (Pause)
   Suggestion of a human body.
   (Pause)
   Two human bodies side by side.
   (Pause)

Quite peaceful.
(Pause)
Great sea slug.
(Pause)
Two lips for that matter.
(Pause)
Somehow sexual look.
Like works of art.
Expresses something; like a woman's anatomy.

2. *Looks like a tired snake to me.*
   Looks pretty harmless.
   Not much to fear.
   All worn out.
   Quite safe for some time.
   (Pause)
   Earth worm; slug; meandering river; slow tempo.
   Something that has lost its sting.
   Meanders along, lazy old fellow.
   Therapist: *Is it connected in any way with the last one?*
   Maybe — very sad if it was (laughs)
   *Said other one suggested a woman's anatomy; if this suggests a
      man's anatomy, a very tired exhausted male.*

Many of the phrases used to describe the male symbol are practically
identical with expressions which she had previously used in reference to
her husband.

INTENSIFICATION OF PSYCHODYNAMICS

In plastotherapy, the therapeutic process is not only more quickly initiated, but it is also intensified. This intensification is seen to take place in at least three distinct areas of psychic activity — in the patient's emotional relationship with the therapist, in abreaction, and in insight.

In formal psychotherapy, there are variations in the emotional relationship between patient and therapist; but in general, these variations are gradual. When the patient is modelling, changes in his relationship with the therapist occur much more abruptly. He reacts against the therapist when he is frustrated in the modelling; then when the therapist moves closer to him emotionally, there is an equally abrupt change towards a positive relationship.

The experience of these rapid changes in relationship in itself tends to lead the patient to the more ready expression of his emotion in abreaction. It may be directed against the therapist, who has disturbed his emotional calm by frustrating him in asking him to model, or who has humiliated him by causing him to express ideas which he had not intended to disclose. More often, the abreaction concerns some deepseated conflict, his hate of his father, or his guilt and shame at things which he has done. In plastotherapy there is a strong tendency to the emotional disturbance of the patient. Real guilt and rage reactions frequently occur in a way which is not common in ordinary psychotherapy.

The intensification of the psychodynamic processes also applies to the way in which insight comes to the patient. In ordinary psychotherapy, precautions are always taken lest insight come too suddenly, or when the patient is insufficiently prepared for it. With the relatively slow processes of ordinary psychotherapy, this is usually easy enough. However, with plastotherapy and the acceleration and intensification of the processes, insight may come very suddenly. Besides the suddenness, there is often an intensification of the process itself, so that the patient suddenly gains an insight with great clarity, as distinct from the gradual clearing of the mists in orthodox treatment. It would seem that this intensification of the process of insight is intimately connected with the permanence

21

of the plastic symbol as compared with the transience of the spoken word.

The psychodynamic processes are not only more quickly initiated and intensified, but they are also accelerated. There is often a great change. Things that were happening so slowly in psychotherapy now take place with a rapidity which may be quite alarming. Quick changes in relationship, sudden bursts of abreaction, and phases of rapid insight, all lead to a general acceleration of the the whole therapeutic process.

The corresponding disadvantage of the speeded-up process is the greater likelihood of acute anxiety reactions. But compared with formal psychotherapy, the therapist is better equipped to deal with the situation, as he has far better means of non-verbal communication, particularly as regards the meaning of his behaviour. When tension is seen to be mounting, he moves closer to the patient emotionally, and so reduces the anxiety.

Figure No. 7

A patient with a severe chronic anxiety state had considerable psychological insight as a result of previous treatment. In psychotherapy he discussed his problems in a disinterested, offhand manner. When introduced to modelling, he spoke about the same conflicts, but they seemed more real to him, so that he now participated in the psychotherapy, instead of maintaining the spectator role as formerly.

> *Restless while I was doing it; wanted to get it over.*
> *Can't see anything in it.*
> *Was just fiddling round with it until a pleasing shape came.*
> *Thinking about bananas.*
> *It's like a shoe.*
> (Pause, sighs)
> *Volcano, senseless, sort of stop thinking.*
> *Can't see anything.*
> *Feel blocked.*
> *Started doing it with two hands at once.*
> *Can't think.*
> *Feeling of impatience.*
> *Bread roll.* (Sighs)
> *Always think of sexual organs.*
> *Frightened to shape it.*
> (Pause)
> *Too restless, too impatient.*
> *Think about sex because I know you are looking for it.*
> *Then the whole shape dissolves, break it up fiddling with two hands, something sticking up like.*
> *Sexual thoughts always in mind unless concentrating on something else.*

EMOTIONAL REACTION

There is a very great contrast in the patient's emotional reaction during modelling in plastotherapy, as compared with his reaction during modelling in occupational or recreational therapy. In these latter, the patient's emotions are in no way disturbed. It is an easy, comfortable, pleasurable experience for him. It is far removed from anxiety and guilt; it is an experience which he enjoys, and he looks forward to the next session.

With plastotherapy, the situation is quite different. From the very beginning, it is an anxiety-producing procedure. The uncertainty of the first session often makes the patient tense and uncomfortable. Even when the first session has gone off quite smoothly, it is common for the patient to say that he would prefer not to use the clay next time. This resistance is a problem which must be faced on the next visit, and it clearly shows that the patient often thinks of the next session with considerable apprehension. Sessions which are productive of psychopathological material are emotionally disturbing, and in an effort to save himself further disquiet, the patient is likely to resist further treatment. The same resistance is often shown when the session has not been productive. The failure to make something therapeutically useful often produces as much anxiety in the patient as does the actual projection of psychopathological material. Similarly with the associations, if they are of traumatic quality, the patient's anxiety is liberated. On the other hand, if the patient is inhibited and blocks with the associations, he is equally anxious and uncomfortable. From these considerations, it is clear that the dynamic nature of plastotherapy evokes emotions in the patient, which are quite different from the case when modelling is used merely as an occupational or recreational adjuvant to psychiatric treatment.

Figure No. 8

A male patient who had deep-seated feelings of inadequacy was compensating in active Don Juanism. Formal psychotherapy was slow and unproductive. However, when he was given some clay he made these breasts. He was emotionally disturbed by what he had made, and the whole psychotherapeutic process was accelerated.

> *Breasts, pleasant.*
> *Just made them.*
> *Made one to start with.*
> *Started to make a column like a statue of Jesus.*
> *Wanted to be happy in front of the column.*
> *Himself leaning.*
> *Wanted my arms outstretched lifting people everywhere.*
> *Could not do it in clay, so made a couple of breasts.*
> *Thought of my mother, maybe she loved me pretty well.*
> (Pause)
> *Feel near tears.* (Eyes moist)
> *Sacrifice wonderful, don't want to cry.*
> *Old man died. Not much money, sent us to good school.*
>   (weeps)

25

Did think she loved us as well as she knew how.
(Pause)
Wanted you to put me in a deep trance.
Disturbing — so right-feeling here, and then go and indulge in bad talk at the gym.
Like not to do that.

The patient's associations show how the whole process has been accelerated. In ordinary psychotherapy, he had been formal and psychologically unproductive.

III

THE TECHNIQUE OF PLASTOTHERAPY

THE MATERIALS

Any form of modelling material may be used. A slow setting plaster of Paris mixture has the advantage that the models set hard and can be kept for future reference. This has been of real value in this project. So little is known about the psychodynamics of the plastic expression of conflicts that it has often happened that the significance of a model has become apparent only some time after it was made. Plasticine models very easily become distorted, and so may lose their exact meaning. The models illustrated in the text were all made with a proprietary mixture of plaster of Paris which contains powdered asbestos to prolong the setting time. Its only disadvantages are that it is rather expensive, and the asbestos makes the mixture sticky, so that it tends to adhere to the fingers. The few patients who had previous experience of modelling usually complained that it did not handle so well as ordinary potter's clay.

Even in the most suitable cases, no attempt is made at plastotherapy for the first two or three sessions with the patient. This delay is necessary for two reasons. In the first place, rapport is an essential pre-requisite to plastotherapy; so sufficient time must be allowed to establish a satisfactory relationship with the patient, or the suggestion of modelling will be quickly rejected. Secondly, a foreknowledge of the patient's likely reactions may make all the difference between success and failure. In addition to this, it is only after a certain amount of verbal exploration with the patient that the need or advantage of plastotherapy becomes evident.

EXPLANATION TO THE PATIENT

The success of any form of psychological treatment very often depends to a great degree on the way in which the proposition is put to the patient in the first place. This is particularly so with plastotherapy. An apparently trivial error on the part of the therapist can have an effect out of all proportion to its factual magnitude. The inapt use of a phrase, a clumsy expression, the show of a little anxiety, or a display of the slightest impatience may provoke the patient to reject the whole idea. It is well to remember that immediate rejection, before the patient has ever touched the clay with his fingers, is easily the most common cause of failure. In fact, once the patient gets as far as to take the clay in his hands, some degree of success is almost assured.

There is no set formula which can be used. The matter must be explained to each individual patient according to his particular personality structure. This is the most difficult part in the whole procedure of the therapeutic use of modelling. As a general rule, the less said the better. Lengthy explanations are likely to arouse the patient's anxiety, and alert his defences. He feels that something which requires lengthy explanation must be difficult, or he feels that there is some trap about it, and he puts himself on guard in order not to fall into it. As the explanation proceeds, he becomes more and more apprehensive. This process is often augmented by another mechanism. The therapist is very aware of the importance of these few moments. Rejection will not only put a stop to the use of plastotherapy, but it will of necessity put back the patient's whole treatment. In these circumstances, the therapist himself is likely to be anxious. This in turn may provoke him into making an unnecessarily long explanation in order to try to ease the difficult situation. The patient may become aware of the therapist's anxiety, or the lengthy explanation may unconsciously put him on his guard. In either case his apprehension is increased, and the likelihood of an easy transition to modelling is lessened.

As with so many techniques in psychotherapy, the idea of expressive modelling will often be accepted more easily if it is first offered obliquely, by non-verbal means. The statement of what is expected then follows in words, rather as an afterthought, when the patient's initial surprise at the proposition has passed off. The idea has already gained some degree of acceptance before the patient is given the chance to reject it. If it has not been expressed in words, there is really nothing for him to reject.

The successful use of this manoeuvre requires real ease and sureness on the part of the therapist. Rapport is essential. The modelling materials can be brought in without comment, and placed on the table by the patient. The therapist's manner expresses the idea to the patient that this is just a part of the ordinary everyday business of psychiatric consultation. There is a complete naturalness about it. The therapist can pick up some of the clay, and mould it with his fingers in an absent-minded kind of way. There is no hurry to rush into verbal explanations. The first comments can refer to some quite inconsequential matter which the patient cannot possibly reject. *"The clay is a little hard. It needs a drop more water."* A little water is added, and the therapist continues absorbed in moulding the clay. The patient's interest can be directed to it. *"You see it is just right now. It goes into all sorts of shapes, any shape you like."* Even at this stage, unless one is very sure of the patient, it is wisest not to put a direct request such as: *"I want you to model the clay into something."* The direct request can easily provoke a direct refusal.

The patient may be offered the clay, but there is still no suggestion that he should model it in any way. An approach such as this can hardly be rejected. *"We use a lot of this. It is fascinating stuff, this clay. Feel it."* A piece of clay is put into the patient's hand. The therapist continues to mould some of the clay. This is a non-verbal invitation to the patient to do likewise. He starts to mould the clay. The therapist all the time maintains a leisurely ease. Then with suitable patients, one can sometimes proceed like this. *"You know there are all sorts of different ways in which we can express ourselves. We can use words, but we also express ourselves by our gestures, by the expression on the face, or by the way we do things. There are all sorts of ways of expressing ourselves. You can express yourself by what you make. You can*

29

*express yourself in modelling. That is why we use this clay. You
see it goes into shapes in your fingers. You make things. Remember this is not art. It is just a way of expressing yourself. It is a way
of expressing yourself without any words. It does not matter what
it is that comes. It is quite easy. You just let yourself go, and you
find you are making something. I will leave you for a little while.
Then I will come back and see what you have made."*

The principles in the approach are that the therapist remains
non-directive; there is a transition from couching the ideas in the
first person, to the second person; and it is made clear that the
process is one of expression and not of art.

A few half-hearted protests at being left are an expression of
transitory anxiety, and should not prompt the therapist to stay with
the patient. *"You will find it quite easy. I will be back in a little
while."*

PROCEDURE WITH DIFFERENT TYPES OF PERSONALITY

It is unlikely that everything will go completely smoothly. The
majority of patients will use defences of one kind or another. The
subsequent moves by the therapist are determined by the nature of
the patient's defences, and his personality structure. The intellectually dull patient may be on guard because he looks upon
modelling as "arty stuff". With him the idea of expression must be
fully explained and emphasized. The sophisticated patient may be
on guard for completely opposite reasons. He realizes that it is
likely that he will disclose himself in the modelling. He is guarded
because he knows that he may reveal himself more than he intends.
With the spoken word, he knows what he is saying; but when he
expresses himself in modelling, he feels that he is giving himself
away to an unknown extent. It makes him guarded. This process
has been noticed in sophisticated homosexuals who have not
ventilated their conflicts, and also in latent homosexuals who have
some vague awareness of their bisexuality. The latent homosexual
who is quite unaware of his condition typically expresses it in his
modelling. The guarded sophisticated patient often presents difficulties. If rapport is good, as it should be, he can be taken into our

confidence. *"This is a means of expression. It is a means of expression just like words. Like words, it is a means of communication. It is a communication to me. Nobody else will know anything about it. It is merely a way of expressing yourself to me."* If the patient we are dealing with is in fact a latent homosexual, this approach is often successful, as it uses his condition to form a close relationship with the male therapist. This is used to the patient's advantage as a means to circumvent his defences.

Other, guarded, sophisticated patients may be too remote for this technique. They avoid a close emotional relationship. With them, another approach must be used. The idea of complete ease and relaxation can be emphasised. *"You let yourself relax completely. You have the clay in your hands. You think of nothing in particular. You are in a kind of reverie, a daydream, and your fingers just fiddle with clay. They make something. You take no notice of what it is. They make it in a daydream. It is easy; you just let yourself go."* This idea of reverie or abstraction often appeals to the sophisticated patient, and so again, a trait in the patient's personality is used to lead him on to expressing himself in modelling.

With other patients, dissociation can be used to advantage. This may be particularly successful with hysteroid persons. *"You just sit there. Your fingers take the clay. They mould it into something. It does not matter what it is. They do it. You really do not take any notice of what your fingers are doing."*

Anxious patients are liable to panic at the prospect of something new. They need a little reassurance. This comes mainly by way of the calm, leisurely and unhurried manner of the therapist. His friendliness is expressed in his behaviour, rather than in words. The patient gains the feeling, *"He will not do anything to hurt me. He will not upset me. I am secure when I am with him."* To achieve this, the therapist stays near the patient. He too can play with the clay. There is very little place for verbal reassurance, but the fact that the patient feels that the therapist is near him gives him security. Then when the therapist is sure that the more acute manifestations of the patient's anxiety are passing, he can withdraw

31

a little, and perhaps remain seated in the room, remote from the patient. As the patient starts to use the clay, and there is no further surge of acute anxiety, he can be left in the room to model by himself. Thus the therapist is continually using his behaviour to communicate with the patient. By these means, one can deal effectively with the initial panic of the anxious patient when he is first confronted with modelling. The anxiety subsides; but the therapist must be on the watch for further exacerbations of anxiety, which are likely to occur as the patient finds himself expressing psychologically significant material in the models.

With the intelligent patient, one can often use a different approach. It may be possible to take him openly into our confidence. He can be reminded that nervous illness may be caused by the activity of repressed conflicts of which the patient is not aware; and that various techniques such as truth drugs, psychoanalysis and hypnosis are used to bring these unconscious conflicts to light. *"In each case it is a matter of getting round the psychological mechanisms which are preventing the expression of the conflict. Your getting well depends on the ventilation of these things which are deep in your mind. There is another way of bringing them into the open. It is by modelling with clay. You just relax, and you let your hands mould the clay. Then you find that your hands are making some shape, or the likeness of some object which is connected in some way with these things in your mind. By this means you can be helped to give expression to these conflicts, and so helped to get well."*

However, when the patient is less intelligent, such an approach may not be practicable. If the patient is not too insecure or too anxious, a direct approach may be possible. *"We use this clay modelling in treatment now. Just make anything at all that comes into your mind. Anything at all, it does not matter what it is."* The patient may have heard of occupational therapy, and in some sort of vague way, thinks that this is the treatment. If he makes some inconsequential object such as a vase or an ash-tray, he is merely reassured, and he is later brought around to making models of psychological significance.

As a rule, the patient takes the clay and starts moulding it into some definite shape. He may need a little encouragement, but in general the therapist remains as passive as possible, and always non-directive. The patient who is experiencing difficulty may be given a few hints as to what is expected of him. *"You express yourself in the modelling. Your fingers make something that is connected with thoughts deep in your mind. You just let yourself go and it comes. It is easy."* It may be necessary to give the patient a clue in this way as to what is wanted, but at the same time he is never given any suggestion as to what kind of ideas to express.

REJECTION OF MODELLING

It must be remembered that in plastotherapy the therapist openly exposes himself to failure by rejection in a way which does not obtain in ordinary psychotherapy. In almost all procedures in psychotherapy, the therapist clearly retains control of the situation. An analytical interpretation is open to rejection by the patient. If it is rejected, it is a manifestation of resistance, and there is no great worry. But in asking the patient to do something unusual, such as modelling, the therapist gives the patient an easy opportunity to reject the whole procedure. The only technique in psychotherapy which carries a comparable risk in this respect is hypnosis. In the first place, it means that the therapist must be really secure in himself. His psychological adjustment must be such that he does not experience anxiety, rather than that he merely conceals it. This absence of anxiety is all the more difficult of attainment when it has to be coupled with an extreme sensitivity to the changes of feeling in the patient. An awareness that one is laying oneself open to rejection is likely to produce anxiety. The slightest trace of uneasiness is observed by the patient, and he is more than ever likely to reject the idea. In the second place, it means that the ground work must be well done. The preparations for putting the idea to the patient must be complete. It must be done calmly and leisurely, so that one step follows the next easily and inevitably.

Suspicious, paranoid types of persons are particularly guarded at the prospect of something new. When confronted with the proposition of modelling, they tend to feel that something which they do not understand is being put over them. In consequence, they are likely to reject the idea, even before it has been fully explained to them. As a general rule, such patients are not very suitable for plastotherapy.

Similarly, people who are very rigid in their thinking and in their pattern of life lack the adaptability necessary for this form of treatment, and will probably refuse it before giving it a trial.

Another group of patients who are likely to reject the idea are the insecure. For these people, any new experience increases their basic feeling of insecurity, and they are likely to reject the idea of modelling on account of the anxiety it would produce. However, it is worthwhile persevering with these insecure patients, as many of them can be helped with plastotherapy. The most important factor in their management is that they should be seen on two or three occasions before modelling is suggested. This allows of satisfactory rapport. Then, with the emotional support which comes of rapport, the new experience is less productive of anxiety.

As a general rule, if it suddenly comes to the therapist that he is in danger of rejection, he must make some direct move to forestall the patient. Under these circumstances, there is a tendency for the therapist to make some indirect display of authority. *This will help you to get well. I cannot help you if you do not cooperate.* This type of thinly concealed authority only alienates the patient, and can have little scope in treatment based on insight. It seems better that the therapist should use the opposite approach, and try to move closer to the patient emotionally. This may be difficult if the move is left too late. If the patient is already threatening rejection, his hostility to the therapist may already be aroused, and the move to a closer relationship must be made with due circumspection. The therapist can make things easier by modifying his demands, and suggesting that the patient make anything that comes into his head, rather than something to express his problems. It is much better to conclude the session with the patient having modelled some object of no psychological significance, rather than that he should reject the whole proposition. In the former case, the door is still open for treatment on a subsequent occasion.

PRECAUTIONS

From the start, there are certain precautions which should be taken. Plastotherapy is a dynamic procedure, and acute anxiety reactions are liable to occur in a way which does not ordinarily obtain in waking psychotherapy.

Once the patient has accepted the idea of modelling, and sets about moulding the clay with his hands, the presence of the therapist may be disturbing to him. He feels that the therapist is waiting for him to do something. He tries to hurry; he becomes anxious. He tends to turn to the therapist for advice. By talking to the therapist, the patient gains time, and postpones the expression of ideas which will be painful to him. Superficial conversation with the therapist destroys the state of reverie, and so hinders the expression of unconscious material. As a result of these factors, it has been the custom to leave the patient to do the modelling in a room by himself. On occasion, the patient has become extremely disturbed by the ideas which he has found himself expressing in the clay. Accordingly, it has been thought wise to slip into the room from time to time, so as to make sure that the patient is not on the verge of an acute attack of anxiety. If the patient is occupied with the clay, he is left again with the least possible disturbance. *"Good, I will come back in a quarter of an hour."* If the patient seems to be likely to reject the clay, he can be given some word of encouragement, or if difficulty in getting started has made him anxious, he can be reassured.

A watch must be kept for any likelihood of the sudden expression of traumatic material. This can sometimes be anticipated from our knowledge of the patient prior to the modelling. It is most likely to occur in the tense and anxious, in latent homosexuals, in unstable pre-psychotic patients. During the modelling, any very intense preoccupation with the clay, or outward signs of anxiety such as tremor of the hands or facial twitching, are an indication to move closer to the patient emotionally, and so give him support in his crisis. The presence of the therapist, with whom he has rapport,

35

makes all the difference in these moments of very acute anxiety.

On the other hand, a certain amount of care must be exercised in alleviating the patient's anxiety in this way. The danger is that the too early or too complete alleviation of anxiety may so reduce the motivation for the expression of the conflict that the modelling ceases. The patient is reassured. He is calm and comfortable again; and he prefers to abandon the clay which was the cause of his temporary disquiet.

IV
THE MODELS
GENERAL CHARACTERISTICS

W HEN ONE COMES TO CONSIDER the actual models themselves, the outstanding feature is their great diversity of form. Some are relatively well executed. Others are poorly made, misshapen, amateurish, or childish. Some are easily recognized as the likeness of a familiar object, a man, a house, a tree. In others can be seen the purposefully distorted likeness of common things. Still other models are carefully shaped, but they are the fantastic symbols of the disturbed mind, the likeness of nothing on earth.

In a general way, we can reduce this apparent chaos into two groups of models — psychoneurotic and psychotic. Each has characteristic features; but it must be made clear from the outset that from mere inspection of the model it is not always possible to determine whether it has been made by a psychoneurotic or a psychotic patient.

One of the outstanding features of models made in this type of therapy is that they almost always have some specific relevance. A human figure is not just a man; it is the father, the husband or the lover. A tree or a house does not represent the object in some vague, generic sense. It is definite and specific. It is the tree or house where some particular incident took place. At first, the patient usually defends himself by denying the specific nature of the object he has made, and its real meaning becomes clear only from the patient's associations to it.

Occasionally it would seem that the process is rather different. It may be that the patient has in fact made some non-specific object, but when he comes to look at it and talk about it, then it assumes a secondary specificity. Experience, however, suggests that this latter process occurs much less frequently than the former.

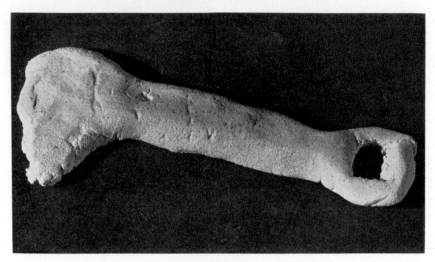

Figure No. 9

A woman with domestic conflicts makes an axe.

Axe

Doesn't look very like one.

Axe my husband used when he broke down the room.

Keeps coming to my mind.

Axe and all the blood.

Wonder where the clothes went.

My nightdress torn and covered with blood disappeared.

This is an example of uncomplicated plastotherapy. The patient makes a likeness of some object which is directly connected with some significant conflict. She has made the axe with the wrong type of handle. It is the handle of a spade, not an axe. It is common for the patient to become very upset while expressing a conflict in modelling, much more upset than in an ordinary interview. Her failure to make the axe with a proper handle is a reflection of her disturbed state of mind while she was doing the modelling.

Figure No. 10

A reality problem may have a deeper psychological significance.

An introvert youth could hardly discuss his problems at all in an ordinary interview. He makes a bottle.

Supposed to represent a bottle.

Mother drinks too much.

Different person when she has been drinking.

Things she says and does.

Just can't condone it.

Don't mind anybody having a drink but the way she goes —
Been like it for years.

Since I was a kid I suppose.

Rows with my father and then takes it out on me.

The bottle thus stands for his mother's alcoholism. However, it has a much greater significance than this because of its indirect relationship with his feelings towards his mother. His ambivalence finds open expression in his associations to the model.

Figure No. 11

The models are almost always specific.

A seventeen-year old girl who was being treated for a convulsive hysterical tic made this figure. At first she denies its specificity.

Made a figure because it is the easiest to make.

(Then follows a long pause in which the patient becomes preoccupied, and fiddles aimlessly with the model.)

Probably a man — because — I don't know — because I am usually with men — where I work there are only four girls and about eighty men.

Don't know anything else.

(Then follows some inconsequential conversation)

Therapist: *Who do you think it might be?*

40

Could be John, I suppose.

(Long pause, in which patient keeps patting the figure with a modelling tool.)

Can't say any more.

Don't know any more.

(After another pause, she says)

I suppose it is him, he has shoulders like that.

This sequence of events is very common in plastotherapy. The patient at first denies the specific identity of the model, but very soon discloses it in the associations.

THE MEANING OF THE MODELS

The model may represent some superficial everyday problem. Business problems, practical difficulties in the home or with the management of the children come into this category. Models referring to reality conflicts of this nature are usually made at one of the early sessions of plastotherapy; then, as the patient becomes more accustomed to the procedure, deeper and more significant conflicts are given expression.

As treatment proceeds, and the deeper conflicts become resolved, and the patient is regaining better mental health, there is often a return to the making of models which refer to the practical difficulties of everyday life. This has been taken as a sign of the patient's better psychic integration, and a probable indication for the termination of treatment.

When the model refers to some superficial conflict, or to some problem of reality, it often happens that the matter represented in the model also has some deeper significance to the patient than is at first apparent. For instance, a slight business setback is a reality problem which might seem of no very great importance, but to a man whose main criterion of success in life is success in business, then the situation assumes a much greater significance.

When expression is given to deeper problems, sexual conflicts frequently become mirrored in the models. About one half of the models produced in this form of treatment have a direct sexual significance. This may or may not be obvious from the appearance of the model. The directness with which a sexual conflict is expressed in the modelling depends on the activity of the patient's defences. This is determined by a number of factors. For instance, the psychotic patient will often express a sexual conflict by modelling the genitalia without any attempt at distortion or symbolism. The psychoneurotic usually expresses a similar idea through the medium of conventional symbols, in which the basic sexual nature of the idea is somewhat concealed. On the other hand, when there is sufficient motivation in the form of intense anxiety, or when he is given the security of a positive emotional relationship with the therapist, the psychoneurotic may also express sexual conflict with stark realism. In these circumstances, it is common for male patients to make clay breasts as symbols of the female. This has been more frequently used than the hollow shape, which literature on the subject would lead us to believe is the most common female symbol. Women who openly express sexual conflict usually make a penis. As a general rule, men make the male organ only when they are troubled with impotence, or when they use the male symbol as a negative expression of general feelings of inferiority.

A model may be used to express an abstract idea. It may be an idea which it is difficult to express in words. The modelling then becomes a means of communication between patient and therapist. Very often the idea is communicated partly by the plastic symbolism of the clay, and partly by words. The patient explains the idea verbally, and at the same time refers to the various symbolic elements of the model. The process is then analagous to the explanation of some idea by reference to a plan or a map. On other occasions, the abstract idea is expressed in the model, but the patient will make no attempt to explain it.

Although there is great variation in the ideas expressed in the modelling of plastotherapy, there are common themes which keep recurring with different patients. On the one hand there is the everyday reality problem and domestic conflict. Then there are the sexual conflicts, which may have been either consciously suppressed or may have been deeply unconscious. The third group of common themes represents the expression of abstract ideas. These may concern such problems as the meaning and purpose of life. Models of this nature are more commonly made by patients of introvert personality, and sometimes it would seem that they represent a sudden crystallization of amorphous ideas which the patient has been pondering for some considerable time.

Figure No. 12

The ship signifies the patient's wish to travel. This is a superficial problem, but it is directly related to a very much more significant conflict. The patient is a schizoid boy in great conflict with his father. The ship represents his wish to travel, but much more important, it represents his wish to leave home. It thus becomes an expression of his wish to escape from the whole Oedipal situation.

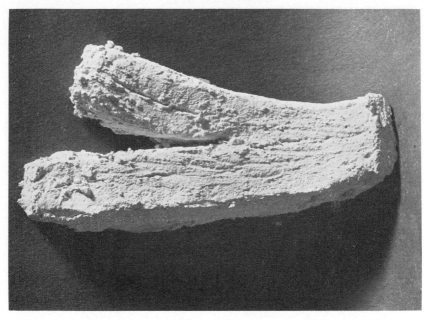

Figure No. 13

The model is used to express a commonplace idea in conventional metaphor.

Somewhere along the road I got off the path.
There is the road I should have gone along.
There is the other path.
The neurotic path gets further and further away.

Figure No. 14

Male patients who suffer symptoms as a result of an unresolved sexual conflict very often mould the clay into the shape of a woman's breasts.

This illustration shows models made by three different men in plastotherapy.

The first was made by a man whose feelings of inferiority were driving him to great sexual promiscuity. He makes a realistic likeness of a woman's breasts. He becomes disturbed while doing the modelling, but instead of talking of his worries about his numerous girl friends, he abreacts his deep-seated ambivalence towards his mother.

In the second model, the shapes are a poor likeness, but nevertheless, the patient identifies them as a woman's breasts. While he was making the models, he drifted into a state of great preoccupation. He kept smoothing out the clay on the surface of the models, but later he distorted the second one, making it flatter and giving an edge to it. Distortion of this nature is very common in plastotherapy, and it would seem to represent an attempt by the patient to deny that he ever made the object. In both of the models made by this patient, the nipples are absent. With some men the nipple is particularly significant psychologically, and this is often reflected in the models made in plastotherapy. These shapes were made by an inhibited obsessive. It would seem that in his preoccupation with the clay, he allows himself to mould the shapes of the breasts, but the idea of the nipples is so disturbing to him that he altogether denies it.

The third shape was made by a man who had suffered from impotence for most of his life. In these models, the process of distortion has progressed a step further. In his associations, he at first denied any knowledge as to the meaning of what he had made. However, he later identified it as a woman's breasts, and then proceeded to speak of his sexual difficulties.

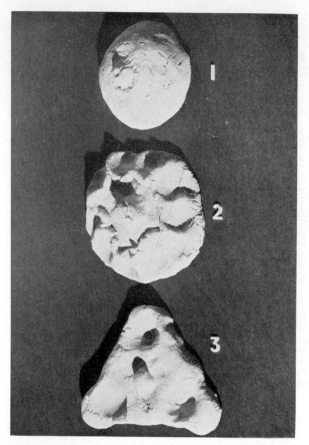

Figure No. 15

The male patient often makes a single female breast. This illustration shows three such models, made by different patients; and it serves to demonstrate increasing degrees of distortion of the models. Following non-directive questioning, the meaning of each was acknowledged by the patient. The first was made by an obsessive patient with phobic symptoms and sexual conflicts. The other two models were made by men who were suffering from impotence.

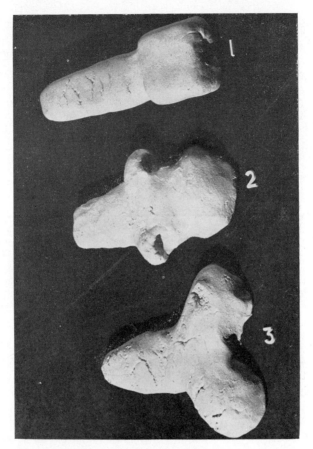

Figure No. 16

During this study, phallic shapes have been made most commonly by men suffering from impotence.

The first two models were made by a schizoid youth who expressed vague ideas of homosexuality; the third model was made by a man who suffered from impotence of many years duration.

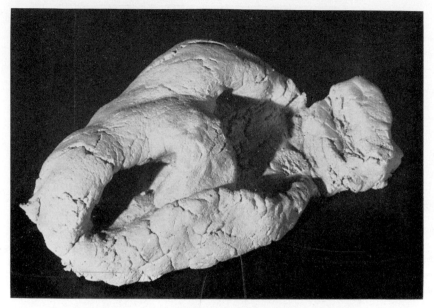

Figure No. 17

This rather odd looking model represents an attempt at the expression of an abstract idea. The patient feels that she is turning into herself. This was true, as she was very preoccupied with her own subjectivity. She explained the idea in words, and at the same time she demonstrated the way the idea is expressed by the turning in of the model. This was the second of two models depicting the same theme. In it she has added the steps, which indicate that there is a way out from her trouble.

The model is interesting in another respect, in that the patient who made it is a professional artist; but she in no way reflects her professional competence when modelling in plastotherapy.

PREVIOUS EXPERIENCE IN MODELLING

An interesting feature of the problem of getting the patient to model is that it is not made any easier by previous experience in modelling. There are always the two opposing forces. The patient wants to express his conflict so that he might be relieved of his symptoms; at the same time he does not want to express it because of the hurt, the shame, or the humiliation which he experiences in doing so. The patient who has had experience in modelling tends to exploit this experience as a defence. He lets it be known to the therapist that one models artistic things. By concentrating on producing something aesthetic, he defends himself from the expression of matters of psychological significance. Even when this defence is interpreted to the patient, he will often continue to persist with it in some slightly changed form. The uninitiated in modelling are denied this defence, and in this respect plastotherapy comes more easily to them.

Patients who are artistic, or who have some skill and experience in modelling, are not only reluctant to model in a therapeutic situation, but when they do come to use the clay, they do not show their ordinary artistic skill. In fact, the models made by persons who have had experience of modelling as a profession or a hobby are usually indistinguishable from the models of those who have had no previous experience.

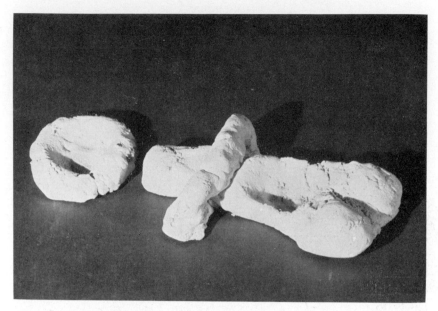

Figure No. 18

This crude model represents sexual intercourse. It was made by a competent professional artist. In it she gives no indication of her artistic talent. The clumsy execution in a woman of artistic capacity might suggest an underlying psychotic condition, but this was not so.

Think it symbolizes a man's sexual organ.

Possibly symbolizes intercourse.

Don't know why I made that hole.

Cup shaped symbol of fertility.

Man's testicles and erect penis.

This is a receiving vessel. (Points to the end of the model)

Felt I must make erotic symbols.

Symbol of vagina. (The arch over the penis)

My desire to conceive.

Erotic symbols come into my painting.

Man's sexual organs came unconsciously.

Before married was obsessed with the idea of having inter-course with my husband.

Feel I was over-sexual.

Feel I might still be like that.

Am more highly sexed than he in some ways.

Last year some difficulty in intercourse.

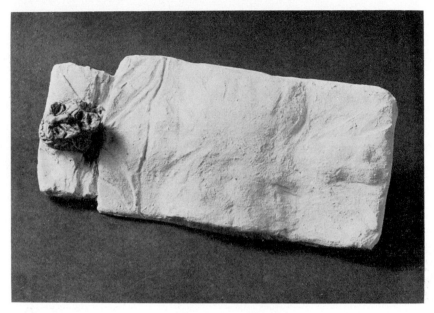

Figure No. 19

As distinct from the previous model, this figure of death was made by a woman who had had no previous experience of modelling or of art of any kind.

PSEUDO-PHALLIC SYMBOLS

A difficult problem of interpretation arises when a model has all the appearance of a phallic symbol, but there is no corroborative evidence from the patient's associations to confirm such an opinion. This is an important point, not only as regards the therapeutic use of modelling, but as regards our basic ideas about the interpretation of symbolism. Some of these models, which would appear to be phallic symbols, have been shown to well trained psychiatrists. Some of these men have been quite definite in their view that a model of this nature is in fact a phallic symbol, and should be interpreted as such, no matter what the patient says about it.

There is always the difficulty of the criticism of a form of psychotherapy which is essentially short-term in nature, that if the associations were pursued further, evidence of the phallic nature of the symbolism would eventually be obtained.

In the therapeutic use of modelling, many patients make shapes which have all the appearance of phallic symbols. In the author's experience, when there is some other evidence, either in the associations or in the patient's behaviour and affect, to confirm the phallic interpretation of the symbol, then in these cases subsequent psychotherapy proves beyond doubt that the phallic interpretation was correct. On the other hand, in those cases in which no corroborative evidence comes to hand at the time of the making of the model, subsequent psychotherapy has produced nothing to substantiate a phallic interpretation.

There is a good deal of evidence, particularly from hypnography, that many of these pseudo-phallic symbols are in fact neologistic individual symbols of the patient. So, in our present state of knowledge, it would seem wise to regard as phallic, only those models for which there is some real corroborative evidence as to the sexual nature of the symbolism.

Figure No. 20

This apparently phallic model represents a lighthouse. The patient was suffering from simple schizophrenia. He seemed lost in the world. He felt that he did not know where he was going, and that he needed something to guide him.

His associations indicated that the guiding light might be material, philosophical or spiritual. He was given ample opportunity to give sexual associations, but he did not do so, nor did his behaviour show the preoccupation or anxiety which usually accompanies the making of a phallic symbol. Subsequent psychotherapy showed nothing to suggest that the model was anything more than a symbol for guidance.

SCREEN MODELS

It has been found that the models are almost always connected in some way with some conflict in the patient's mind. This in itself is a rather surprising observation, as it might be thought that patients would produce inconsequential objects quite unrelated to any intra-psychic tensions. Experience has quite definitely shown that this is not so. However, there is one exception to this generalization. It is the production of what is called a screen model.

Occasionally the psychoneurotic patient deliberately goes out of his way to comply with the request to model something, but at the same time he purposefully aims not to disclose himself in any way. This of course is a defence against the anxiety or guilt of expressing his conflicts. It seems to occur most frequently when the patient is aware of some significant conflict, but for reasons of shame or hurt he is unable to bring himself to express it.

Screen models most commonly occur either at the first session of plastotherapy, or at a session following a session at which some particularly disturbing matter was ventilated. These models usually fall into one of three different categories. The commonest is the making of a likeness of some non-specific object. When the patient is questioned, he explains that it is just a man, or a house, or a dog or a cat, whatever the case may be. Sometimes such models are in fact true screen models, but very often it is a matter of the patient defending himself by denial of the specific identity of the model. In which case, further associations or subsequent psychotherapy will disclose the particular identity of the likeness produced. The man turns out to be the father. The house is the scene of some particular traumatic incident; and the dog or cat is connected with some incident of childhood.

Another type of screen model is the production of a likeness of some particular element of the patient's immediate environment. In the present study, much of the modelling has been done at a table in front of a window overlooking a park. Occasionally a patient will defend himself by making a likeness of some particular tree or distant building.

A third type of screen model is produced when the patient misinterprets the instructions as to what he is to do. He turns to the idea of occupational therapy, and makes a vase or an ashtray. In the case of some intellectually dull patients, and a few who have seemed to have rather fixed preconceived ideas about the use of modelling in occupational therapy, it has seemed that the misinterpretation of instructions has been genuine enough. But with others, it has been quite clear that the misinterpretation was purposeful, and was used as a defence in an attempt to ward off the disclosure of painful conflicts.

When a patient has made a screen model, it is usually not wise to confront him immediately with his defence. Such a procedure is likely to arouse hostility, and rapport deteriorates. This is to be avoided, as the successful use of modelling in psychotherapy is very largely dependent on the maintenance of a satisfactory positive relationship with the patient. If the patient has made a screen model, it means that, at the moment, he has some need to defend himself. Instead of interpreting his defence and so lessening rapport, in this type of therapy it is usually more effective to give the patient greater security, so that the need to defend himself is no longer so urgent. So he is given the feeling of greater security by non-verbal moves which increase rapport. It is all quite leisurely. He is given more clay and the instructions are repeated, and the patient usually produces a model of some psychological significance.

If this move is unsuccessful, further active steps must be taken, or the patient will continue to make other models which are psychologically sterile. He must be brought to make something which has meaning. The idea of expressing himself in the modelling is again explained to him. Emphasis can be made on his allowing a state of relaxation and reverie to develop in his mind, or alternatively, emphasis can be made on dissociation. If the patient does not seem suitable for this type of approach, he may be led to plastotherapy by a process of conditioning and education. It is probable that some minor conflicts of the patient are already known. He can be shown how these could be expressed in plastic form. He is then told, *"Now you make other models. You make models which ex-*

*press something. With the models, you express ideas which are
deep in your mind."*

In actual practice, screen models are made much less frequently
than might be expected. In retrospect, it would seem that they
have often been associated with a hurried, and perhaps inadequate
explanation of plastotherapy. Their occurrence is practically confined to work with psychoneurotics in the waking state; as they are
very rare indeed with both the psychotic patient, and the psychoneurotic who is modelling under hypnosis.

Figure No. 21

The patient had been very disturbed by the disclosures of a previous session of modelling. On this occasion, she at first resisted attempts to persuade her to use the clay again. She finally agreed; but she made this model of a book, the idea of which was suggested to her by a book which was lying on the table where she was modelling. The model effectively screened the expression of any traumatic conflict which might be disturbing to her.

V

THE ASSOCIATIONS

ELICITATION OF THE ASSOCIATIONS

P LASTOTHERAPY functions purely as an adjunct to general psychotherapy. It is not sufficient that hitherto unventilated conflicts should be expressed in modelling. They must be resolved. They must be integrated with the general psychic structure of the patient. For the most part, this must be done at a verbal level.

The first step in this process is the conversion of the plastic expression of the idea to its expression in words. This is merely a change from one form of symbolism to another; from plastic to verbal symbols.

Often the patient will comment spontaneously and freely about the model he has made. He is quite anxious to talk. He can then be encouraged to keep talking by an occasional *"Um"* or *"Ah,"* or a nod of the head. If words cease, the flow of his thought can often be started again by a gesture in the direction of the model, or even the manoeuvre of moving the model a little closer to the patient. It usually comes about that the patient is soon expressing some deep-seated conflict which is somehow obliquely related to the model.

The all-important factor in this procedure is that the therapist remain passive. This becomes more difficult with the patient who does not talk spontaneously. The therapist asks about the model, but he must do so in a completely non-directive fashion, so that he does not suggest any particular line of thought to the patient, or invite any specific comment. It would seem important that this rule should be followed scrupulously in the early stages of treatment, and in the initial phase of any session of psychotherapy around any particular model. In the later stages of treatment, when the psychotherapy is directed towards resolution and integration rather than ventilation, then the therapist's enquiry may assume a slightly more active form.

However, in the initial stages, the patient who does not talk spontaneously can be asked simple questions. *"Tell me about it." "What is this you have made?"*

It is found that the patient's associations come more easily if an atmosphere of abstraction or reverie can be maintained. The therapist encourages this, both by his own manner, and by direct suggestions to the patient. His manner is calm and leisurely. He says very little. He can appear thoughtful and remote. By this means, an atmosphere of pensive reverie is suggested to the patient. Sometimes more active steps can be taken to help the patient to this easy, relaxed state of mind. *"You are relaxed, and calm, and comfortable. There is the model. You just talk. You look at the model and you talk about whatever it is that comes into your mind."*

The insecure patient may lack sufficient confidence to allow himself to drift off guard in a state of reverie. He defends himself by trying to engage the therapist in conversation. He talks about the clay; his lack of skill; how he used to make mud pies as a child. By this means he strives to maintain the conversation at a super-ficial level, and at the same time keep himself alert so that he will not say more than he intends in an unguarded moment. This type of situation arises quite commonly in treatment. The therapist re-mains imperturbable, passive and calm. His attention is focussed on the model, which the patient would ignore. He is so preoccupied with the model that he hardly hears the patient's attempts to engage him in inconsequential conversation. His only answer is *"Um"* or *"Oh"*. The attention of the patient comes to be fixed on the model with which the therapist is so much preoccupied. The therapist is calm and unruffled. The patient himself takes on some of this reverie; and he is thus led into a state of mind in which his associations to the model come easily and smoothly.

The patient may be tense and anxious as a result of conflicts which have come to expression in the modelling. Mental tension is the antithesis of calm reverie. The patient's anxiety must be re-

61

duced. The therapist must resist any inclination to verbal reassurance, as this only opens the way for the patient to use superficial
conversation as a defence. The patient's anxiety is allayed by the
suggestive effect of the therapist's own calm, and by his moving
closer to the patient emotionally. The anxious patient is supported
by being given the feeling that *"he is here; he will help me."*

In other cases, it may be possible to use the patient's anxiety to
provoke a sudden catharsis of associations. In his highly anxious
state, the patient is very receptive to non-verbal communications,
and is very susceptible to suggestions conveyed by this means. At
the opportune moment, a glance or a gesture from the therapist
may be sufficient to give the patient the idea that the therapist now
knows all about him from the model he has made. This breaks
his reserve, and a flood of associations is poured out with the pent-
up pressure of his anxiety.

In appropriate circumstances, this manoeuvre can be developed
still further. Instead of using the patient's anxiety and general state
of tension to precipitate the ventilation of his thoughts in relation
to the model, his emotion connected with some particular object
can be used in a similar way. It really amounts to a matter of
deliberately provoking the patient to abreaction. It may be clear
from the nature of the model and the patient's reaction to it, that
his emotions regarding some person or event are fully mobilized,
and are on the point of ventilation. It may be that he is struggling
with feelings of guilt or love or hate. When it is seen that this
situation is developing, the mere introduction of the idea of guilt
or hate or love, by some comment, will often precipitate an abreaction with ventilation of the relevant conflicts.

MANNER IN WHICH THE ASSOCIATIONS ARE GIVEN

There is great individual variation as to the way in which the
associations are given. These variations often provide valuable
information about the patient.

They may be given in quite a matter-of-fact manner. This
usually implies a relative absence of anxiety. It is frequently seen
in psychotic patients, and in psychoneurotics, when the model has

reference to some problem of everyday life. Other patients, who are more disturbed, particularly those who are sophisticated in matters of psychology, may be able to maintain a matter-of-fact attitude for a short time; but this facade invariably breaks down when further associations are sought.

Sometimes the patient will make no response to questions about the model. He may be so preoccupied with the model that he becomes statuesque. This is often a warning sign of impending abreaction. The therapist remains silent and passive. Any comment only distracts the patient from the ideas which are seeking expression. Furthermore, the patient may use any intervention by the therapist as a defence, by engaging him in conversation and so lowering the tension, and thus allowing easier suppression of the ideas which are on the verge of expression. If the therapist refrains from intervention, the tension usually builds up until there is a sudden explosive catharsis of traumatic material. The words come quickly from the pent-up pressure of ideation. There are the usual accompaniments of abreaction, coloured by the particular emotional tone imposed by the nature of the ideas being expressed.

With other patients, the associations are given very obliquely. The patient continues to express ideas peripheral to the central theme. The process goes on and on in a circular fashion. It soon becomes apparent that the patient is avoiding some particular area; and the defensive purpose of his way of giving the associations becomes obvious. The therapist must now make some estimation of the patient's drive to defend himself in this way, and decide whether the patient has a real psychological need to defer the expression of the particular idea, or whether he is merely hedging to avoid embarrassment. If the former is the case, the therapist may decide to move to a closer relationship with the patient, in order to support him; while if the latter is the case, the matter can usually be brought to finality by continually bringing the patient's attention back to the model. This confronts the patient with the central idea, as the model itself has some direct connection with the significant conflict.

With still other patients, the associations are inconsequential, but they lack the conscious or unconscious evasive quality of those just described. They are not purposive in the same way. At the start, it seems that these patients have no knowledge at all of the meaning of the model. As the patient talks about it, the underlying meaning seems to come closer to his awareness. The associations become more relevant, and then the meaning comes, first to the therapist and then to the patient. This may be a relatively slow process, and on occasion may extend over two or three sessions, in which the patient spontaneously makes similar models, and the associations become more and more pertinent until the conflict finally gains expression.

COMMUNICATION BY NON-VERBAL ASSOCIATIONS

It sometimes happens that the patient tells us about his model by his expression, gesture and behaviour, rather than by words.

Psychotic and pre-psychotic patients often make a model, and believe that its meaning is perfectly obvious to the therapist. To them it is so obvious, that it is just as clear as if it were written down in black and white. The patient points to it and nods. That is all there is to it. There is no purpose in his talking about it. If he is questioned too much, the patient may become irritable at what appears to him to be such an extraordinary lack of comprehension on the part of the therapist in such a simple matter.

A similar mechanism may operate with the psychoneurotic, when he is under sufficient stress of anxiety and guilt. The process rather resembles the formation of ideas of reference, when the patient sometimes believes that people can tell what he has done by merely looking at him. In the same way, the patient believes that the therapist can tell all about him from the shape which he has made. This mechanism usually applies to sexual conflicts, and the model usually contains thinly veiled sexual symbolism. The patient makes the model, and then looks pitifully at the therapist with a gesture expressing the idea that he has now told everything. The situation is analogous to the physical examination of the guilt-ridden youth, who believes the physician knows all about his masturbation from having seen his genitalia. The ideas seem to the patient so terrible that they are not put into words. They are communicated non-verbally, by subtleties of expression and gesture. The therapist understands the patient's communication, and replies to him in the same non-verbal language. To translate the ideas into words at this stage would be an unforgivable assault on the patient's sensitivity.

If the patient believes that he has told the therapist everything in the model, a demand that he repeat it all over again in words is not only exasperating, but informs the patient that the therapist does not understand him. In such circumstances, it is better that the therapist remain passive, and give the patient the impression that he understands the meaning of the model. The patient benefits by the calming effect of his imagined confession. At the next session, his guilt is not so pressing, because he feels that the therapist knows all about the conflict, and has not rejected him. He is now better able to talk about the model, and the therapist, by continuing in his passive role, is gradually able to piece together the threads of the story. But it may be wise not to venture into the interrogation of the patient about the conflict in verbal psychotherapy until the therapist is confident that he understands the nature of the area which he is about to explore.

DEFENCE BY DENIAL

When the psychoneurotic patient is first asked about the model he has made, unlike the psychotic or hypnotized patient, he almost invariably counters with some defence. He is inclined to deny that he knows anything about it. *"It is nothing." "I don't know what it is." "I just made it for fun."* This type of initial defence is very characteristic of plastotherapy. It is in marked contrast to the reaction of the patient who has been modelling in occupational or integrative therapy. In this case, the patient will usually answer any question as to what he is making, in a direct and uncomplicated fashion.

The following are the exact words used by a patient.

This is very hard on me.
I am not talkative.

Right hand was doing it, then the left.
Did it with two hands.
Can't think of anything.
Always feel tired.
Want to lie down and go to bed.
My mind is a complete blank.

Most patients commence with a few phrases such as this. However, the majority quickly proceed to give relevant associations to the model without any active intervention by the therapist.

Sometimes the patient shows a real reluctance to talk about the model. It is clear that he is somehow disturbed and distressed by what he has made. If any attempt is made to force him to speak, his resentment will be aroused. The therapist can sit and wait. There is no hurry. The therapist communicates by non-verbal means that he is in a calm and leisurely state of mind. Perhaps he can draw the patient's attention to the model by leaning forward and moving it a little; or perhaps he can make it easier for the patient to start talking by making some unverbalized interrogatory, *"Eh"* or *"Um."*

Although the patient has already expressed the conflict in the modelling, he may be still reluctant to express the same idea in words. As a result, we find that we run up against a further set of defences. The patient may deny any knowledge of the meaning of the model. As would be expected, this occurs most frequently when the idea of dissociation was used in order to get the patient to start modelling. *"You don't worry about it. Your hands just pick up the clay. Your fingers work it. Just quietly and easily, and you will find that they make it into something."* This defence by denial is very common in hypnosis, when a similar dissociation is used. As in hypnosis, the defence is circumvented by leaving that particular model and proceeding with another. This time, the suggestion of dissociation is avoided. When a patient has once made one model, he will usually make others without the same need for dissociation. He is then denied the use of this defence for subsequent models.

Sometimes when the patient makes a model in the mental abstraction of deep reverie, he will deny knowledge of its meaning. In this case, it may be that the model gives expression to deeply unconscious material which still remains repressed. This can sometimes be guessed from the bizarre nature of the symbolism. The meaning is disclosed by getting the patient to give a series of free associations to the model. If there should be difficulty with free association, the matter can be met by getting the patient to make another model which will explain the first. *"Make another model. You let yourself go completely. This model will somehow explain the first one. It will be the key. You let yourself go completely and the shape will just come."* Associations to the second model will often explain the first one.

When the model is badly integrated, or bizarre in any way, and the patient is reluctant to talk about it, it is always wise to get his associations to what appear to be the individual elements of the piece. The patient may refuse to express in words the central theme of the idea which he has expressed in the model, but at the same time he may talk quite freely and naively about each individual element which it contains. The meaning of the complete model then becomes clear.

Figure No. 22

Sometimes it is found that the patient is vague and evasive in giving the associations.

A middle-aged bachelor was being treated for a severe chronic anxiety state, and impotence of long standing. He makes this model.

> *Didn't like the feeling of the clay.*
> *Think of a shoe again.*
> *Not a thought in my mind.*
> *Didn't think about anything.*
> *Some people have an ease of thought which I haven't.*
> *Just didn't think about anything.*
> *A complete blockage today.*
> *Always feel like that.*
> *Tired, but not really tired.*
> *Feel impatient.*
> *Want to get it over.*
> *It does not provoke any thoughts at all.*
> *Feel a heaviness.*
> *Sleep too much.*

The patient was told that at the next session he would be hypnotized, and asked to speak about the model. Two weeks later he was hypnotized. Closure of eyelids and automatic movements of the arms were obtained. He was then shown the model, and asked what it was.

Very hard to talk.

Very sleepy. (He could hardly keep his eyes open.)

Can't keep my eyes open.

Can't talk.

Am still aware of my thoughts.

That is the whole trouble, I can't relax enough.

Lunch appointment twelve o'clock.

Female sex organ.

That is all I can see.

It won't be any good.

Therapist: *Whose sex organ?*

(Shrugs his shoulders. He falls asleep, using sleep as a defence.)

On waking, he is asked if he had associated the model with the female sex organ when he was making it. He states that it had not occurred to him.

NON-SPECIFIC ASSOCIATIONS

Instead of denying knowledge of the model, sometimes the patient will defend himself by giving non-specific associations to a model which, in fact, is specific. This is much more difficult to detect in the waking state than in hypnosis. Models made in hypnosis are almost invariably specific in the sense that they refer to some particular person or object. But in the waking state, patients occasionally defend themselves by making non-specific objects which have no real psychological significance. The patient may say of the model, *"It is just a man. It is just any man."* We do not know whether he has defended himself by making a non-specific model, or whether the model does represent some particular, psychologically significant person; and he is now defending himself by refusing to disclose its true identity. It is important that we resolve this problem without delay, as its outcome determines the way in which we will proceed with the patient. If we accept the patient's statement as to the non-specific nature of a model which is in fact specific, we only encourage him in the use of this defence in subsequent treatment. There are various signs which will help us to come to a decision. If the model is really non-specific, there is no anxiety about the patient. As it is non-specific, talking about it is not in any way a threat to him. On the other hand, if the patient is denying the real identity of the model, he is experiencing a certain amount of anxiety. The more he is asked about it, the more anxious does he become. We come to feel that he is concealing something from us. It may be conscious, just vaguely conscious, or quite unconscious. We proceed to free association, and the meaning of the model becomes established. With the patient who remains calm throughout, we discard his model as non-specific, and get him to make another with greater emphasis on dissociation or reverie, whichever may be indicated.

Sometimes another mechanism operates which further emphasizes the importance of continuing the enquiry when the patient describes his model in non-specific terms. The model may be genuinely non-specific. However, while the patient's associations are being obtained, it may act as a matrix on which to project significant conflicts. The shape is non-specific, but while he is being asked about it, he focuses all his attention on it, and ideas become projected in much the same way as in the Rorschach Test. The model may thus provide the means of bringing about the expression of significant psychological material, or the patient may actually come to identify the model in some particular way. By such a process, the originally non-specific model gains a secondary specificity as a result of projection stimulated by persistent enquiry for associations.

DEFENCE BY CIRCUMSTANTIALITY

Psychoneurotics often give very verbose, diffuse associations. This is itself a defence. The patient's anxiety is aroused by the awareness of what he has expressed in the modelling. The idea of it disturbs him. He tends to tone it down, as it were. In talking a lot about unimportant details, he feels that he is keeping the therapist's attention from the horrible central truth. In this way, he becomes circumstantial. He is frightened to stop talking, for surely the therapist will ask the dreaded question. In dealing with this type of situation, there is no need to rush things. The patient's anxiety and distress call for some consideration. One must consider the meaning of such a defence in terms of behaviour. It is a plea for mercy. *"Please do not ask me that question about the model."* As he continues to stave off the question, one can see him saying, *"Please do not ask it, you see how it would upset me."* The therapist is now in a position of power. He can use his power, or he can withhold it. He has been striving to get the information from the patient, and now he is in a position to demand it. If he does demand it, the patient's dreaded conflict is exposed. But the patient's inner turmoil is increased because he was not ready to disclose it. The patient feels hostile to the therapist because he was forced into disclosing something against his will, and inevitably rapport deteriorates. On the other hand, the therapist can refrain from using his power. Some subtlety is required here. At this stage, it is an error in technique to let the patient believe that he has mastered the therapist, that he has bluffed the therapist, and put it over him in avoiding the question. The therapist's aim is to give the patient the idea that he had the question in mind all the time; that he was going to ask it; and that he refrained from doing so only out of consideration for the patient. This idea can be expressed by reference to the model. Because the idea is uppermost in the patient's mind, an appropriate gesture towards the model, or a glance at the patient, is sufficient to communicate the meaning. One of the great advantages of plastotherapy is the way in which it facilitates this type of non-verbal communication. The patient's anxiety is now relieved. He is aware of the way in which the therapist spared him. Rapport is greatly increased. As a result of these influences, the patient will soon spontaneously disclose the meaning of the model; and the therapist is now in so much the better position to use his relationship with the patient in treatment.

Another variety of the same defence is the giving of screen associations. The patient, perhaps in a state of reverie, makes a model. He then finds that he has disclosed himself more than he had intended. In the model, he has expressed the thing which nobody was ever to hear about. To cover up, as it were, he purposefully gives inconsequential associations of no psychological significance. The situation is easily recognised. He is seen to be evasive. There is an obvious incongruity between the real disquiet of the patient, and his would-be bland comments about the model.

EMOTIONAL DISSOCIATION

Sometimes the associations to the model are given in a different way altogether. The patient makes a model which expresses a lot of psychopathological material. When he is asked about it, he surprises the therapist by explaining the whole of the psychopathology in a matter-of-fact way. In the author's experience, this has occurred most frequently with patients who have read a great deal of psychology, and those who have elsewhere had previous treatment by formal psychoanalysis. The first time this is encountered, it is really quite alarming. The patient knows all the relative psychopathology. He makes a model and builds the psycho-

72

pathology into it. The key to the situation is the patient's matter-of-fact attitude. He understands the psychopathology, but there is no emotion about it. He stands off, and views his own conflicts simply as if he were studying a case. His feelings are dissociated from it. This is defence by intellectualization. It is a difficult defence to meet, and the aim must be the integration of the patient's intellectual and emotional life. The patient must be made to give some emotional response to the present situation. A start must be made with this first model. If the matter is postponed, the defence by intellectualization only becomes so much the more firmly established. The ideal is to provoke some emotional response about the central idea expressed in the model. The whole of the conversation turns towards feeling, as opposed to thinking or to facts. *"What did that feel like?" "How did you feel about it?" "That must have hurt him, how did it affect you?"* and so on. It may be possible to get the patient to express some emotion towards the model. He may handle a female figure gently, or he may handle a male figure roughly. This is at least a start of some emotional involvement. The fact of the model being there, in front of the patient, with his hands actually on it, tends to precipitate the expression of emotion in a way which does not obtain in a purely verbal interview. The expression of emotion is also facilitated by the greater ease with which the personal relationship with the patient can be varied in plastotherapy. The use of modelling gives the therapist the chance to move close to the patient by way of encouragement, or even helping him; likewise he can employ the modelling to become more distant by using it to frustrate the patient. In fact, if defence by intellectualization is really well established, it is better, as a last resort, to provoke the patient into some display of emotion against the therapist, rather than allow him to maintain an emotional dissociation for the whole session. This requires a good deal of judgment, as rapport obviously deteriorates for the time being, and care must be taken to prolong the session sufficiently after the display of emotion to re-establish an adequate positive relationship for the patient to continue treatment.

73

One of the conspicuous advantages of plastotherapy is in dealing with these patients who use defence by intellectualization; and these are the patients who are often the most difficult to handle in simple verbal psychotherapy.

BLOCKING

With other patients, when the associations are being sought, other defences come into operation. In the ordinary interview, the patient may have been unable to give verbal expression to his conflict. He makes a model which is somehow related to the problem. This becomes the means through which he is finally able to ventilate the conflict in words. But there is often an intermediate stage in which the words will not come. He makes as if to speak, but just as the words would seem to be on his lips, he suddenly stops. This is psychological blocking. He says nothing. He usually keeps looking at the model. His mobilized anxiety shows itself in his fidgeting and restlessness.

The therapist can now make moves to help him. These moves must be made in the right way, or the patient will use them to relieve his feeling of tension, rather than in expressing the conflict. This happens if the therapist is himself embarrassed by the silence, and speaks to break the silence and relieve his own anxiety, rather than to help the patient. In these circumstances, the patient seizes on the therapist's comment to introduce some inconsequential, but anxiety-relieving topic of conversation.

When the patient blocks, the therapist must communicate to him a number of ideas. He must inform him that silence is no embarrassment. He should also aim to communicate the idea that there is a calm inevitability that the patient's conflicts will be expressed. It is obvious that these ideas cannot be expressed in so many words. Any attempt by the therapist at a logical verbal formulation would be so incongruous as to provoke the patient either to panic or to mirth. The ideas must be communicated by non-verbal means. Just as the patient in his modelling is using non-verbal means to give expression to his conflict, in the same way the therapist in his turn uses his behaviour as a non-verbal means of informing the patient that he is not worried by silence, and that the patient will soon be able to ventilate his conflict. The adequate communication of these ideas by the therapist requires more than his mere passivity. It requires some definite, but extremely subtle change of attitude in his behaviour. The patient in this anxiety-ridden state is quick to perceive these changes in attitude. They have meaning to the patient. The proof of this is that they produce observable changes in the patient, which lead to the more ready expression of his conflict.

There is another situation which calls for some communication from the therapist. The patient has made the model. He starts to say something about it, and then he blocks. No words come. The therapist must quickly assess the degree of anxiety or guilt which the patient is feeling. If the patient is experiencing acute anxiety, it is usually a mistake for the therapist to simply reassure the patient, and so relieve his anxiety. This desire to relieve another's distress is a reaction of normal human kindness; and it needs a constant awareness of the psychotherapeutic situation to prevent oneself from impulsively making this mistake.

In these circumstances, verbal reassurance has two important effects on the patient. By introducing words and another train of thought, it provides him with a ready made defence against expressing the painful conflict. He quickly picks up something which the therapist has said and talks about it, and in a few seconds the focus of the interview is far distant from the traumatic area. Secondly, the relief of anxiety by reassurance robs the patient of motivation. He is reassured; he feels better; perhaps he need not talk of these horrible things after all.

If instead of verbal reassurance, the therapist can move closer to the patient emotionally, then a rather different set of reactions is induced in the patient. Again, this move to a closer emotional relationship must be made by non-verbal means. An expression, a gesture, or merely the drawing of one's chair a little nearer to the patient informs him that you understand his distress of mind, that in fact you feel for him. This move, although it would often seem that it is hardly perceived by the patient, evokes a change in his

75

emotional tone. At last someone understands. The emotion of it loosens the resistance and the patient ventilates the suppressed material.

If it seems to the therapist that guilt rather than anxiety is the patient's predominant affect, then the move to a closer emotional relationship with the patient can be appropriately structured. In this case, the idea to be communicated might be paraphrased, *"I know you have done something wicked; I understand; I shall not forsake you; I shall still help you."* The experience of guilt evokes in the patient the feeling of being apart, of being separated from those he imagines are not guilty. If the patient looks at the model he has made, and he experiences guilt, he feels shut off from the therapist. The ventilation of the conflict becomes even more difficult. The therapist must move closer to the patient. To accomplish this, he can use a simple but powerful symbolic mechanism. The guilty patient feels different from others, he feels apart. He feels unworthy, and because he feels unworthy, he knows that people would wish to keep their distance from him. The therapist, aware of this, can bring into play the powerful symbolic mechanisms of touch. He touches the patient. It must be done with absolute naturalness and sincerity. The patient typically scrutinizes the therapist. If he finds him completely natural and secure in himself, he feels that he is no longer apart, and comes more easily to voice the conflict expressed in the model.

Figure No. 23

This model was made by a male patient with a longstanding sexual conflict. It would seem that he was about to make a shape of a woman's breasts. However, he was unable to let himself go sufficiently to make a real likeness, and ended up by camouflaging the model. The breasts are grossly asymetrical, and the model is surrounded by a kind of ledge which leads one's attention from the central theme. By this means, he would deny the idea which he has already expressed.

He continues to defend himself by blocking and denial in the associations; and he does all he can to lead the therapist into irrelevancies.

> *Twin peaks of California.*
>
> *A couple of hills sticking out of a lake.*
>
> *A couple of sombreros stuck together.*
>
> *African natives have breasts like that, pointed.*
>
> *At first* (the sentence is mumbled and I cannot hear it, so I ask him to repeat it.)
>
> *No thoughts come.*
>
> *Used to be day-dreaming a lot.*
>
> *Now just think about nothing.*

77

*Think about things I would like to do but just can't be
    bothered.*
(Pause)
Can't think at all.
Nothing comes to my mind.
It's like a blank wall.
Cars passing in the street.
Feel tired.
Must be a bad subject for this.
*Read a book, and read two pages and don't know what I
    am reading.*
Smoke too much.

The associations illustrate how the patient defends himself. Almost
every phrase he utters is an attempt to lead the therapist from the idea
of a woman's breasts, which he has expressed in the model.

VI

SOME PSYCHODYNAMICS
OF PLASTOTHERAPY

MODELLING AS A CATALYST

I N SOME CASES, the modelling seems to act as a catalyst, as it were, for the whole process. There is some conflict which is denied expression in vis-a-vis phychotherapy. The patient is asked to model something with his hands. Then suddenly, without question, he unburdens himself of psychologically significant material. It comes abruptly and forcefully, and is often unexpected by both patient and therapist.

This type of catalytic action shows plastotherapy at its best. Somehow the making of the model weakens the retaining mechanisms, and a flood of repressed ideas bursts forth. The psychodynamics which bring about this effect seem to vary in different cases. Sometimes the process would seem quite clear. The conflict is seeking expression, but it is held back by suppressive or repressive mechanisms. In his reverie, the patient makes his model. Because he is off guard, the conflict finds some kind of indirect expression in the clay. He looks at the model, and a sudden awareness of the conflict surges to his mind, and is given immediate expression in words. He becomes stirred, and the ventilation of the ideas is accompanied by the feeling and display of appropriate emotion.

On the other hand, there are cases in which it would seem that the mechanism is much simpler. When the significant conflict is being withheld by conscious suppression rather than by unconscious repression, the modelling may be used by the patient as an excuse to himself for ventilating the conflict. He feels, *"This modelling is the treatment. This is where one tells everything."* Such a mechanism often operates when the patient is being held back by a sense of shame or humiliation. In these cases, the patient seizes on it as a face-saving mechanism which is not available to him in an ordinary interview. He uses it to express a conflict which he would have expressed in formal psychotherapy, if he were given the necessary time.

Figure No. 24

A schizoid girl, who is on the verge of a psychotic breakdown, demonstrates the effect of the changing shape of the clay, as she moulds it.

> *That is an incredible thing.*
>
> *Watched the changing shapes of it, each time a different shape.*
>
> *Rolled it; and it went hollow of its own accord.*
>
> *Thought anything which it did itself better than anything I could construct.*
>
> (Pause)
>
> *Looks like a uterus or womb.*

Figure No. 25

A very inhibited young girl makes a car. Formal psychotherapy had been very unproductive, but the modelling has the effect of disinhibiting her and catalysing the expression of ideas.

> *Like cars.*
> *Just made a car for the sake of making something.*
> *Would rather go out in an old car.*
> *Can have better fun in an old car.*
> *Young people who have got new cars are "stuffed shirts".*
> *Young people that I like have old cars.*
> (Pause)
> Therapist: *Any particular people?*
> *Friend of mine has an old car.*
> (Patient fidgets restlessly)
> *My mother thinks we should be wowsers.*
> *People in churches are mean and horrible types, the majority of them.*
> *Mother thinks I should join in the Church more.*
> *Do not believe in spending all my time in the Church.*
> Therapist: *And what does she think about cars?*
> *If I go out with a boy in a sports car she condemns him.*
> *She doesn't like any young people with cars.*
> Therapist: *Why is that?*
> *She thinks they are skites and show-offs.*
> *The boy I was out with yesterday was a very sporty type.*
> *I was waiting for the remarks about him.*
> *She doesn't believe in drinking, even in moderation.*

She is brought back to the car, and it becomes clear that her real problem does not concern a car in itself, but is the matter of what she might do with a boy in a car.

DEFENCE BY CAMOUFLAGE

Sometimes the patient will make a likeness of some object, and then, after he has made it, he may alter it so as to make the original meaning less obvious. This process occurs most commonly when the patient has made a model of some object of sexual significance. It would seem that the patient lets himself go in the uncritical way suggested to him. He allows the expression of some significant conflict by projecting the idea in his modelling. This is probably the likeness of some sexual object. It then often happens that he becomes preoccupied with the model. He studies it intently, and then alters it, camouflaging its real meaning.

When the patient's associations to such a model are sought, he usually continues the defence by verbal denial, and it is usually only after some persistence in seeking his associations that he will acknowledge the meaning of the model.

The patient distorts the model, and then denies knowledge of its meaning. The degree to which this is a conscious process can be the subject of interesting speculation. It might be thought that the psychotic may not be fully aware of what he is doing; but the fact that the patient is awake might lead one to the opinion that with the psychoneurotic, the whole procedure is in his full awareness. Experience with plastotherapy would suggest that this is not always the case. There seems to be irrefutable evidence that the waking psychoneurotic may project his conflicts in modelling without being aware of what he is doing. During the process, some patients become so intent on the model that they develop a state of reverie or mental abstraction. In this state, it would seem that the normal syntonic function of the ego loses some of its integration. Some degree of dissociation is present. On occasion, it has seemed that the patient was not any more aware of what he was doing, when he was distorting the model, than he was when he was actually making it. At present, such problems are largely a matter of conjecture; and proof or otherwise will depend on the closer examination of patients in this area, which would probably need to be carried out as a matter of research rather than by way of clinical observation during treatment.

On the other hand, there can be no doubt at all that at times the distortion and denial is a fully conscious process. The patient makes a model; he then feels that he cannot bear the disgrace of expressing such an idea, so he consciously alters the model in order to disguise its meaning from the therapist.

Figure No. 26

An impotent male patient with a sexual conflict makes this model of a woman's breast. It would seem that he cannot bear the idea that is in his mind. He distorts the model so as to camouflage the likeness which brings to him such disturbing thoughts.

He denies that he knows what he has made. However, in another session, he is hypnotized, and is shown the model. In hypnosis he acknowledges it as a woman's breast.

ABREACTION

One of the outstanding features of plastotherapy is the way in which it leads patients to abreact. As the patient talks about the conflict which he has expressed, he becomes more and more worked up. This process is observed in simple psychotherapy, but it is much more pronounced in plastotherapy. It is no mere statement by the patient of his feeling of emotion; it is a matter of really experiencing the emotion. Very often it is more than this. It is a matter of being temporarily overwhelmed by the emotion. Hate, guilt and love are the emotions which most frequently take possession of the patient in this way.

When we think of abreaction, our thoughts are likely to turn to hypnosis, narco-analysis, ether abreaction, or other psychiatric techniques used for this purpose. However, experience with plasto-therapy has proved that many patients will abreact in the waking state with extreme violence, when they realize that they have expressed some deep conflict with the clay. Such abreaction may occur with a minimum of active interference by the therapist; and on occasion it may occur in the complete absence of any prompting by the therapist, when he is actually out of the room.

A point which is particularly important from the point of view of treatment is that these severe abreactions may occur in patients who consistently maintain a complete control of their emotions in formal psychotherapy. Even patients who have persistently defended themselves by emotional isolation or intellectualization have been brought into acute abreaction while modelling.

These abreactions are clearly distinct from the anxiety reactions which may occur in plastotherapy. Nevertheless, it would seem that they are brought about by similar mechanisms. In the first place, plastic expression allows the ventilation of the significant conflict by circumventing habitual defences which are applicable only to verbal expression. Secondly, the patient becomes emotionally involved because the permanent quality of plastic expression does not allow him to dismiss the disturbing thoughts from his mind. The model is continually there in front of him, all the time reminding him of his problem.

There is one very important consideration which concerns abreaction in plastotherapy. Abreaction such as this, with the patient in the waking state, has different psychodynamic qualities from abreaction with the hypnotized or narcotized patient.

Abreaction with the hypnotized or narcotized patient often has an "as if" quality about it. Sometimes it almost gives the impression that the experience of the emotion was not really genuine. This stems from the role-playing element of hypnosis. With the waking patient, this is usually absent, or at least very much reduced.

When the abreaction takes place in the waking state, there is an enhanced therapeutic effect on account of the patient's awareness of his emotion. When the hypnotized or narcotized patient abreacts, one is always left in doubt regarding the degree to which the patient felt it as a real experience. This doubt is increased when the abreaction is followed by amnesia, either spontaneous or induced. In fact, after abreaction in hypnosis or narcosis, the patient is often left with the feeling of having had a bad dream. It is an event which is experienced as rather remote from reality. There is nothing of this quality about abreaction in the waking state. It is a living experience, which the patient accepts as part of life. He is thus brought to full awareness of his emotions.

This process of coming face to face with one's emotions as a result of abreaction in the waking state, is allied to, but at the same time different from the process of coming face to face with the conflict expressed in the model. In many cases, the two processes occur concurrently, and are complementary, the one to the other. In other cases, however, they take place more or less separately. On one occasion, the ventilation of some significant conflict is the main feature; on another occasion, there is great display and deep experience of emotion, and the ideational content of the session would seem to be of secondary importance.

Abreaction in the waking state is a much more significant event to the patient than it is in hypnosis or narcosis. It is a more dynamic situation, and has much greater therapeutic possibilities. The usual problem is the technical difficulty of inducing abreaction in the waking state. This difficulty is significantly reduced by the use

87

of modelling.

However, against these technical therapeutic advantages of abreaction in the waking state, there is one definite disadvantage.
Abreaction in the waking state is much more difficult to control.
In hypnosis, if the expression of emotion tends to take possession
of the patient, as it were, the situation is easily met, either by reassurance which is possible through the close rapport with the hypnotized patient, or by simply increasing the depth of hypnosis. With
the narcotized patient, the situation is met in a similar way, by
simply giving more of the drug. These ready means of control are
not available with the patient who is abreacting in the waking state.
There is not only the question of control during the actual process
of abreaction, but the waking patient takes a good deal longer to
recover from his abreaction. No matter how severe the abreaction,
it is a rarity for the hypnotized patient not to be fully recovered,
and fit to return home after half an hour's hypnotic sleep following
the abreaction; but the waking patient often recovers his composure
only very slowly.

Figure No. 27

Sometimes the modelling evokes abreaction in patients in a quite extraordinary fashion.

The patient is a woman in her middle thirties, who has suffered from bronchial asthma for twenty years. She seeks psychiatric help because it is noticed that her asthma is worse when she is subject to nervous stress, particularly so following differences with her husband.

She works with the clay for a few minutes, and then becomes acutely disturbed.

> *It's terribly difficult.*
> (Pause. Patient becomes very tense.)
> Therapist: *Just let yourself talk.*
> (Patient trembling, and tears roll down her face.)
> *All I want to do is to cry.*
> *Have not cried since I was here last* (About three months ago).
> (Patient weeps, and then pulls herself together.)
> *I didn't make anything.*
> *It looks like hands, I suppose.*
> *Can't talk at all.*

I really can't.
(Patient very disturbed, too disturbed to continue the interview.)

The reader who has had no personal experience of plastotherapy may well be incredulous that a patient should become so very disturbed by the simple matter of modelling without any intervention by the therapist at all.

In the absence of relevant associations, the shapes she has made in the clay have no meaning at all. It can only be assumed that the process of modelling brought some particularly disturbing idea near to the point of ventilation, but its final expression was actually inhibited at the last moment.

The patient was much too distressed to be taxed further, and quite some time passed before she was able to compose herself.

Figure No. 28

The patient is a big, good looking man, of particularly fine physique, and about thirty years of age. He was being treated on account of his emotional difficulties with women. During considerable verbal psychotherapy, he had always been well poised and well controlled. He had never expressed any strong emotion, and had never shown any sign of abreaction.

He was left by himself with the modelling materials, in a state of normal mood and complete composure. About fifteen minutes later, when the therapist returned, he was sobbing convulsively, with tears streaming down his face. He pulled himself together enough to make the following comments.

Knew I wanted to shape it into a breast.
It was warm.
I was contented.
I felt at peace, as if nothing mattered.
Was thinking of my mother.
Don't think she always liked me.

He was so disturbed that it was some time before he was sufficiently composed to leave the premises.

The clinical impression was that the modelling involved the patient emotionally in a way which would not have occurred with any amount of formal psychotherapy.

THE PATIENT'S REACTION

The patient reacts both to the model, and to the therapeutic sessions as a whole. Sometimes the very sight of the model is terribly distressing to the patient. When asked about it, he pushes it away. He may become very upset and refuse to look at the model at all. *"No, no. Take it away. Take it away; it is horrible."* It would seem that he regards it with real horror, something which he simply cannot contemplate. In the case of pre-psychotic schizophrenic patients this reaction at times has been one of great violence; but the reaction may also occur with psychoneurotics. In view of the fact that the patient has made the model himself and nothing has been said about it, this is a very strange reaction. It would seem that the very process of modelling, without any psychotherapeutic interference by the therapist, has brought to the patient's awareness some very disturbing idea which has been previously repressed, or perhaps merely suppressed. There is another important factor. In ordinary psychotherapy a patient will express some terrible conflict. It is expressed in words. But the spoken word is easily denied and forgotten. This defence comes into play to save the individual from oppression by too great anxiety. But when the conflict is expressed in modelling, the situation is different. These defences are no longer applicable. The patient sees the expression of the horrible idea; it is there in the model before him. That is why it is pushed away. He cannot tolerate the sight of it.

Of course there are other defences available for the patient to use to save himself from the hurt of awareness of the idea expressed in the model. But a feature of plastotherapy is that a patient's defences may be very active and effective as regards verbal expression, and at the same time they may be inactive and ineffective in the field of plastic expression.

There are some further observations on those patients who recoil in horror from the shape they have created. It is not the horrible appearance of the model in the factual sense, which causes the patient to recoil from it. Some patients make shapes of figures which would ordinarily be described as revolting. Yet the patient may show no revulsion from them. But other patients make apparently innocent shapes, and are caused great distress by them. The actual physical shape of the model is not in itself the disturbing factor, nor is the actual idea expressed in the model. Many patients make models which express horrifying ideas without being disturbed by them. The factor which determines the patient's response is his own particular reaction to the idea projected in the modelling, that is, the psychic significance of the idea in relation to his own particular personality structure.

There is another point. There would seem to be a qualitative difference in the patient's revulsion from the model, and in the usual type of anxiety reaction which occurs from sudden awareness of traumatic material in verbal psychotherapy. It is difficult to express the subtlety of the difference. The anxiety experienced in psychotherapy seldom has the persistent horror and loathing which is sometimes seen in the patient's reaction to the model.

Instead of being disturbed by the model, the patient may react with open incredulity that he could have made such a thing. When this reaction has occurred, the patient has often been very resistive to modelling on subsequent occasions.

Besides reacting to the model, the patient reacts to the therapeutic session as a whole. At the conclusion of a session, it is usually seen that the patient has some fairly clearly defined attitude to the situation. This is so because of the patient's emotional participation in the treatment. If there is no emotional involvement, as in a session of recreational modelling, the patient leaves in a neutral state of mind, without any clearcut attitude being established. With plastotherapy, on the contrary, the patient may go out of his way to make known his attitude, either in words, or by some non-verbal communication. This attitude of the patient varies with different persons and in different circumstances. The patient may express open amazement or incredulity that this thing which he has made with his hands should in fact be a reflection of the deep-seated conflict of which he was hardly aware. He is pleased, and feels that the treatment can do something for him. On the other hand, there are many patients in whom anxiety is aroused by

the ventilation of their conflict, or by the half expression of repressed material. At the end of the session, these patients are often
uncomfortable within themselves, and sometimes quite disturbed.
Their attitude is often one of resentment. They may be openly
hostile to the therapist for making them feel uncomfortable in this
way. Such resentment is usually shown obliquely rather than
directly. The patient makes disparaging remarks about the situation. *"Sort of thing kids do." "Have not had my hands in a mess
like this since I was a child." "I was really expecting some help by
psychotherapy."* Such expressions are the product of the patient's
temporary hostility. If his aggression is passively tolerated, it ceases
in subsequent sessions, as the patient begins to realize the help he
is gaining from the treatment.

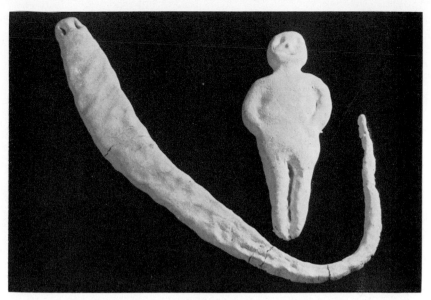

Figure No. 29

A girl had been treated in hypnosis for the removal of an hysterical tic. She was now undergoing waking psychotherapy. She makes a human figure and a snake; she then gives the following associations.

Looks as if it's dead.

Don't like the look of it.

Think it's a man.

Think it must be my father.

(Loses her concentration, shrugs her shoulders.)

I know what this other thing is.

A snake I saw a long time ago.

Saw it when I was picking up some wood.

(Gives an account of the circumstances of seeing the snake.)

Therapist: *Just talk the thoughts as they come to your mind.*

Nothing comes to my mind.

Therapist: *Just talk about what comes into your mind.*

(Patient blocks and says nothing.)

When she was seen a week later, she asked if she was hypnotised when she made *"those horrible things."* She was reassured that she had not been hypnotised; then she said, *"When I was making them I knew they were silly, but I felt I could not make anything else. Felt I had to keep on and on fiddling with the snake's tail. If I were making something with clay I would not make a snake, surely"* (i.e., if not hypnotised).

For several sessions after this she flatly refused to have anything more to do with the clay.

95

Figure No. 30

The evaluation of the patient's reaction to the model may be just as important as the evaluation of the actual model itself. This model was made by a woman who had previously suffered from organic brain damage. She had been admitted to hospital on account of grossly hysterical behaviour; and the matter was further complicated by the fact that, just at times, she gave the impression of being out of touch, in a way which suggested the possibility of a schizophrenic process. This, however, was quite overshadowed by her florid hysterical behaviour. She was given the clay, and she made this model, which shows two recumbent figures lying side by side. The patient was known to have an acute domestic conflict. The only feature for comment about the model is the obvious camouflage.

The patient was asked about the model, but she would say nothing at all. She then came to react to the model in quite a peculiar way. It was as if the therapist must know all about it. Her reaction to the model clearly showed the odd schizophrenic quality, in contrast to the dramatic hysteroid quality of her behaviour in the ward.

FAILED SCREENS

Sometimes it is quite clear that the patient intends to defend himself by making a screen model, but somehow the process breaks down. This demonstrates very forcefully the dynamic qualities of modelling when it is used in plastotherapy. His associations often show how the patient purposefully set out not to disclose himself; but in making the model it somehow comes about that he actually makes something which is directly connected with this very conflict. Sometimes the patient is aware of the change as he works the clay, but in other cases the patient believes that he has produced a model with no psychological implications whatever. In these cases, it is interesting to note the change in the patient's reactions as awareness comes to him. He usually starts off easily and confidently because he feels secure, since he does not associate the model with any personal problem or psychological conflict. As he is encouraged to talk about the model, his attitude changes. As the model begins to be associated with his inner conflict, his previous easy confidence gives way to tension and anxiety. As he is led to talk further about the model, he realizes that he is discussing some basic problem which he had not intended to ventilate. Patients who have had this experience have afterwards commented that they would never have brought themselves to discuss the subject if it had not been for the use of the clay.

Figure No. 31

A failed screen model.

> *Dirty old man lacking in intelligence.*
> *An unpleasant person to deal with.*
> *Was thinking of the prostate gland.*
> *Feeling that I would have done something sexual if I had been*
> *sure the girls would not see it.* (i.e. made a sexual symbol
> if he were sure the therapist's secretaries would not see it.)
> *It suggests the General Manager, more trouble with him.*

It seems that the patient made a screen model in the form of a face.
It then appeared to him as an unpleasant face. He then realised it was
the face of the General Manager, a man whom he hates. It was actually
his conflict with this man which precipitated the illness which brought
him to consultation.

Figure No. 32

A failed screen model.

The patient was a man of minor executive status. He was inclined to be resentful of authority, and conscious of matters of wealth and position. In a number of sessions he had been very resistive to modelling. Previously, he had had considerable treatment by psychoanalysis; and he felt that the modelling was merely an invitation to make sexual symbols.

> *Sheep with a good fleece on it.*
> *Saw the big hat of your other patient, assumed he must be a sheep farmer.*

After a good deal of irrelevant talk, he associated the sheep with wealth. The original comment that the sheep had a good fleece on it suggests that it is in fact a symbol of wealth. (The reader is reminded that, in Australia, the sheep is commonly used as such a symbol.)

It would seem that the patient was determined to avoid the projection of the sexual material which he felt the therapist wanted. He makes a screen model of a sheep, the idea being suggested to him by the sheep farmer's hat. But it so happens that the model, which is made purposefully to avoid the expression of psychologically significant ideas, comes to express his very active conflict as regards matters of wealth.

99

Figure No. 33

A girl of seventeen years suffered a sudden onset of a severe tic of the shoulder, which at times involved most of her body in convulsive movements. The tic had been controlled by suggestive hypnosis. She was now being treated in psychotherapy. The complete absence of anxiety when she had finished the model made it obvious that she had made a screen, and that she was secure in her defence.

> (Laughs) *I have just been reading about the Loch Ness Monster.*
>
> (Laughs again and looks sideways at the therapist. There is no trace of anxiety, and her manner is rather like a naughty child playing a game, teasing her parent.)

Therapist: *So it's a monster.*
The back reminds me of a mouse, the front of a crab.
Therapist: *What about monsters?*
Weird, imaginary, I suppose.
Therapist: *Ever think of present-day monsters?*
There are no such things.
Therapist: *But people often talk of monsters.*
But just on an occasion.
Therapist: Mmmm.
I sometimes say he is a monster.
Therapist: *Who would you say that about?*
Met a boy last Saturday night, he followed me around.

He followed me.

I said to Jean he was a monster.

Therapist: *You said he was a monster?*

Suppose I meant horrible.

Therapist: *Why did you feel he was horrible?*

Kept on all the time.

Very persistent.

Suppose he expected me to fall in with him and I just wasn't going to.

Therapist: *In what way would he expect you to fall in with him?*

Take me home; go for a drive.

(Pause)

Is it true that opposites attract opposites?

Therapist: *Was he your opposite?*

I hope so.

Therapist: *Talk a little more about these things.*

Over Christmas four of us had photos taken in Bill's car.

Didn't turn out very well.

Dreamed Bill turned into a monstrosity.

Went eccentric.

Therapist: *Bill seemed a bit of a monstrosity?*

(Pause)

Therapist: *Just talk.*

(Pause)

Therapist: *About Bill?*

(Patient becomes restless, some tic movements develop in the shoulder. Pause.)

Therapist: *Just let yourself say these things.*

You must think I have a one-track mind, always talking of boys.

Therapist: *That's normal enough.*

I think about them, then I get disappointed.

Therapist: *You think about them, and you get disappointed?*

Don't know what I get disappointed over.

Therapist: *Just talk.*

(Pause)

Last Saturday night I imagined if I went to the Town Hall, I imagined Bill would be there.

I went, but I didn't see him.
(Movement of shoulder increases.)
Later on I heard he was there.
Therapist: *You missed him.*
(Pause)
Therapist: *Would you like to make another model now?*
(very definitely) *No.*
Therapist: *You said you felt disappointed when you thought about boys. Do you think that has anything to do with the monster idea?*
Could be, I suppose.
Therapist: *Just talk.*
Well, I don't like boys.
Wouldn't like a monster.
Therapist: *Why do you say you don't like boys?*
I suppose you have got to have boys.
That's why I force myself to flirt.
Therapist: *You like flirting a bit?*
No.
(Pause)
Therapist: *Just talk.*
I have to have a boyfriend, otherwise people would think something was wrong with me.
That's why I go out with boys.
Have never been out with a boy and enjoyed being there.
Sooner be by myself or with a girlfriend.

This is a perfect example of the psychodynamics of a failed screen model. It was quite clear from the patient's laughter and her teasing attitude that she felt that she had fooled the therapist by making something silly and of no possible psychological significance. In a few minutes, her conversation about this frivolous model brings her to the open ventilation of her significant conflict, which had remained unexpressed in several sessions of formal psychotherapy.

SECOND SESSION RESISTANCE

The difficulty which is experienced in inducing some psycho-neurotics to express themselves in modelling has already been dis-cussed. It often happens that, when such a patient is brought to model, the procedure goes particularly well. Conflicts are disclosed in the modelling which had not been expressed in formal psycho-therapy. The patient is emotionally involved in the expression of the conflicts, and it would seem that everything is going very well. At the next session, however, it has been a very common experience in such cases to find that the patient is extremely resistant. In the early stages of the work, this second session resistance used always to come as a great surprise and shock to the therapist. The first session had gone so well that it was assumed that subsequent ses-sions would go likewise.

However, it is this very success of the initial session which un-consciously puts the patient on guard. He realizes that he disclosed himself more than he had intended. He senses that he was no longer master of the situation, as he felt he was in formal psychotherapy. He has the feeling that somehow he had lost full control, both as regards what he was expressing, and also the way in which he was stirred up in his emotions. He tends to approach the next session with apprehension and caution.

Second session resistance may show itself at any or all stages of plastotherapy. The patient produces specious rationalizations to avoid modelling. He feels that he is not suited to this form of treatment. He has another appointment; there will not be time to do any modelling today. The resistance may be shown in the actual models. It may be that, on the first occasion, in an unguarded way, the patient expressed his sexual conflict in sexual symbols. He wants to avoid doing this again, so he deliberately uses the clay to express some relatively unimportant reality problem. A change of this nature, from the expression of significant biological material in the first session to inconsequential reality problems in the second session, is quite a common occurrence, and is taken as a manifesta-tion of second session resistance. This mechanism must not be con-fused with the gradual transition from deeper to more superficial material which takes place as the deeper conflicts become resolved over a period of treatment.

Second session resistance often shows itself in an attempt by the patient to make a screen model. To avoid a repetition of the embarrassing disclosures of the first day, he sets out deliberately to make a model of no psychological significance. It has been shown how the subtle dynamic mechanisms of plastic expression very often lead the patient on, so that he ends up by expressing the very ideas which he purposefully set out to avoid. It thus comes about that the second session of plastotherapy is a common occasion for the production of failed screen models.

The patient may make what appears to be a significant model, and then manifest second session resistance by refusing to talk about it. The more the patient is pushed for associations, the more tense and anxious he becomes. Some judgment may be needed to avoid precipitating an anxiety reaction. Sometimes the situation can be met by peripheral enquiry, rather than by seeking an explanation of the central theme. By this means, the patient may be led to disclose the conflict bit by bit, rather than all at once. With this type of resistance, when the defences are persistently maintained, and the patient's anxiety is mounting, it may be a help to give the patient a face-saving excuse to disclose the problem. Hypnosis can be used to this end. The patient is ready to accept the opportunity of ventilating the conflict, and at the same time denying responsibility.

Figure No. 34

1.   *A foetus.*
        Have only one son.
        The others I was not allowed to have.
        Love children.
        Feel very sad about it all.
2.   *Just a vase.*

These two models, made directly the one after the other, illustrate the same principle as is seen in second session resistance. In the first model, the patient has expressed a psychologically significant idea which is disturbing to her. She realizes that she has expressed rather more than she intended. As a result of this, her defences become alert, and she then tries to make a vase which is only a screen model, and is of no psychological significance at all.

105

VII

ANXIETY REACTIONS

ANXIETY IN PLASTOTHERAPY

Anxiety reactions may occur in ordinary psychotherapy, as any form of insight therapy mobilizes a certain amount of anxiety. These reactions most commonly result from frustration by the therapeutic process; or fright at the emotions released in abreaction; or the sudden awareness of repressed material; or a reconsideration of basic values. In plastotherapy, the dynamic processes of psychotherapy are accelerated. In fact, this is the whole purpose of plastotherapy. In its turn, this acceleration of psychodynamics has the direct effect of increasing the likelihood of anxiety reactions. This is necessarily so because the mechanisms of toleration and adaptation work only slowly. The more rapid therapeutic process does not always give these mechanisms time to function effectively. A patient may be able to tolerate the gradual awareness of repressed material, which would cause acute anxiety if it were disclosed more quickly.

In any form of psychotherapy, the control of the patient's anxiety from moment to moment during the interview is a fundamental necessity. The experience of anxiety has a profound effect upon the ventilation of repressed material. Too great anxiety may inhibit the patient; too little anxiety may make him feel comfortable and secure, and thus work to rob him of motivation to express conflicts, the thought of which distresses him. A mounting anxiety may drive a patient on and on, faster and faster, like a runaway horse, until thoughts which he is at present unable to bear surge into his consciousness. The therapist is continually regulating the amount of anxiety which the patient is experiencing. It is reduced by reassurance or by emotional support; it is increased by diverting the patient's awareness to anxiety-producing areas. In plastotherapy, with the acceleration of the dynamic processes, the therapist must be more than ever observant of the patient, so that he can lessen the tension at the critical stage, and so forestall an uncontrollable attack of anxiety.

An interesting aspect of the anxiety reactions which occur in plastotherapy is that they are not related to the model as such, but are only related to the patient's reaction to the model. A patient may make a shape which clearly symbolizes a sexual conflict but the patient may not react with anxiety. Thus a psychotic patient made homosexual symbols without being disturbed in any way, although the models would seem to be of a nature which would disturb most patients. Similarly, a neurotic patient made a shape representing sexual congress. The open expression of such an idea is very disturbing to many neurotics, but this woman showed no undue anxiety. The reason was that the symbol was made in response to her desire to have a child, and not an expression of sexual conflict. On the other hand many models, which on their face value would not appear to be in any way disturbing, may in fact produce very acute anxiety reactions. The patient may make a simple human figure. It is his father. He talks about him, and becomes more and more disturbed. Finally, he may become aware of his hostility; and he may then experience acute anxiety. Thus the anxiety-producing effect is not inherent in the model itself, but is only a product of the patient's reaction to the model.

ANXIETY FROM FRUSTRATION

The patient very often experiences some initial anxiety when he is first asked to model something. It is a new experience. He is rather caught unawares. Anxiety which he was able to control in the verbal interview is now mobilized. The therapist observes the signs of mounting tension. He reassures the patient. *"There is nothing difficult about it. We use it frequently. Many patients get great help through it."* The patient's anxiety is further allayed by the therapist's calm, leisurely, and at the same time sensitive approach. Anxiety of this nature is rarely any trouble, as it is easily controlled by these simple means.

The patient may become anxious through frustration in another way. He may accept the idea of modelling; but when he goes to do it, he may find that he cannot get started. He holds the clay in his hands, but, try as he may, he is unable to think of anything to make. He complains that his mind has gone blank. He wants to be co-operative, but he finds it impossible. Something holds him back. He is frustrated. Tension mounts, and the usual symptoms and signs of anxiety appear. This reaction has occurred most frequently with highly inhibited patients. In retrospect, it would seem that the patient has usually not been adequately prepared for plastotherapy, or has not been given adequate emotional support in the critical initial phase. A similar type of reaction may occur with an obsessive patient who may find that he simply cannot come to a decision as to what to make. Sometimes these reactions may be quite acute. One patient who had been left for a few moments found that she was unable to make anything. She became acutely disturbed, and rubbed handfuls of clay into her hair.

A less common type of anxiety reaction occurs in the obsessive patient who does not like to touch the clay because he feels that it is dirty. On one occasion, a man was too sensitive to disclose that this was the cause of his reluctance to make something. He was encouraged to take up the clay in his hands, and he promptly had a very acute reaction with sweating, tremor and general distress. It was only then that he explained that he could not bear to touch the wet clay. It conflicted with his obsessive ideas of cleanliness. A woman patient reacted rather similarly, and it was disclosed only in subsequent psychotherapy that the slimy feeling of the wet clay was associated in her mind with a sexual assault which she had suffered as a child.

Sometimes the frustration and the associated anxiety reaction occur at a later stage in proceedings. All goes well; the patient makes a model; but when he is asked about it, he finds that he cannot say anything. He blocks. This, of course, is a defence. It saves the patient the hurt of ventilating the traumatic conflict; but at the same time it frustrates him in the reality situation. He wants to say something, but he cannot. The more the therapist pursues his enquiry, the more does the patient become tense and anxious.

The management of the situation requires judgment. It is clear that something of significance is on the threshold of expression. It is in the patient's interests that it should be ventilated. On the other hand, persistent enquiry runs the risk of precipitating the patient into an acute anxiety reaction. Although this is very unpleasant for the patient, in intra-mural psychiatry it may not have any untoward effect on the general progress of the treatment; but in consulting room practice, any acute anxiety reaction is to be avoided, as the patient has to be in a fit state to return to his home at the end of the session. If, to avoid this danger, the patient's anxiety is alleviated by reassurance and emotional support, there is the risk that he will not express the conflict. The management of the patient consists of a compromise between these two attitudes — that an acute anxiety reaction is avoided, but at the same time the patient is left with sufficient anxiety to provide motivation for the expression of the conflict.

Whatever happens, the anxiety must be reduced by the end of the session; otherwise the patient may be too disturbed in the interval until the next session of treatment. If the blocking persists, and it seems likely that the significant conflict will not be expressed during the session, then it is wise to lead the patient to talk of some inconsequential matter which can be related somehow to the model. In this way, anxiety between sessions is reduced. Such a procedure may be necessary, although it has the obvious disadvantage that the patient may try to use this experience as a defence during the next treatment.

SUDDEN AWARENESS OF REPRESSED MATERIAL

It is often wise to warn the patient that he may find himself expressing ideas which would not ordinarily come to his mind, and if this should happen, not to worry about it. In this way, an attempt is made to reduce the likelihood of anxiety reactions. This, of course, is not necessary with psychotic or hypnotized patients. However, with the psychoneurotic patient in the waking state, there is a very real danger of sudden acute anxiety reactions arising from the abrupt awareness of ideas which have been expressed in the modelling. Latent homosexuality presents a danger in this respect; but in actual practice, it would seem that the defences usually remain active, so that the symbols which are so clearly bisexual to the therapist may remain meaningless to the patient. This is the ideal situation. The therapist, if he thinks fit, can then, at a suitable time, allow the patient a gradual awareness of his conflict, by psychotherapy around the symbol.

However, many patients suffer transient anxiety reactions as a result of the sudden awareness of much more superficial conflicts. This may occur merely through the patient's awareness of the intensity of his love or hate. He may have been vaguely aware of his emotion, and at the same time refused to acknowledge it to himself. It is usually someone whom he should not love, or someone whom he should not hate. He models a figure which represents the person concerned, and suddenly finds himself expressing the full strength of his emotion. Such a reaction may be very disturbing to the patient. Even if it may be desirable from the point of view of treatment, there is the practical difficulty of working with ambulatory patients who have to be in fit condition to return home after the consultation. An occasional patient has been so disturbed by an anxiety reaction following the sudden revelation of superficial conflicts, as to refuse further treatment. Such reactions can be anticipated to some extent by the following type of suggestion: *"You just let yourself go. You let yourself express anything at all. It does not matter what it is. Do not be frightened by what you find yourself expressing. You just let yourself go."*

Once the anxiety reaction has occurred, there are two different ways of dealing with the situation. One aims at increasing repression; the other at giving the patient insight. Which method is used will be determined by circumstances. Reassurance is a direct means of facilitating the repressive mechanisms. If necessary, half a grain of phenobarbital and a cup of tea will help the patient to feel more composed. On the other hand, if the moment is opportune, the patient can be led to insight by psychotherapy round the model and the conflicts expressed in it. Before starting on psychotherapy in this way, one must always be sure that adequate time is available, as the patient will at first usually become more disturbed before he settles down.

Quite a number of different ideas have had the effect of producing anxiety reactions. The patient's sudden awareness of his ambivalence towards a parent or marriage partner is a common cause. So is the sudden awareness of the sexual component of love, particularly so in young, inhibited, or idealistically minded schizoids. The idea which is likely to produce the most acute and uncontrollable anxiety is the patient's sudden awareness of homosexual drives within his own personality. This reaction may occur in latent homosexuals of either sex. Experience suggests that latent homosexuals should be treated very carefully when in plastotherapy, just as they should in any form of insight therapy.

Instead of a sudden, clear insight with an immediate surge of anxiety, the process may be much less dramatic. The patient may merely become intensely uncomfortable and show an extreme dislike for modeling. There is no sudden insight, but the patient becomes disturbed. He pushes the clay away. At any attempt to get him to continue, he offers very firm resistance. He may get up from his chair and pace round the room. *"I have had enough of that."* When taxed for further explanation, he can give very little reason for his sudden rejection of the clay. *"It gives me thoughts."* Sometimes it would seem that he is aware of the nature of the thoughts, but on account of the pain they bring, or owing to their ill-defined quality, he is unable to give them verbal expression. On other occasions it has seemed that the patient has never really been aware of the idea; but its approach to the threshold of consciousness has been sufficient to precipitate this type of anxiety reaction. The experience must be very disturbing to the patient, as in subsequent interviews, some patients have said that they would willingly have treatment by any means at all, except by modelling.

There is another factor concerning the management of anxiety in plastotherapy. The anxiety reactions which occur in response to the sudden awareness of repressed material in plastotherapy are generally much more difficult to control than are similar anxiety reactions occurring in verbal psychotherapy or in hypnotherapy. In verbal psychotherapy the patient can defend himself by the simple defences of amnesia and denial. In hypnoplasty, the therapist can save the patient from undue anxiety by increasing the depth of hypnosis. But the patient who has made a model in the waking state is continually confronted by the symbol of his disturbing ideas, with the result that his anxiety is both more severe and more persistent.

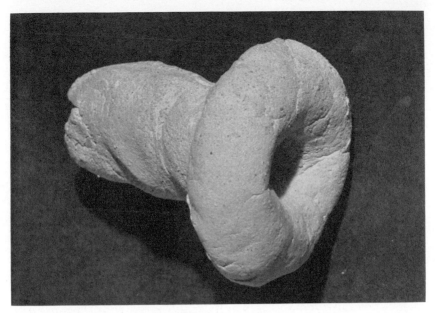

Figure No. 35

A schizoid youth, who complained of various anxiety symptoms, was rather vague and uncommunicative in the usual verbal interview. In the next session, he was given the clay, and in a state of intense preoccupation, he made this model, which consists of a phallic shape which is hollowed out behind.

It was immediately thought that the model was a bisexual symbol, and that it probably represented a projection of the patient's own latent homosexuality.

The patient spontaneously made the following comments, which tended to confirm the interpretation of the model as a homosexual symbol.

> *When I started to make something, that started unconsciously.*
> *Then thought—could be connected with* (very softly) *the*
> *penis.*
> (Pause)
> *Nothing more I can say about it.*

The conversation was promptly steered on to superficial matters. The patient gradually lost his intense preoccupation and was able to return home in a reasonably calm state of mind.

In subsequent sessions, the same type of symbolism was repeated, and the patient gradually came to talk of his homosexual conflict.

It was felt that the way in which the patient was deliberately led from the conflict which he had expressed in the model saved him from an acute anxiety reaction.

113

VIII
INTERPRETATION OF THE MODELS
THE MEANS OF INTERPRETATION

EXPERIENCE IN plastotherapy has made one thing abundantly clear. The models must be interpreted in the light of all the available information. Any glib interpretation of a model on the basis of its apparent symbolic appearance is fraught with danger. The occurrence of screen models, pseudo-phallic models, and the deliberately sexual models of the sophisticated patient, is sufficient reason to put one on guard when it comes to the problem of interpreting the meaning of these productions.

In coming to an understanding of any model, the patient's associations to it are equally important as is its actual shape. But in considering the associations, we must bear in mind that they may be used by the patient as a second line of defence, as it were. The conflict has found plastic expression in the model he has made. Now that he comes to talk about it, his defences may become more active. In fact, the defences concerning verbal expression are consistently more active than are the defences concerning plastic expression. So it comes about that the patient may use the associations, and in fact the whole of his verbal contact with the therapist, as nothing more than an elaborate defence screen to cover up the meaning of the awful idea which he has expressed in the model. However, we must not confuse this mechanism with conscious prevarication. The patient is not deliberately misleading us. He just finds that he is discussing the model in a light other than its true shade of meaning. It is clear that we must be just as chary in accepting what the patient has to say about a model as we are in our evaluation of the actual shape of it.

Some incongruity in the patient's affect, while he is actually making the model, will often lead us to suspect that he is making a screen model or a deliberately sexual model. Similarly, when the patient is making an apparently sexual symbol, the absence of pre-occupation or anxiety suggests that the model may be only a pseudo-phallic symbol. In the same way, by considering the patient's affect at the time, we get valuable clues as to whether or not the associations which he is giving reflect the real meaning of the model, or whether they are in fact a defence to obscure the real meaning.

Of course, it so happens that the patient sometimes consciously misleads the therapist in his comments about the model. After making it, he is suddenly overcome with panic at the prospect of disclosing such a matter to the therapist. He knows what he is doing. His prevarication is now quite conscious, but at the same time he is driven on, by forces within himself, to continue it.

Any furtiveness, hedging, or side glances at the therapist suggest that the patient's defences are functioning at a conscious level.

The patient's actual behaviour at the time he is making the model may give us valuable information. The patient may become pre-occupied while he is making the figure of a man. We may notice that his lips become tighter, or that there is a change in colour of his face. It may be that the figure he is making is prodded roughly with the modelling tool. If the patient tells us that the model is just the figure of a man, and no particular man, and that he just made it for fun, then we realize that he is using his comments as a defence. We can be quite sure of this because the signs noted in his behaviour were the manifestation of anger; and one does not display anger towards a non-specific object.

In the same way, we must use all the background information which is available in interpreting the models. Thus, a patient may make a model of ambiguous bisexual symbolism. If the patient has clear clinical signs of latent homosexuality, we are probably quite justified in interpreting the model as a projection of his latent homo-sexual drives. On the other hand, if the patient had given a history of satisfactory, normal heterosexual adjustment, one would seek some other corroborative evidence before making an unequivocal pronouncement as to the homosexual significance of the symbol.

115

In considering the patient's background in relation to the interpretation of a model, we must always refer to a clinical assessment of the patient's psychological background. We must not be unduly influenced by the patient's social background in the community, and be led into any false belief that a man in such a position would not harbour the thoughts which appear to be expressed in the model. Nevertheless, account must be taken of the patient's background or sophistication in matters of modern art and psychological theory, as this may have a distinct bearing on the character of the models produced.

If the patient shows resistance, by either evasion or blocking, in giving associations to the model, then hypnosis may be used as an aid in the interpretation. The patient is hypnotized; and while hypnotized, he is shown the model which he has made in the waking state. He can be asked what it is, or his association can be obtained in the same way as described in hypnoplasty.

Figure No. 36

The model was made by a schizoid youth who was on the verge of schizophrenia. From the appearance of the model, the therapist had assumed that it was a female breast, which is a particularly common production for inhibited young men to make.

> *Don't know what this could be at all.*
> Therapist: *What is the thought in your mind?*
> *Just doesn't seem to make sense at all.*
> (Pause)
> *Still feel — sort of — a bit nervy.*
> *Don't think it could be connected with sex.*
> *Wheel or —*
> Therapist: *Just relax, and tell me the thoughts in your mind.*
> *Could be — could be connected with sex.*
> *Suppose it could be.*
> *Could be the top of a penis.*

The patient's associations came as a great surprise. He was given further opportunity to associate the model with the female breast, but he persisted with his phallic interpretation. This illustrates the importance of the associations in the interpretation of a model.

In this case, the nature of the patient's associations was taken as evidence that the patient was in fact psychotic, although no clear evidence of psychosis was forthcoming from ordinary psychiatric examination.

Figure No. 37

If a patient confronts the therapist with consistent denial of the meaning of a model, and provided there are no contra-indications such as incipient psychosis or latent homosexuality, the patient may be hypnotized and questioned about the model while in the hypnotic state.

The patient denied the meaning of this model in the waking state, but when hypnotized, referred to it as a woman's breast.

TYPES OF SYMBOLISM

Patients who model clay in plastotherapy produce pieces which show four different grades of symbolism.

The most superficial may be called representational symbolism. The patient makes a model which aims to be a likeness of some particular object. A representational symbol can often be recognized by its having some peculiarity which identifies the particular object which it represents. Thus the particular house where some traumatic incident took place may be shown as a real resemblance to this particular house.

The great majority of the models produced in plastotherapy are conventional symbols. There is no attempt to produce an individual likeness. Thus a man may be represented as a round blob for the head, an oval body with two arms and legs. The fact that the model represents a man is quite obvious to any observer, but he cannot tell which particular man it is. In plastotherapy, the figure almost always represents some particular individual. However, his specific identity lies only in the patient's mind, and cannot be determined by the appearance of the model, but is disclosed in therapy by the patient's associations.

A third grade of symbolism occurs in the individual symbol. The patient invents some particular symbol to express some particular idea. He characteristically uses the same symbol to express the same idea on different occasions. As it has been made up by the individual, the observer cannot tell what it represents. We learn its meaning only through the patient's associations.

The most profound type of symbolism is the universal symbol of the unconscious in the Freudian or Jungian sense. Here we have the common phallic male symbol, and the hollow female symbol. In plastotherapy, these occur most commonly in the models of psychotic and prepsychotic patients.

Many patients make a model of the penis. However, it must be remembered that only a small proportion of these phallic shapes are true universal symbols. A neurotic male patient may make a model of a penis, and then start talking about the difficulties brought about by his impotence. In such a case, the phallic model is a conventional symbol as it represents something clear in the patient's consciousness. This is obviously a much more superficial type of symbolization than is the case in the following illustration, in which a pre-psychotic woman makes a phallic symbol and identifies it as her husband.

Figure No. 38

The four levels of symbolism are here demonstrated in the models of four different patients.

1. Representational symbol:
   The patient makes a model of a house, and ventilates problems in her life which concern the running of her house. It is a representational symbol because the two chimneys identify it as her particular house.

2. Conventional symbol:
   This is a conventional representation of a man. There is nothing about the model to identify it as any particular person. However, the patient identifies it in her associations as her boy friend.

3. Individual symbol:
   This is the "mouth-can't-swallow" symbol of the patient described in Chapter XI. Without the patient's associations the model is quite meaningless. It is only after two or three sessions with the patient that the meaning becomes clear. The indentations are recognized as tooth marks, and the twisted appearance of the model is seen to represent the idea of the food blocking in her gullet. As is usual with individual symbols, this model was repeated, with minor variations, on a number of subsequent occasions.

4. Universal symbol:
   This is a universal phallic symbol. It was produced by a young

woman who had been behaving rather strangely. Some years previously, she had had a craniotomy on account of a subarachnoid haemorrhage. The question now arose as to whether her disordered behavior was due to organic brain damage, or due to a schizophrenic illness. She was given the clay, and spontaneously made this phallic symbol. When asked about it, all she would say was that it was her husband. She made no mention of its being a penis, but maintained that it was her husband. This was taken as evidence that it was likely that she was schizophrenic, and the subsequent course of her illness proved this to be so.

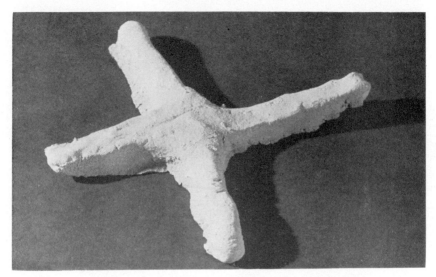

Figure No. 39

A mildly depressed patient makes this conventional symbol. She feels that she has neglected the spiritual aspects of life, and now plans to seek the help of God.

Figure No. 40

This is a typically conventional way of expressing an idea. The top two figures are the patient and his wife as they have been. At the bottom they are shown as they should be, and as they are going to be.

Figure No. 41

The patient was unable to give any associations at all to this symbol of the female.

Figure No. 42

A mildly euphoric schizophrenic woman makes this shape. She says it is *"The sound of Alleluja."* It is thus a good example of an individual symbol expressing an abstract idea.

LEVELS OF INTERPRETATION

There would seem to be no doubt that some models are capable of valid interpretation of different meanings at different levels of psychic integration. This occurs most commonly with models which have a direct reference to some present-day reality problem, and which at the same time represent some form of classical sexual symbolization. The patient will often give a series of comments or associations referring to the present-day situation. Then there may be a pause in which the patient becomes more intent and more preoccupied. He then comes to give a further series of associations relating to the latent sexual symbolism. The content of these latter associations may have no direct connection with the previously expressed, more superficial ideas.

Various manifestations of the principle described above are common enough in psychoanalysis and psychoanalytically orientated psychotherapy. However, the modelling has provided many examples of the same principle as applied to the expression of abstract ideas, which are clothed in the garb of present-day reality problems. In these cases, there may be no obvious sexual content.

Sometimes representational or conventional symbols may be used in such a way as to express a profound abstract idea. If the deeper meaning is not especially sought, it may easily be missed, as the patient is often sensitive about the deeper meaning which he has expressed, and he is happy for the therapist to accept the model on its face value, and so avoid discussion of the abstract meaning.

Figure No. 43

The patient is recovering from a severe psychosis. She produces a well integrated model of three poplar trees. The branches of the smaller central tree are arranged in the shape of the letter "K," and a path in the form of a "K" leads up to the trees.

The patient's associations indicate that she is still much more disturbed mentally than is indicated by the model.

> *I was thinking of blind people when I made it.*
> *How they can feel distances.*
> *I was thinking of that Katy again.*
> *The two big ones are looking after her.*
> *There is "K" on her, and "K" in the front, it is also the pathway.*
> *It was Katy that I saw in the vision.*
> *Joan who came into the ward represented Katy.*
> *When I went to Joan she had half of what I had.*
> *She had visionary words too.*

From the appearance of the model, and from the patient's associations, we can assume that the rather artistic composition of the three trees really represents two people looking after her friend Katy.

However, it so happens that we know a good deal more about the patient, and this additional information allows us to make a further interpretation of the model at a deeper level of psychological integration.

Besides the plastotherapy, the patient has also been painting, and is being treated in psychotherapy in relation to the conflicts expressed in this way. The theme of the three poplar trees has occurred several times in her painting. Sometimes she has referred to the two larger trees as Adam and Eve, and the small one as representing all their progeny. However, on other occasions, she has referred to them as the Trinity, a symbol of Godhead. In these paintings, there has been a long path leading to the three poplars. This is the path that one must travel in life to finally reach God. In the present model, the idea of the path has been contaminated with her thoughts about her friend Katy, and it has turned into the letter "K." So, with this additional information about the patient, we can now interpret the model, not only as three poplar trees, and Katy being looked after by two other people; but also as an expression of creation and a belief in the Godhead of the Trinity.

Figure No. 44

The patient gives this model the title, "Anaesthesia." Dramatically and with feeling, she demonstrates the sensation of relaxation and profound flaccidity which the patient experiences when she is being given an anaesthetic.

These ideas are openly expressed when she talks about the figure. But a knowledge of the patient makes it clear that the symbolism also gives expression to other, deeper ideas of which the patient did not speak.

She is a religiously minded woman. Although she is not psychologically depressed, in her illness she became preoccupied with matters of religion. This idea finds expression in the way in which the anaesthetized figure is shown so clearly as a cross. But the symbolism goes a stage further than this. The figure shows how she gives herself up to the oblivion of the anaesthetic, but she gives herself up in the form of a cross. She thus comes to show that she not only abandons herself to the anaesthetic, but she abandons herself to the care of God.

In such a case, the full meaning of the symbolism may come to us only when we have both the patient's associations to the model, and the history of her state of mind at the time of making the model.

REALITY PROBLEMS

If we come to consider the actual thought content expressed in the models, we find that these productions fall roughly into three groups. There are models which express reality problems, models which express basic psychological conflicts, and models which express abstractions. It must be emphasized that such a grouping is incomplete, as there are many borderline examples. More than this, a reality problem is often found to be a problem only because of some basic psychological conflict; and again, such a conflict may be seen by the patient as an abstraction. Nevertheless, some such grouping is convenient for descriptive purposes.

The significant reality problem will always be disclosed in ordinary conventional psychotherapy, provided sufficient time is taken. The patient is held back usually by guilt or shame, or by loyalty to someone dear to him. If it is not ventilated in the first session, then it will be on some subsequent occasion. In such cases, plastotherapy merely has the effect of hastening the process.

The problem is usually expressed in conventional symbols. The model represents some person or object which is connected in some way with the problem. In such circumstances, very often the patient makes a human figure, and in his associations, identifies it with the father or wife or lover, or some person connected with the particular reality problem.

When the patient has come to ventilate a reality problem in this way, he nearly always feels better for it. He has at last brought himself to discuss the awful thing. Consequently, there is an easing of tension and a reduction of anxiety.

Figure No. 45

An insecure, dependent girl presents her reality problem with complete directness.

My home.

Maybe I am frightened of leaving it.

In this case, as with many others, the reality problem is secondary to some deeper psychopathology.

BASIC PSYCHOLOGICAL CONFLICTS

The patient may have some vague inkling as to the basic psychological conflict, but unlike the reality problem, it is something which is not in his clear awareness.

These conflicts will ultimately find expression in formal psychotherapy, but it may be quite a time-consuming affair. As a general rule, such conflicts are ventilated much more quickly by means of plastic expression in modelling.

In these cases, the conflict is very often expressed in models by using universal symbolism. The expression of basic psychological conflict is usually accompanied by uneasiness, tension and anxiety. In this respect, the situation differs from the expression of a reality conflict which leaves the patient with less anxiety.

The anxiety-producing effect of the situation is such that it is wise to see to it that awareness of the idea comes to the patient only slowly, so that it is within his capacity to bear it without the mobilization of undue anxiety. It must be emphasized that when the basic psychological conflict concerns latent homosexuality, the patient should not be allowed to become aware of his condition, unless proper means are available for adequate treatment.

It is frequently found that a patient's model is a direct expression of some reality problem, but at the same time, in another way, it also represents some basic psychological conflict. The same model thus comes to have different symbolic values at different levels of consciousness. In such a case, there is always the temptation to bring the patient to work at the deeper level; but it may well be wiser to ignore the deeper symbolism, at least for the time being, and evaluate the patient's condition after the resolution of the more superficial conflicts.

Figure No. 46

This model was made by a psychotic female patient. It represents an expression of basic psychological conflict. During her psychosis, she spoke a good deal of homosexuality, as regards both herself and her husband.

She makes this shape with a female breast and a phallic tail. It would seem to be a clearly homosexual symbol. This is confirmed by her irrelevant reference to homosexuality about her husband.

> *Looks like a baby worm.*
>
> *Does an embryo look something like that?*
>
> *One day, a fair, pansy, effeminate creature called out to my husband and said he need not look as if he did not know him.*
>
> *It looks like a tongue — very smooth.*
>
> *What do circles and curves mean in psychology?*
>
> *Negative personality not amounting to much.*
>
> *It looks like a little baby.*

It is interesting that she makes no reference to the sex of the creature which she has made. Earlier in her illness, she would make ready comment about the sexual aspects of her models. However, at the time of making this piece, she was beginning to recover from her psychosis. The repressive mechanism is more effective again, and prevents the expression of the sexual ideas in words, even though they have been given clear expression in the plastic symbolism of the model.

134

ABSTRACTIONS

As distinct from reality problems and basic psychological conflicts, the patient sometimes uses modelling to express some abstract
idea. It is often something which is very vague, but at the same
time very significant to the patient. It may concern his evaluation
of fundamental matters such as life and death, or it may be that
some incident of the utmost triviality inspires in him some thought
which he feels as profound or significant. As one might expect,
young schizoid persons of either sex are the main source of such
models. In fact, it is quite common for the vague idealism of
introvert youth to find expression by this means. The idea may be
expressed in conventional symbols, in which case the patient discloses its deeper meaning in his associations. Very often the idea
is expressed in individual or universal symbols, and the therapist
senses from the start that the patient is striving to give expression to
some abstract idea.

There is a further feature about these models. Sometimes they
express ideas which are extremely difficult, or may be almost impossible, to express clearly in words. This applies particularly to
cases where individual and universal symbols are used. The individual symbol, which is the neologism of plastic expression, is
created for this very purpose. It is essentially a neat way of expressing some idea which cannot be expressed with equal simplicity
in words.

In our everyday life, from time to time we have the experience
of thoughts and feelings coming to the mind which seem to be
beyond our power of expression. They often concern very basic
problems, matters which may change the whole course of our life.
They may concern the strange accompaniments of love, or the
lack of love. It is not so much love itself, but the ephemeral intangi-
bilities which accompany it. Sometimes the urge to communicate
these ideas is very strong, but words fail. The ideas seem to exceed
the limits of verbal expression. So also with other basic problems.
There are those of life and death, of God and the spirit. Mankind
has accepted the fact that words are inadequate for the expression
of such ideas. We fall back on symbolism. This is seen in the

135

Church; and we must not forget that the ancient Church and modern psychiatry are two disciplines of learning which share much of the same raw material. Thus the patient who comes to us for help is often unable to communicate his problem, through the sheer inadequacy of words. When the verbal symbol fails, the idea may find expression in the plastic symbols of his modelling, or it may be that the verbal and the plastic symbols together can express something which cannot be expressed in words alone.

Figure No. 47

A crown, because I have had to fight.
Know when I have won the battle, I shall have the crown
of achievement.
Achievement of winning the battle against illness and slander.
This model is typical of the way in which an abstract idea may be expressed in conventional symbolism.

IX

PLASTOTHERAPY AS AN AID IN DIAGNOSIS

INCIPIENT PSYCHOSIS

THE DIFFERENCES in the models of psychotic and psychoneurotic patients can be turned to practical use in the field of diagnosis. In the vast majority of cases, diagnosis is a matter of no great difficulty, and is determined more easily by simple clinical methods than by plastotherapy. But all who practise psychiatry will, on occasion, have difficulty in deciding whether some particular patient is psychoneurotic or is in fact pre-psychotic, a schizophrenic who does not yet show the signs of schizophrenia. This is one of the most important differential diagnoses in psychiatry, as on it will depend future treatment and management. It is just in this field that plastotherapy may be extremely useful. It is with projection that the pre-psychotic schizophrenic most readily discloses himself. This is seen in the Rorschach Test. The pre-psychotic will usually model without reluctance, and in so doing will often disclose his disordered thinking in the material projected symbolically in the model.

In a similar way a patient, who on clinical examination is just a little over active and mildly euphoric, in plastotherapy may give clear evidence of early hypomania. The unstructured situation of modelling allows him to give full rein to the pressure of his ideas, which may still be quite well controlled in a diagnostic interview.

In the use of plastotherapy for diagnosis, the decision should not be made only on the examination of the model; but the manner in which it was made, and the patient's verbal associations to it must always be given full consideration.

Much valuable information may also be obtained from negative

138

results. A highly introverted, schizoid youth came to consultation because he could not get on with his fellows at work. When anyone would whistle, he thought they were whistling at him. There was a history of his having run away from boarding school. He had had some kind of nervous breakdown which had kept him home from the university for a year, and he had recently considered a monastic life, and had only been dissuaded by his parents. From this history, and from psychiatric examination in which he showed himself to be very reserved and withdrawn, it was considered likely that he was an early schizophrenic. However, when given the clay, he modelled only objects which were the practical concern of his life as an engineer. He made none of the bizarre objects which are commonly made by patients in the early stages of schizophrenia. This negative result of his modelling was taken to mean that his grip on reality was much better than that which formal psychiatric examination had led the therapist to expect. It was interpreted as indicating that the patient was a highly sensitive introvert, rather than schizophrenic. Further investigation proved that this assessment of the patient was correct, and treatment was modified accordingly.

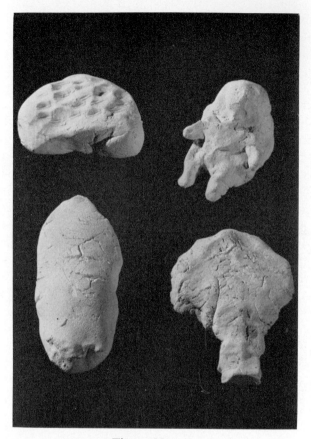

Figure No. 48

A young business executive, who was still working, had been restless and overactive for a few days. On examination, he was talkative, but rational, and showed no clear evidence of thought disorder. He made this series of four models to represent human life.

The complexity of human nature.
One — a child alive.
Two — needs bread to survive.
Three — when he grows up his brain is bigger.
Four — in search of knowledge explodes the atom.
Man must go in search of knowledge for the ultimate benefit
of the child.
Why did I start with a child — because I want another.

The bread is like a Polish roll.
The cells of the brain are so complicated that one doesn't
know what it all represents.

The thought content of this series has the pseudo-philosophical quality which is so often seen in early schizophrenia. The impression is that biologically significant ideas have just gained the threshold of awareness, and that their expression is clumsy and inarticulate. The whole is incongruous with the patient's background as a business executive.

In this way, plastotherapy gave much more definite evidence of thought disorder than was obtained in clinical examination.

Figure No. 49

At the time of making this model, the patient was still working in a responsible professional capacity. He was a young man of schizoid personality. He had always been shy and retiring, but he came to consultation on account of increased anxiety in meeting people. Psychiatric examination disclosed some ideas of reference, but the patient gave no evidence of gross thought disorder.

> *Yes, top of a penis.*
> *Thought it was when I was making it.*
> *Just seems pretty big.*

While the patient was making the model, it was thought that it might be a symbol of the female. The patient's associations came as a complete surprise. They were taken as evidence of the probable onset of the psychotic process, which was not demonstrable in an ordinary interview.

Figure No. 50

A young man came to consultation. He was a little vague, and it was hard to nail him down to any specific complaints. He had recently had an unsatisfactory affair with a girl. He openly expressed both love and hostility towards her. He was finding his work increasingly difficult. In a general way, it seemed that he just felt that all was not well with him.

On examination, there were well marked obsessive traits, and a tendency to rigidity of thinking. He was not hallucinated, and there were no ideas of reference. On clinical examination he could be considered a fairly normal young man.

For diagnostic purposes, he was given clay and asked to model something. He made this very poorly integrated shape, which he called a mouth.

> *A mouth.*
> *I put some teeth in it.*
> *Don't think it is much of a mouth.*
> *Would like to have put big lips and some teeth but couldn't.*
> *But couldn't work the clay.*
> *Don't think it looks like a mouth.*
> *If the mouth had been open I would have had the tongue hanging out to make it comical.*
> Therapist: *Is it comical now?*

No, just a mouth.
I am not impressed with it.
Don't want to talk about it.
Therapist: *Whose mouth might it be?*
Thought never occurred to me; can't attach it to anyone.
As far as a mouth goes I like a woman's mouth to be attract-
ive, with full lips.
Doesn't look like a woman's mouth, more like a deadbeat's
mouth.
Would like to have a nice mouth.
Betty once said I had an attractive mouth. I wasn't thinking
of that. She often complimented me on my mouth and
teeth.
Flattery.
Flattery is hard to refuse.
Wasn't thinking of that, just took the clay and made a cleavage
and there was a kind of mouth.
With these film stars the mouth is a prominent feature.
Like to see a good set of teeth.
Therapist: *Whose mouth do you think it is?*
Only my own which I have in my mind.
Don't like to talk about my mouth.
Marlon Brando and James Dean have good mouths.

The patient's associations to the model showed an incoherence which was quite absent from his conversation in an interview situation. In fact, both the poor quality of the model and the apparently psychotic nature of the associations came as quite a surprise to the therapist.

An important diagnostic problem presents itself here. Can the nature of the associations be explained on the grounds of obsessive thinking about the mouth and lips; or has the session of plastotherapy given evidence of an incipient psychosis which is masked in the ordinary clinical interview? The absence of obsessive features in the model itself, the poor integration, and the fact that it represents a part rather than a whole, would all suggest a schizophrenic process; and the associations are more disordered than one would expect in a psychoneurotic.

Modelling was discontinued for fear of precipitating the patient into a frank psychosis. He was treated with chlorpromazine, with improvement.

144

Figure No. 51

At the time of making this model, the patient was still working. It had been noticed that he was behaving a little queerly; but his wife did not think there was anything wrong with him. On clinical examination, he was restless, active and euphoric, but his thinking was still ordered and controlled. He makes a rocket ship which is surmounted by a cross. The modelling provided a situation which allowed free expression to his uncontrolled thinking, which was not disclosed in a clinical interview.

> *Guy Fawkes Day my son was born.*
>
> *A rocket scientist.*
>
> *My father creator of all things, has built blocks of flats, fishing boats, toys; he is a creator.*
>
> *My father will create the rocket ship.*

I must be the electric and computing engineer for the
rocket ship.
My brother is going to be —
He is a pilot of jet planes.
It will be a 5-stage rocket.
Five people in it.
Father, brother who will navigate, son will discover how to
run through the hydrogen and nitrogen.
One Christ on earth.
No man in the moon.
Who will we bring back from the moon?
We will be carried along by the rocket ship.
A cross on the top of the rocket ship. (Points to the model).
Come back from the moon piloted by Jesus Christ.
Have a lot to do.

The uncontrolled situation in plastotherapy has unleashed his hypo-manic flight of ideas. The process is of particular interest in view of the fact that in a reality situation the patient could still exercise judg-ment, and control his thinking. This was demonstrated after the session of plastotherapy. The patient had composed himself, and was about to return home. He was again asked about the model. He glibly rationalized what he had said as a phantasy. Nevertheless, a firm diagnosis of hypomania was made. However, in spite of heavy medi-cation, the patient had a florid hypomanic episode a few days later.

Figure No. 52

A sixteen year old girl was brought to consultation because she had been asked to give up the training as a nurse which she had just started. Neither the hospital matron nor the patient could give any very good reason for this action, and the parents were rather baffled.

During the interview, the girl would talk quite freely and pleasantly on matters of little consequence; but as soon as she was brought to any difficult subject, or any matter of psychological significance, her thought would block, and she would be able to say nothing. Each time she would remain silent until the spell was eventually broken by the therapist's re-introduction of some inconsequential topic. There was no

147

abnormality of affect, and her behaviour appeared normal. The parents considered that there was nothing untoward about the girl.

On account of her blocking, psychological enquiry at a verbal level was practically impossible. She was given the clay, and made this face with its protruding tongue. She was unable to give any associations at all. Subsequent events proved the model to be a projection of ideas of reference.

THE HALLUCINATED HYSTERIC

There is another important differential diagnosis in psychiatry, which is often a matter of considerable difficulty, and in which plastotherapy may be a considerable help or may even give an unequivocal decision. This is the matter of the differential diagnosis between an hallucinated case of hysteria, and a schizophrenic who may be using hysteric mechanisms of defence. Sometimes such a diagnosis is easy enough to make on the character of the hallucinations, or some other positive evidence of schizophrenia. However, a definite decision is not always possible in either clinical examination or projective psychological testing. These patients may be given clay and asked to model. The schizophrenic typically makes a model which is bizarre or disorganized. The hallucinated hysteric, on the other hand, makes a model with the characteristic neurotic features. It is an interesting fact that there are some schizophrenics of this nature who do not disclose their abnormal thinking in the more structured projective situation of the Rorschach Test, but who will nevertheless disclose it in making bizarre models. A difficulty in interpretation arises with the sophisticated hysteric who is familiar with modern art, and who consciously sets to work to make something bizarre. In this case, the patient's attitude to the model is quite different, and the associations disclose logical thinking about the model, in place of the bizarre ideas of the schizophrenic.

Figure No. 53

The patient who made this model was subject to vivid visual hallucin-ations, and was given to grossly hysterical behaviour. There were no signs of disintegration of her personality; and she was at first regarded as an hallucinated hysteric.

The model shows a horse's head with a snake on it. The patient was unable to give any account of what she had made. Like the models of many psychotic patients, it displays a contamination of ideas, and a mixture of different grades of symbolization. This was taken as evidence that in spite of her grossly hysterical behaviour, the patient was in fact schizophrenic.

It was later found out that she thought that the therapist's name was "Mare" or "Mares" (instead of Meares). The representation of the therapist by a horse's head is a conscious and superficial use of symbols. However, his masculinity is represented by the phallic snake on the mare's head. This is the product of a much deeper and clearly un-conscious process of symbolization. This juxtaposition of symbols re-lating to different levels of consciousness is one of the reasons why the typical model of the psychotic appears to us as odd, or bizarre, or incomprehensible; and at the same time it attracts our attention. It is intriguing to us because the deeper symbolic elements are related to unconscious material in our own minds.

150

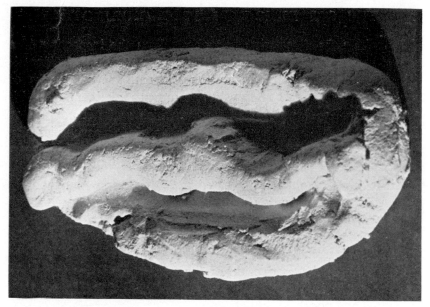

Figure No. 54

A young married woman was displaying grossly hysteroid behaviour by way of exaggeration and dramatization. She made this model. It represents a figure with the hands held above the head in the attitude of a diver. The figure lies in a kind of bed. The patient would not discuss the model, further than to say that it was herself.

The model has the bizarre quality which is so often seen in the productions of schizophrenic patients. There is something odd about it which is not ordinarily seen in the work of an hysteric. It is not usual to think of a recumbent figure with the arms held above the head. This was taken as evidence to suggest that, underneath the obvious hysteric defences, the patient was in fact schizophrenic.

THE SOPHISTICATED PSYCHONEUROTIC

In making the diagnosis of psychosis from the inspection of a bizarre model, there is one particularly important hazard. That is the sophisticated psychoneurotic who is familiar with works of modern art, and who consciously sets out to make something bizarre. There are a number of factors which make it possible to distinguish such productions from the models of psychotics. In the first place, our knowledge of the patient may clearly suggest the operation of such a mechanism. Furthermore, the actual model which is made by the sophisticated patient is often too good, in the sense that the execution of the model is too good; it is too well integrated, or the symbolism is too clearly expressed. In other words, when the sophisticated psychoneurotic decides to make something bizarre, he does so in a rather text-book fashion. On the other hand, the production of the psychotic patient is seldom so clear-cut in its bizarre quality, and the model is often poorly integrated and poorly executed.

There is also a marked difference in the attitudes of the sophisticated psychoneurotic and of the psychotic to their bizarre models. The psychoneurotic has a matter-of-fact attitude towards it. He made it consciously and he knows what it is. He is realistic about it; he may even laugh at it. This is in marked contrast to the psychotic, who is characteristically vague about it. This is because he does not fully understand it himself. As against the psychoneurotic's matter-of-fact attitude, the psychotic often seems as if he is half frightened of the model. He may push it away. He does not want to look at it. This of course is due to his half awareness of the repressed ideas symbolically represented in the model. There is none of this effect with the sophisticated psychoneurotic, because he was quite aware of what he was making. He may even be quite proud of what he has made, and may invite the therapist to examine it.

These differences become even more clearly marked when it comes to obtaining the patient's associations. The sophisticated psychoneurotic will explain the meaning of his production like a guide in a museum. Because it is, in fact, rather a fake production,

152

he can explain it without experiencing any disturbing affect. He may be rather pleased with himself about it, and refer to it as his work of modern art. The psychotic's associations to his model are usually vague. He cannot explain it because he does not understand what he has made. His associations are rambling and elusive; and as he looks at the model, he is often both fascinated and disturbed by it.

The recognition of these differences between the modelling of the sophisticated psychoneurotic and of the psychotic is of vital importance in the use of modelling in psychotherapy. If it were not for our ability to distinguish between these two cases, there would be doubt as to the validity of much of the work in plastotherapy.

Another mechanism sometimes comes into play. The sophisticated patient may have preconceived ideas about psychiatry and psychiatrists. To him it is a matter which deals with sex. When he is given the clay and invited to make something, he immediately thinks that the psychiatrist wants him to make something sexual. When the patient interprets the situation in this way, he may be provoked to react in either of two ways. His reaction may be one of purposive resistance to what he regards as a rather crude invitation from the therapist. He deliberately goes out of his way not to make anything with a sexual significance. Patients have disclosed this reaction in subsequent psychotherapy. Sometimes the result has been that they have simply made screen models. However, not uncommonly, when there has been some significant sexual conflict, the patient has tried to make a screen model but has failed, and he has unwittingly communicated the idea which he was deliberately trying to conceal.

Other patients, who believe that the therapist has given them the clay in the anticipation that they will model something sexual, react by doing what they imagine is expected of them. They set to work to make something sexual. *"If he wants sex, I will give it to him."* When the patient is a man, he usually makes a woman's breast, and a female patient usually makes a penis. This type of reaction occurs most frequently in disinhibited or insensitive persons. When the reaction occurs in pure form, the breast or penis is, in fact, a screen

153

model, as it does not represent a conflict. The patient has used what he regarded as the therapist's wish for something sexual as a defence against the expression of his real conflicts. This reaction is recognized when he talks about the model. There is an absence of anxiety. He may be rather pleased with himself. He is matter-of-fact about it, as it is not psychologically significant to him. On the other hand, some patients who show this reaction do in reality have significant sexual conflicts. They make the breast or the penis just to please the therapist, as it were, but in so doing they are unable to avoid expressing their own sexual conflict. This becomes clear when the patient is asked to talk about the model. He becomes tense and anxious. He is likely either to become very preoccupied with the model, or alternatively to show obvious dislike of it. He may push it further away. It may be noticed that he deliberately avoids looking at it. These reactions all show that the model is psychologically significant to the patient; and as he is kept talking about it, he will sooner or later ventilate his own problem. In this case, the model, which was made just to please the therapist, actually brings about the ventilation of the patient's conflict.

It is obviously very important that models of sexual organs which are made in this way, as a response to the mistaken belief that the therapist desires such models, should be recognized for what they are. Otherwise, they could be taken as an indication of psychosis. However, the patient's reaction to the model, and the nature of his associations to it, will usually settle the matter beyond doubt.

Figure No. 55

If this model were examined without reference to the patient or her associations to the model, in spite of its well integrated appearance, it could perhaps be mistaken for the production of a psychotic. However, the patient's associations leave no doubt in the matter.

> *I have made a horrible looking face.*
> *It's as well I know Picasso.*
> *Have been worried about my painting.*
> *So many modern paintings express uncertainty.*
> *I could not paint that way.*
> *My paintings, landscapes, give security, but feel they are not interpreting the present era.*
> *Have felt they are not an experience of today.*
> *Will have to face that.*
> Therapist: *What do you feel the model expresses?*
> *Tense, uncertainty, horrible face.*
> *These things always frightened me in art.*
> *I love having beauty like Mozart or Beethoven.*

Figure No. 56

This shape has some resemblance in character and form to the previous production. However, the associations make it clear that the model is the product of a psychotic, and is not the work of a sophisticated psychoneurotic, who consciously shapes something in the surrealistic manner.

> *This is the sea and a live bird, fish and all sea things.*
> *That was a head in the sea.*
> *The hand here.*
> *It's a sea hand, waves push it.*
> *Don't know what the fish is doing there.*
> *It has an old man in its eye — the other eye has nothing.*

DIAGNOSIS OF BASIC PERSONALITY

It is common clinical experience that a patient's basic personality structure may be more or less completely masked by some rather florid defence mechanism or reaction formation. In this way, it is not uncommon for gross hysterical reactions to camouflage, as it were, an obsessive personality, or even an incipient schizophrenia. In the same way, a reactive depression may disguise the basic personality. The depression is treated, only to disclose an early schizophrenia, or perhaps a severe obsessive neurosis.

The recognition and evaluation of the underlying personality structure is of importance, both in treatment and in prognosis. This sometimes comes quite dramatically in modelling. Hysteric defences are most effective and most easily used in interpersonal relations. This situation holds in the circumstances of the clinical interview. Modelling, on the other hand, is more impersonal, and many patients whose everyday life is crowded with hysteric mechanisms may show little of it in their modelling, and reveal more of their basic personalities.

Similarly, we learn a lot about the patient's attitudes from the way in which the model is made. A man makes a representation of his loved one. But he models only her head. This suggests that, although he loves her, he completely avoids her womanly body. Is he frightened of it? Is he too immature to think of her sexually?

Then again, she may be represented as a full length figure; but her figure may be shown asexually. There are no feminine curves. There is no bust. Such a model suggests that the patient does not think of her in terms of sex. On the other hand, the loved one may be represented in all her womanliness. Great attention is given to the shaping of her body, and the moulding of her breasts. It is clear that the patient thinks of her as a sexual being.

Just as in the ordinary interview we learn much about the patient from the things he does not tell us, so in plastotherapy we learn much about a patient from the things which he does not express in his modelling, and from the features which he omits from his models.

Figure No. 57

Sometimes the model reflects the patient's basic personality structure rather than any particular conflict.

This model was made by a patient suffering from a severe phobic condition which was elaborated with a gross hysterical overlay. His agoraphobia was so intense that crossing the street would occasion him terrible distress. He would cling to the security of the buildings on one side, and could cross to the other side only when a number of other people were doing likewise. His accounts of his symptoms were interspersed with the hysterical grinding of teeth and clenching of fists; and the initial interview disclosed an intensely hostile reaction to any suggestion of authority.

The model gives a clear indication of his underlying obsessive personality, which was masked by the florid symptomatology. He thought he would make the clay into a cube, but he found that the material was so soft that he could not make the corners exactly square. He persevered for over half an hour. He was quite unable to leave the task and make a transition to another project. The model was placed on one side and he was engaged in conversation. During the psychotherapy, he continued to stretch across the table, still bent on further attempts to straighten the corners of the cube.

X

PLASTOTHERAPY WITH PSYCHOTICS
MODELS OF PSYCHOTICS

T HE APPROACH OF THE psychotic patient is usually direct and un-complicated. In contrast to the psychoneurotic, he will frequently start to model something with little or no delay. This readiness to express oneself in modelling is quite a feature of early schizo-phrenia. The patient may not be able to give any very clear idea as to what the model is about, but he makes it readily, and is quite prepared to do more. In fact, if left to themselves, many schizo-phrenics will continue modelling until the supply of material is exhausted. Sometimes, of course, the nature of the illness will make the production of models impossible. A patient exhibiting stereotopy may go on and on moulding the clay for hours at a time, in very much the same way as is sometimes seen in hypnotized psychoneurotics.

Usually with the psychotic patient the defences are down, and there is nothing to prevent the spontaneous expression of conflicts. This process is well seen in schizophrenics whose illness runs a recurrent course. When the patient is psychotic, he models freely and without hesitation. As he improves, it becomes more difficult to get him to express himself in modelling. Then, when his illness is in a state of remission, his defences are active, and it may be quite impossible to get him to model at all. He behaves again like a normal person. He may rationalize the situation, or produce screen models of no psychological significance. Then, if there is a recurrence of the illness, he will again project significant material in modelling.

In general, the models made by psychotic patients show different characteristics from those made by psychoneurotics. They are usually more disorganized. Even when the parts of the model are well formed, the model as a whole still gives this impression of disorganization. The psychotic finds difficulty in organizing into a unity the various components which go to express facets of the idea. But there is more to it than this. Models made by psychotic patients characteristically have a bizarre quality about them which is not usually seen in the work of psychoneurotics. It is difficult to analyse the factors which make the models appear bizarre. Fragmentation is often a feature. There are bits and pieces with no apparent cohesion. Parts of objects are often used to represent the whole. Pre-psychotic and psychotic patients have a tendency to use individual and universal symbols in place of the conventional symbols of the psychoneurotic. There is an obvious similarity in this process of making individual symbols, to the schizophrenic production of neologisms. In both there is the creation of some new symbol which is specific to the particular patient, and is used to communicate some idea which the patient finds difficult of expression. In one case the symbol is verbal; in the other it is plastic.

The models of psychotic patients are often incomprehensible to the observer. If he is uninitiated in matters of symbolism, he may still be drawn to the model because of the direct appeal of the universal symbols to elements in his own unconscious. In this way he may feel fascinated, as it were, by the model. It has some kind of attraction for him, but he does not know why. The bizarre quality of the work of psychotics is further enhanced by the juxtaposition of objects which ordinarily are not in close apposition. It is odd, incongruous. It is the language of the unconscious, bizarre, just as it is seen in modern surrealistic works of art.

There is usually nothing commonplace about the ideas expressed in the models of psychotics. For the most part they are the ideas of basic biological conflict — of love and hate; of sex and sexuality; of life and death. These conflicts may be expressed in a starkness which is not seen in the models of psychoneurotics. A male figure is distinguished by his genitalia, not by his clothes, as with psychoneurotics. There may be a constant repetition of the same idea in succeeding models, which is foreign to psychoneurotics. The latter are aware that they have expressed an idea, and so proceed to the expression of further ideas. With the psychotic, the one idea often demands constant repetition. This process would seem to be analogous to stereotypy.

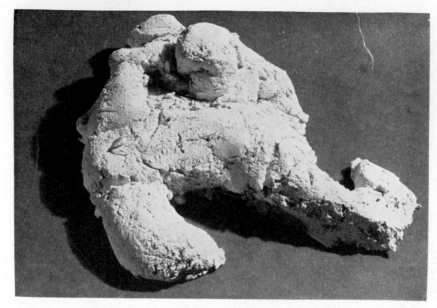

Figure No. 58

Although the psychotic patient took great care and time in forming this model, in reality it is nothing but a shapeless mass. However, in a rambling and incoherent fashion, she went to some pains to point out various persons and parts of persons in the clay.

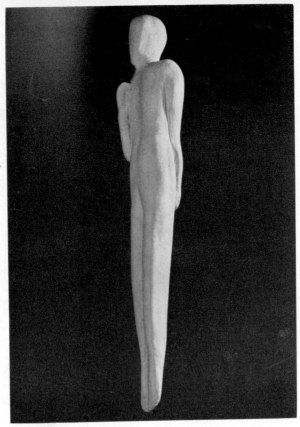

Figure No. 59

There is often something bizarre about the model made by a schizophrenic. Something incongruous, something which we cannot quite understand. It is as if the model were signalling some message to us, but we fail to comprehend it.

This model illustrates these points, and the patient's comments really do very little toward making the matter any clearer.

> *You could call it Russia.*
> *Are you sure you did not say anything about Russia?*
> (The patient apparently refers to some hallucinatory experience.)
> *You said you did not say anything about Russia.*
> *How could I hear that?*
> *Since the revolution, Russia is a young country.*
> *General idea of where they are going — like the figure when it was half finished.*
> *The left arm — diplomacy, must hide one side of your political thoughts.*
> *The right arm — asking for a blessing for guidance.*

Figure No. 60

A psychotic female patient with homosexual conflicts makes this likeness of the female external genitalia. There has been some attempt at secondary disguise.

Looks a bit like a face.
Looks like a cockeyed face.
Just sex thoughts.
Don't want to talk about them.
(Patient then abreacts.)

Figure No. 61

Schizophrenic and pre-schizophrenic patients not uncommonly speak in enigmas; so that what they say seems to have meaning to the patient, while it has no meaning to others. This tendency may find expression in the modelling.

A young schoolteacher comes to consultation because she has lost control of her class of young children. She is rather unconcerned about it. She has some slightly odd mannerisms, but she is in complete touch with reality. She has no ideas of reference, and is not hallucinated. She talks quickly and logically.

She makes the above model, and spontaneously makes the following comment.

> *There is nothing to talk about, that is as obvious to you as it is to me.*

This was said in a way which showed that the model had some meaning to the patient, and that she assumed that the meaning was also obvious to the therapist.

This is a typically schizophrenic comment from a patient in whom there is no clear clinical evidence of psychosis. It indicated that the patient was on the verge of schizophrenia.

Figure No. 62

This model of a face shows the enigmatic quality which is so often seen in the modelling of schizophrenics.

MODELLING AS COMMUNICATION

One of the basic problems in the treatment of acute psychosis is the failure of communication. The patient is unable to tell us what is wrong. In our everyday parlance, we say, "The patient is out of touch". We have learned to communicate with such patients by means of our behavior. The disturbed patient can understand the meaning of our actions when he cannot understand our words; and we in turn can learn something from his behaviour. We can let him know that we like him, that we want to help him, and care for him. This simple communication is often of vital importance in our management of the acute psychotic. However, this form of communication is limited to the expression of a few very primitive ideas. Modelling can sometimes be used to further this process as a means of more complex non-verbal communication.

The psychotic patient may use the clay as a means of communication in more than one way. The process may be entirely unconscious, and apparently without purpose. He makes some shape. He does not know what it is, but by its symbolism, or by its relation to other models, or by the patient's reaction to it, or by his verbal associations to it, the therapist may learn the meaning communicated by the model.

In other cases, it would seem that the model has some real meaning to the patient, although on account of his psychosis he is quite incapable of translating the symbolism of the model into the symbolism of words. In these cases, although the patient is out of touch with reality, there is something quite purposive about the modelling. It is a message. It is as if the patient writes down his problem; but instead of forming letters with a pen and ink, he forms his own symbols with his fingers in the clay. The meaning is clear to him, and he expects the therapist to be able to read and understand. He invents shapes to express some idea which he cannot express in words. This is an individual symbol. The first task of the therapist is to decipher it. This becomes possible because these symbols tend to keep recurring in subsequent models. The patient's associations to it are always obtained and noted. So also are other things about the symbol; its relation to other symbols, the meaning of which might be known; the patient's mood, and his behaviour in relation to the symbol. By these means the significance of the various symbols is discovered. A stage is sometimes reached in which it is possible for the therapist to use these symbols to communicate with the patient in psychotherapy.

In the case illustrated (figure 63), a young schizophrenic woman repeatedly made models of a human figure with a bird's wing attached to it. In her associations, she always referred to the figure as "he." However, it gradually became clear that she identified herself with the figure. From the beginning she would say that she knew that the wing should not be there, but she felt she had to make it. If she did not make the wing, she would become distressed and have to go back and add the curious appendage. Then she would be disturbed on account of the wing. When talking about it, on more than one occasion she broke up the model in a bout of impulsive violence. On two or three occasions, she spontaneously switched from talking about the model to rambling about being bathed with her brother when she was a child. This was the clue. In talking about her baths in childhood, she disclosed her castration anxiety. It was clear that the male figure was herself, and that the wing which should not be there was the appendage which she believed she lacked. In this way, the plastotherapy was used as a means of symbolic communication with the patient, who had lost through her psychosis the power of logical verbal communication. After psychotherapy with the models, and some paintings which expressed a similar theme, she showed the figure and the wing separately, to indicate that they did not belong to each other. This coincided with a dramatic clinical improvement.

In still other cases, the process is clearly a conscious one. The patient expresses some idea in the modelling which is already in his awareness. He could express the idea in words, but he is held back by various psychodynamic processes. Communication at this level occurs both with psychotics and with psychoneurotics.

Figure No. 63

A psychotic patient used the modelling in an apparently purposive way to communicate to the therapist ideas which she herself did not consciously understand. A figure with a phallic bird's wing attached to it was used to symbolize her castration anxiety.

MODELS ACT AS A GUIDE TO PROGRESS

If the models made by a single patient in the course of his illness are arranged in chronological order, they often reflect in a dramatic way changes in his mental state. In the case of psychotic breakdown, the models made when the patient first comes under treatment are characteristically bizarre and disorganized. As his condition improves, the models become better integrated and are more easily understood. Then as the illness clears, it is quite characteristic for the patient to introduce a new style into his modelling. The shapes are better formed, but the profound ideas so often expressed in psychosis give way to the expression of everyday trivialities. Instead of the stirring symbolism of the unconscious, the ideas are expressed in the conventional symbolism of the chocolate box and the advertising poster. The models made by patients deep in a psychosis seldom have any artistic merit because the craftsmanship is usually poor; but the ideas expressed in these models are often the profound truths of the disinhibited unconscious. This is the stuff that goes to make great art. But as the patient recovers, this material of potential artistic value is replaced by the trite ideas of everyday urbanity. At the same time, he characteristically tries to dress up these platitudes in the form of art. He tends to lose sight of modelling as a mode of expression, and returns to his conviction that modelling should be artistic. Thus it often happens that the models of the recovered patient are but the pale shadow of the work done in mental illness.

The course of the illness is reflected in another way. As a general rule, the psychotic patient will project his conflicts in a quite uninhibited manner into the shapes he makes with the clay. As he gets better, the repressive mechanisms reassert themselves. He finds he cannot use the clay as he did before. He becomes reluctant to model. It is not uncommon for patients who would model freely while psychotic, to refuse absolutely to model when they have recovered. Two such patients had recurrences of their psychosis, and they again modelled freely; and as their illness remitted a second time, they again refused to use the clay.

The situation during the course of a psychoneurosis is quite different. Initially it is very hard to get the patient to model. However, as he becomes more accustomed to it and less insecure about it, and as his anxiety is relieved by treatment, he comes to model more easily and freely; which is just the reverse of the march of events with the psychotic patient.

This progression in the changing character of the models has applications in therapy. It is found that it can be a useful adjunct to clinical examination in assessing the patient's mental state. Experience suggests that on occasion it is a very sensitive guide as to the patient's condition, a more sensitive guide in fact than the ordinary estimate that one makes of a patient in talking to him. On more than one occasion, a distinct change has occurred in the character of a patient's modelling, but no significant change could be observed at clinical examination; yet a few days later the clinical change became obvious. As the change in the models definitely preceded any observable clinical change, it would seem that, with some patients at least, changes in the quality of their modelling may be a very sensitive guide to changes in psychic integration.

This march of progress of the models, and its link with the patient's condition, is interesting in yet another way. Sometimes it is clear that it is related causally with psychotherapy which is being given to the patient around ideas expressed in the models. Thus some conflict is expressed in the models. It is resolved in psychotherapy, and is replaced by other conflicts. At other times the process is different, especially when the patient is receiving concomitant physical treatment in the form of electro-convulsive therapy or insulin coma. In these cases the change in character in the modelling is often only a reflection of the patient's improved condition as a result of the physical treatment, and there is no observable relationship with ideas expressed in psychotherapy.

THE PSYCHOTIC'S ASSOCIATIONS

As compared with psychoneurotics, there is a noticeable difference in the way in which psychotic and pre-psychotic patients give associations to their models.

In general, they do not evoke defences in the same way when

asked about the shapes they have made. On account of the psychotic process, their peripheral defences, as it were, are down, although their central defences by way of repression may still be functioning in varying degree. The result is that the patient tells us openly what he knows about the model. When the model represents repressed material, he will not be able to tell us much, but evasive defences such as denial and the giving of screen associations do not commonly occur. Sometimes the idea expressed in the model is an abstraction, and the patient may have great difficulty in explaining it in words. He is likely to get cross with the therapist because he cannot follow the meaning, which seems to the patient to be so obviously expressed in the model.

The pre-psychotic schizophrenic may make a model and then refuse to talk about it, in the belief that the therapist immediately knows its inner meaning. This is really an extension of the phenomenon of ideas of reference. The patient believes that people look at him. They can tell what he has done by merely looking at his face. *"You are the doctor; you know all about me from the model. Why ask me about it?"* Of course the therapist might know something about it, but he never knows all about it without the patient's associations.

XI

PLASTOTHERAPY WITH PSYCHONEUROTICS

MODELS OF PSYCHONEUROTICS

As a general rule the plastic productions of psychoneurotic patients are better organized than those of psychotics. The patient may have little competence in modelling, and the shapes may be poorly executed, but nevertheless the model is integrated into a whole. There is some unity about it.

The ideas expressed in the modelling of psychoneurotics are often rather superficial. They tend to the commonplace. This may be because the immediate conflicts of life are often expressed. Although these are real and disturbing to the patient, they may appear trivial to the observer.

It is not only the idea which may seem commonplace, but also the way in which the idea is expressed in the model. In their modelling, psychoneurotics tend to use conventional symbols of everyday life. Because of their familiarity, they come to appear trite or superficial, or perhaps lacking in sincerity. When concepts of right and wrong are expressed, the idea may be represented in much the same terms of symbolism as used in the children's picture books of moral stories which were in vogue a generation ago. It is seen that this manner of expression tends to the puerile, but it is always conventional, and being conventional, it is socially acceptable. This is a feature of the modelling of psychoneurotics. There is little about it which offends. Sexual conflicts are often expressed, but they tend to be expressed in a socially acceptable manner. The sex of the figure is indicated by the clothes or the hair, rather than by showing the genitalia as in psychotic productions. Nevertheless, as treatment proceeds over a number of sessions, the psychoneurotic's defences become less active, and conflicts then come to be expressed in a less conventional and more realistic manner.

There are many exceptions to these generalizations about the models of psychoneurotics. It would seem that the above account could be taken as an accurate description of the models made by psychoneurotics in the early stages of this study. However, over the six year period during which this work has been carried out, there has been a significant change in the character of the models of psychoneurotic patients. They have tended to become more fundamental and less conventional. This change in the character of the models has coincided with more care being taken to establish a positive relationship with the patient prior to modelling, and a greater emphasis on the patient working the clay in a state of calm reverie.

Figure No. 64

The typical model of a neurotic.

The cottage with the roses over the gate and the comfortable hearth are conventional symbols of domestic happiness.

House with rose garden and roses over the gate.

A comfortable house.

Nice warm fire where you could be happy (Patient weeps.)

Figure No. 65

A typical model of a neurotic. A young married woman makes a wall.
> Seems to be a wall that I cannot get over.
> If I could get back to being, without wondering why, every-
> thing would fall into place.
> Worried by the death of my friend who took her life.
> She loved so many beautiful things.
> Feeling of futility.

The wall that one cannot climb is a simple conventional symbol. It expresses a commonplace idea in a way which anyone can understand. It is a dramatization of the patient's inability, so that all can see how difficult things are for her. This type of plastic symbolism, expressed in a socially acceptable form, is characteristic of the neurotic.

MANNER OF APPROACH

The psychoneurotic is nearly always very wary of the idea of modelling. He does what he can to avoid a new situation. He is inclined to produce excuses and rationalizations as to why he should not do it. *"But this is silly."* As he talks, his anxiety becomes obvious. The idea of doing something new is a further threat to his waning security. The anxious, timid and often suspicious approach which the psychoneurotic makes to modelling reflects his fear of disclosing himself. This fear makes him more tense and more inhibited. He fiddles with the clay. With panic near at hand, he looks to the therapist for advice and reassurance. *"How do I do it?" "What shall I make?" "I have no ideas." "My mind seems to have gone blank." "Would you like me to make a cat, or a house?"* This type of behaviour is very characteristic of the psychoneurotic, and is evidence of active defences.

Getting such a patient started may be quite a problem. Success or failure usually depends on the degree of rapport established prior to putting the proposition of modelling. With a difficult patient, it may need up to half a dozen interviews before such a state can be attained. It is often hard to predict the psychoneurotic's reaction to modelling, and there are always a few patients who react with unexpected anxiety and hostility to the idea. Experience has shown that these are usually persons who have a fairly severe, deepseated psychoneurosis; but who have developed effective defensive attitudes so that in ordinary circumstances they can carry on, showing little evidence of their nervous condition. When they are confronted with modelling, they find themselves in an unfamiliar situation, and their facade breaks down with an apparently disproportionate mobilization of anxiety.

This cautious, anxious manner of approach of the psychoneurotic is in marked contrast to the psychotic or pre-psychotic, who will usually take to the modelling without much delay, and with very little show of anxiety.

When the psychoneurotic is making a model, there may be a general air of abstraction about his behaviour; and then, when he has finished the model, he very characteristically shows signs of

177

anxiety. At this juncture, he is quite likely to make some sudden move to take back the model from the therapist, or to destroy it. He quickly rationalizes his action. *"It is not good enough." "It is only silly." "I really did not mean to make that."*

Anxiety reactions occur much more frequently with psycho-neurotics while they are modelling, than they do with psychotics. The reason for this is simple enough. The psychotic patient is already expressing repressed material in his conversation and in his behaviour. In these circumstances, any further expression or additional awareness in modelling does not disturb him. On the other hand, the psychoneurotic's defences are still active, and re-pression is effective. Anxiety reactions may result from modelling, giving the psychoneurotic sudden awareness of repressed material.

When it comes to getting him to talk about the model, the psychoneurotic is always guarded. He very typically starts by deny-ing that the model has any meaning at all. *"It does not mean any-thing." "I just made it for fun." "I don't even know what it is."* The patient will use this type of defence even when it would be obvious to the most casual observer that the model does in fact have some meaning. One of the extraordinary things about plasto-therapy is the way in which a patient will change in a few moments from complete denial of a conflict which is expressed in a model, to its full ventilation.

GRADUAL EXPRESSION OF CONFLICT

Sometimes at the first session the patient will make a model which would seem to have no particular significance, but at the same time it does not fit very well into our ideas of a screen model because the patient seems rather too concerned about it. At the second session, he may repeat the model in slightly different form, and so again in subsequent sessions, until he finally makes some slight change or addition to the model which immediately has the effect of giving expression to some important conflict. In retro-spect, on reviewing the earlier models, it is seen that the idea was actually striving for expression in all of them. It would seem that the desire for expression of the idea becomes more and more com-

PLASTOTHERAPY WITH PSYCHONEUROTICS

pelling until it finally breaks through, and achieves open ventilation. Series of models of this nature give objective evidence of
the way in which repressed or suppressed conflicts gain expression.

A point of practical interest in this work has been the difficulty
of collecting such series of models. The early models of a series
always appear to be of little significance, and hence they have
often been discarded; and it has been only later in treatment that
the meaning of the earlier models has become apparent.

The following four illustrations represent successive models.
They show how the conflict gradually gains expression over a number of sessions.

The patient is a young woman in her early twenties. She had
had a long and rather unhappy attachment to a man, and now has
a very satisfying affair with another man, but he is on the point of
leaving her. She presents herself with the rather unusual symptom
that she feels that she is not emotionally mature. However, it soon
becomes clear that she is in fact quite a mature young woman, with
the empathic and intuitive aspects of her femininity well developed.
She had entered upon this second love affair rather lightheartedly,
but has fallen deeply in love with the young man, although he had
made it clear to her from the start that there was no possibility of
marriage. She has grown to depend upon him, both emotionally
and sexually.

Figure No. 66

It was going to be a little puppy dog.
Then I decided to make a little fat old man.
He was very tired and contented.
He sat down by his tool.
This is his tool. (Points to the modelling stick.)
He was just tired and comfortable.
He went to sleep.
He did not mind if anybody woke him and told him to go on
 with his work or not.

The clay was rather moist, and the original shape has sagged somewhat. It represented a man sitting down, draped in a cloak and leaning on his tool, a hoe of some sort.

It was assumed that this was a screen model, and had no particular psychological significance.

The patient continued to talk about values in life. Someone was encouraging her to take lessons in dress modelling and colour sense. This would help to give her outward security, but she felt that inner security was more important. She said that she wanted to be able to face the particular problems that would be her lot in life, with inner calm, and not to mind who told her to get on with the job. She expressed great surprise when her attention was drawn to the fact that this was the exact idea which she had expressed in the model. At the end of the session, I made the note, "The possible phallic significance of the tool is undetermined."

Figure No. 67

Fountain.
Was thinking about the patient in the waiting room.
Could a mother be partly the cause with all her love and
  attention.
Book I read "The Fountainhead."
Hardest part of being a mother would be not giving too much.
To sit back and let the children have their own life.
Like to have a large family.

The thought content of the initial associations was suggested to the patient by the presence in the waiting room of a mother with a mentally deficient child.

The patient was given ample opportunity to comment about the way in which she had used the modelling stick as the central part of the fountain, but her only reply was that she just used it to make a fountain. From her manner, her naturalness, and the absence of anxiety, it seemed definite that she had no conscious awareness of the phallic symbolism which she was using.

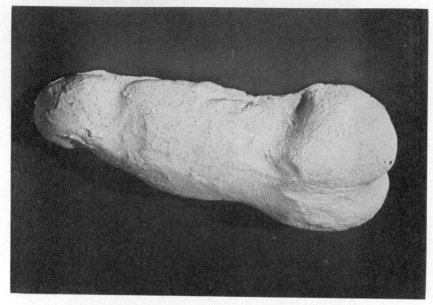

Figure No. 68

Patient has become very distressed in modelling the clay.

Re-living some moments.

It is all bound up with John.

To find the strength not to miss him too much.

I am going to miss the sex terribly.

Looking back, have been most contented when having sex regularly.

It was like a battery.

Very important to him.

If I am going to be good and not have sex, I am going to be frustrated.

Now I do not know if I want to be good any more.

Feel rather an outcast in a way.

Really like it sometimes.

Would not like other people to know. Would people sense it in me?

(Patient is extremely distressed and she makes some inconsequential conversation as a defence to relieve her tension.)

Frightened of growing old and lose attraction.

Need something to take the place of it.

182

Helping others.
Motherhood.
(Pause)
Feel I have slipped back this morning.
Suddenly insecure if not having sex.
(After a pause, says)
I could not have told you this without the clay.

The patient has openly ventilated her sexual desire, which it would seem was seeking expression in the phallic symbolism of the two previous sessions.

Note the spontaneous comment that she could not have brought herself to discuss such matters without the help of the clay.

Figure No. 69

Little clock with a little key in it.
That's me.
That clock needs winding; if someone doesn't wind it, or if
*   there is not some sort of stimulation, it won't go.*
Terribly lazy.
Different tick to everyone who winds it.
Takes on something of the winder.
Needs continual pushing.
No energy.
Therapist: *Tell me about the clock.*
I would rather be a winder than a clock.
Rather frightening with a different winder, the clock is not
*   itself at all.*
Therapist: *Who is the winder?*
Can be anybody — meeting new people — find myself a
*   different person with different people. Not sure which*
*   is yourself.*
(Pause)
Therapist: *Tell me about the winder.*

184

*If it is the wrong winder, the clock will probably tick the
wrong way.*

Most constant winder is John.

Wonder if I am as unselfish as I thought about him.

Am I doing it for my own gain, or do I love him deeply?

*When he leaves me I think of the things he teaches me, atti-
tude, discussion, sex, everything.*

Admire him tremendously as a person.

The patient has reverted to her original phallic symbolism, but now
she uses accepted figures of speech to discuss her sexual desire.

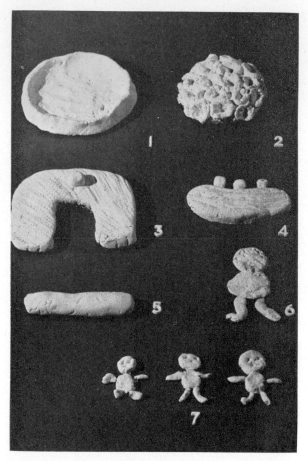

Figure No. 70

This illustration serves to show how a patient gradually comes to give expression to more significant ideas.

  1. An ashtray.—The patient was extremely difficult. She understood quite well what was expected of her in the modelling, but she makes an ashtray as a conscious defence.
  2. A lady's hat.—It is a new fashion. Again, she is determined not to give anything away.
  3. Her House.—She had been very proud of her house, and resented the fact that she had foolishly sold it.
  4. Her three sons in a fishing boat.—From the beach, she had seen

their boat catch fire when some petrol was accidentally ignited.

5. A phallus.—She says she is never satisfied sexually.

6. Her husband.—She says how she is repulsed by his fat body.

7. Her three children.—Then she speaks of the three people in her life whom she has really loved—her girlhood lover, her father, and her girl friend.

The later models thus show a vastly different ideational content from the ashtray and the lady's hat.

XII

EXCERPTS FROM CASE HISTORIES

THE READER IS REMINDED that the dynamic use of modelling is not a form of treatment in itself; it is merely technique in general psychotherapy. As a result of this, full case histories contain much material which is not concerned with modelling; so in order to avoid the inclusion of too much irrelevant matter, only those parts of the case histories which deal directly with modelling are presented. Of necessity, these will appear to the reader as rather fragmentary. In actual practice, it has happened very often that some significant conflict has been ventilated in the modelling, and then the patient has been able to continue with productive psychotherapy. Thus the history, as related by the models, often ends abruptly just at the climax of the story.

In each case, the patient's associations or comments have been obtained by non-directive enquiry. Thus the patient is invited to talk by pointing to the model, or by some general question such as, *"Tell me about it."* The patient is often kept talking by an occasional unverbalized grunt: *"Um";* or if this fails, *"Just let yourself talk about it."* These non-directive comments were not recorded, and are thus not included in the case histories. But any question or comment by the therapist, which is in any way more than a mere invitation to talk, has always been included in the record.

CASE NO. 1

HYSTERICAL HALLUCINOSIS? SCHIZOPHRENIA?

The following excerpts from the case history are presented on account of their interest in relation to modern art; and also in order to illustrate the use of modelling in the diagnosis of early schizophrenia, and in the assessment of the patient's progress.

On account of her difficulty in swallowing, the patient, a married woman with a young family, was admitted to hospital with a diagnosis of probable carcinoma of the oesophagus. While being x-rayed, she appeared to behave rather queerly, and was transferred to the psychiatric ward. She was described by the staff as pleasant and co-operative, and the only abnormality noticed was her rather hysterical manner and behaviour.

On examination, she was well in touch with reality. Her mood was normal, and her emotional tone was consistent with her thought. She was inclined to gesticulate and pose in a grossly hysteroid manner. On direct questioning, she admitted that she had recently had an unusual experience, in which she had seen three mysterious figures in a kind of vision. She identified one figure as a doctor, but was unable to identify the other figures. She later rationalized the experience as a vivid dream. There were no auditory hallucinations.

On the basis of her obviously hysteroid mannerisms, the vivid visual hallucination with the absence of auditory hallucinations, and her intact personality, a provisional diagnosis of hysteria was made, and her presenting symptom, the difficulty in swallowing, was regarded as functional.

Because she described the hallucination of the three figures very clearly, she was asked to draw it. She did this so readily that she was given painting materials and clay, in the hope that she would project psychopathological material. She produced a great number of paintings and models. Illustrations of some of the more significant models arc reproduced. The patient was of working class background, and was quite uninformed in matters of psychological theory. She had had no previous experience in modelling, although on some half dozen occasions she had taken her children to the museum, and said that she herself had been very interested in the statuary.

In this case, the patient was in hospital; the models were made in the absence of the therapist, and were discussed with the patient in twice weekly sessions of psychotherapy.

The models of this patient are filled with deep psychopathology, but in addition to this, they have real aesthetic merit. They thus gain a particular interest in relation to modern art, as they become an aesthetic expression of psychopathological motives. If we go to a collection of modern sculpture, we can see artistically created shapes which, to us as psychiatrists, seem to contain the blended elements of various psychopathological symbols. However, we can never be really sure, because we do not know what was in the mind of the artist when he was making the shapes. Here the situation is different. A young woman, ignorant of psychological theory and untutored in matters of art, has the native ability to create aesthetic shapes. Her psychological repressive mechanisms have failed through the onset of psychosis; and the psychopathology of her unconscious finds direct expression in the shapes which she creates. Here there is no vague speculation as to the symbolic meaning of the pieces, as when we view modern sculpture in our collections. Because of the failure of the repressive mechanism, she is able to tell us the exact meaning of her strange creations.

The photographs of the models are arranged chronologically in the order in which they were made. It will be noted that there are very considerable variations, both in aesthetic quality and in psychopathological content, according to changes in the patient's mental health from day to day. However, it is seen that the early works, made when the psychotic process was more active, contain a number of bizarre, poorly integrated pieces, and a number of well executed pieces which appeal to us as powerful because of their psychopathological symbolic content. As the patient's condition improves, the repressive mechanism reasserts itself, and more superficial ideas come to be expressed in terms of conventional symbolism. With further improvement, deep, biologically significant ideas give way to the expression of the mundane and commonplace.

Following psychotherapy centered around her models and paintings, she recovers and leaves hospital. Some two years later she relapses. Her plastic and graphic productions again express fundamental biological conflicts. Again she improves, and again the character of the models returns to the superficial and tawdry.

EXCERPTS FROM CASE HISTORIES

The work with this patient was done very early in the present study. Even from this very brief account of the models and the patient's comments, the reader will be aware of many missed opportunities for more active psychotherapeutic intervention.

CASE NO. 1

Figure No. 71

"The Guardian."

Life is given in the mother.
She must still lean out and watch over the child.
This arm is incorporating all love and goodness, also clutching
  as if it could strangle the child.
This arm has to be strong and right.
It did not want to be strangling like it ended up.
The strength of my husband is in that strangling.
She leans on a rock of light and right for strength.
The other hand is raised for protection, but could smack
  them judiciously.
The two faces look up for guidance.
There are apexes (apices) on her head.
Everything works out to apexes.
In my own marriage I have walked to the top of the hill
  as far as I can go.
It is a smooth pleasant sensation when I draw these curves.
Big breasted, because woman, goodness, sustenance for the

192

children; yet I did not feed my own babies.
The big arm is love and strength, holding them away, so as
not to smother them in the fulness of herself.

This is the patient's first model. Prior to making this, she had made several drawings and coloured paintings.

This piece is a well-integrated whole, and forms quite a pleasing composition. It is painted yellow. In her paintings she has consistently used yellow to represent light, spirit and goodness. The degree of integration is in marked contrast to her earlier drawings and paintings.

The patient identifies herself with the mother. The breasts are full because she failed to suckle her own babies. The full breasts also suggest femininity. The patient is very tall, although not unduly masculine in appearance. On other occasions, she expresses the wish for greater femininity.

The exaggeration of the right arm is symbolical in the artistic meaning of the word. There is some strong bond joining mother and children. When thinking of the strength of the arm, she associates the idea with the strength of her husband, and her hostile feelings towards him find expression in the idea of strangling.

The idea that the protecting left arm might also smack the babies is inconsistent with the poetic concept of the piece. So also is the thought of strangling. This suggests that the patient's mind is not as well integrated as the model suggests.

The comment about the "apexes" is odd, and suggests a neologism. But the patient has had little formal education, and it is probable that she means "apices," and is using the word to express the idea of a halo.

CASE NO. 1

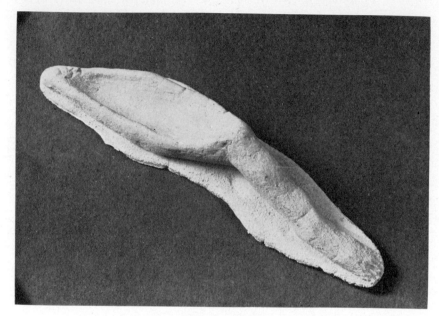

Figure No. 72

"A Leg."

Mother visited me while I was doing it.
I had made a shape I like, but when she started to tell me
of pre-natal influences I changed it to a leg.
I kept rubbing this part at the end.
I thought it was a boat going out to sail.
Mother said it reminded her of a vagina.
The beginning of the sowing of the seed often starts with
that knee.

This model, as distinct from the first one, seems to have all the appearance of a production of a psychotic patient. It would appear to represent a boat with a leg attached to it. There is no manifest meaning. It is bizarre. It is a very marked departure from the rather poetic quality of the first model made only two days previously.

During the session, the patient kept rubbing her finger firmly over the piece. It is clearly divided into two parts, the boat and the leg. From the symbolic point of view, it resolves itself into a kind of hermaphrodite symbol, a vagina with a phallic leg attached. It is not known whether her mother actually discussed the resemblance of the piece to a vagina, or not; but it would seem that this is very unlikely. A more probable explanation is that the remark attributed to the mother is in fact a projection of the patient.

This theme of bisexuality recurs in different forms in subsequent models.

At about this time, the patient was shown to a meeting of psychiatrists with a view to discussion of the diagnosis. Clinically she was in complete touch with reality, and her only obvious disorder was her grossly hysterical manner. The Rorschach test was inconclusive. Her previous talk of a kind of vision had been rationalized to a dream. The only real evidence to suggest an underlying schizophrenia was this strange model, and a couple of drawings which showed rather similar characteristics.

CASE NO. 1

Figure No. 73

"The Man."

Dominating brute.
Had to make him big because I feel he smothers me.
Feet big because he stamps on me.
Mouth shows impatience, no laughter.
Nose like a beak of a bird, cruel.
I felt I would like to stick the modelling tool in the eyes.
They are always seeing what I have not done.
It's fat and round, that means indolent, lover of food, lover
of self.
The wrinkles in the forehead express fiery temper.
He said he would kill me without anybody knowing.
Lots of times he says, "You're mad".

Here is depicted all the resentment and hatred of her husband, which she had found so hard to express verbally. There is a really satanic air about the piece. She has painted it black. When talking of her paintings, she had explained that she used black to express earthiness. This is in contrast to the bright yellow of "The Guardian," which symbolized light and the spirit.

In spite of the complete absence of a body, the piece forms a well-integrated whole in the shape of a pyramid. There is an artistic distortion of those parts of the body commonly associated in the mind with specific qualities—*"Nose like the beak of a bird, cruel." "It's fat and round, that means indolent,"* etc.

The patient was seen two days after making the model, and by that time the plaster had completely set. When talking about it, she became extremely disturbed. She took a wooden modelling tool which she had been using, plunged it into the eyes of the model, and tried viciously to gouge out the eyes of the plaster figure. The intensity of the abreaction was such that it would seldom be equalled even in hypnosis.

During the course of treatment, the patient subsequently made several models referring to her husband. In each of these, the idea of sexuality or bisexuality is very much emphasised. However, in this piece, there is no reference to sex, other than the idea of masculinity conveyed by the great nose, and hands and feet. The ideas expressed here are rather evil, loathing and hate.

CASE NO. 1

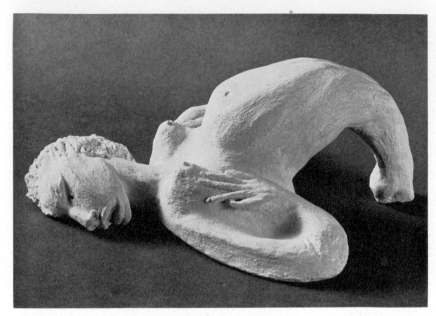

Figure No. 74

"Cherishing Time."

Motherhood; love, honour and cherish. Need cherishing at this time particularly.

My husband was never interested in the child coming. Some men would not make you feel big and cumbersome all the time. They would be full of regard for the new life that is coming.

All these savage thoughts were going through my mind while I was making it.

The legs are small because in childbirth you only feel the upper part of your body.

Arched because I have to go up like that. Combines intercourse in the same action. Arching up to receive life in intercourse.

Arching up to give life in childbirth.

The arms move in a pattern. To draw in, in intercourse, and to expel in childbirth.

There is both tension and relaxation in the fingers.

*The breasts are youthful. The nipples ready to give succour
to the new life.*

The face is straining, being drawn back with pain.

Mouth open with noise.

*Turning away of the head. I don't want to do it, it is too
awful.*

Distended nostrils, you can't get enough air to breathe.

Hair felt electrified.

Arms are big.

Must move them in the pattern of the pains.

Must follow the pattern of the pains with your arms.

In hospital they want to stop you doing it.

The pattern reminds me of maleness.

The rounded arms are like testicles.

The legs are like a penis.

I did not have this thought in my mind when I made it.

In spite of the gross distortion and exaggerated posture, the piece forms a well-integrated whole. The parts of her body where feeling is most intense are exaggerated.

The patient associates in her mind the ideas of parturition and intercourse. She then spontaneously comments on the phallic symbolism.

CASE NO. 1

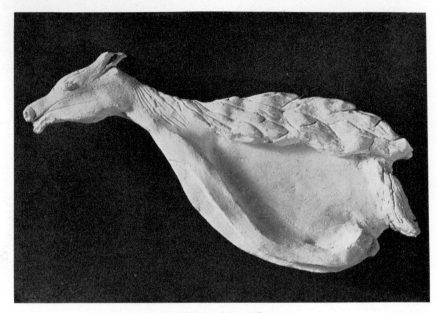

Figure No. 75

"Impression of a Racehorse."

So swift.
Only the feeling of swiftness.
I used to feel like a racehorse.
Run and run on the beach. Feel good.
All straining effort in the face.
Eyes sticking out; nostrils distended; mouth open.
Promised I would take myself to the races in a glamour
costume with a girl friend.
Husband thinks races silly.
I just want to watch the movement of the horses.
To me they have no bodies when racing.

This is the first purely aesthetic work she has produced. The idea of speed and movement is well expressed in the bent-up legs and the flowing mane. The repressive mechanism is reasserting itself, and no psychopathological material finds expression in the modelling.

CASE NO. 1

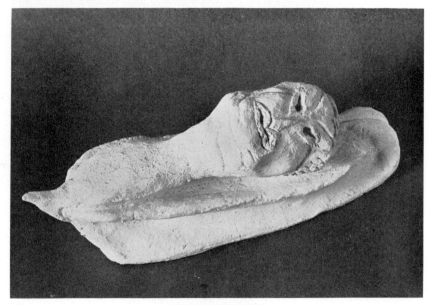

Figure No. 76

"The Figure on the Boat, or Temper."

I was angry when I did it.

I started off to do something beautiful.

I just wanted to do a nice thing.

I started to make a figurehead on a boat, then I thought of my husband and marriage.

I pushed it back, I poked in the mouth and dug in the eyes.

Perhaps it is me now.

Not nice inside.

You could call it temper.

I was thinking of my husband and all the things he has done to me.

I hate him most for spitting on me. Smacks and kicks I can take.

You think you're making me better, but I'm just as bitter towards him.

Every time I think of him I feel I could scratch his face.

He will hold it against me that I have been unbalanced.

He is always saying, "You're mad, you're mad, you're mad."

201

I put this projection on afterwards, I thought it would complete the prow of the boat. But it's on the wrong end of the boat.

The contrast with the pleasing aesthetic qualities of the previous model is a reflection of the variations in the patient's mental state. The quality of the modelling appears to be a sensitive guide to the patient's real condition, as no gross changes in her behaviour were noticed by the hospital staff, or observed in a clinical interview.

The piece is a return to the bizarre. A large head on a boat has no manifest meaning. The projection which was to have completed the prow of the boat is on the wrong end. It is obviously a phallic symbol.

When talking about the piece, she again abreacted her emotions with such violence that the model was in danger of being destroyed from the way in which she was thrusting the modelling tool into the eyes and mouth. It seems clear that the figure is her husband.

CASE NO. 1

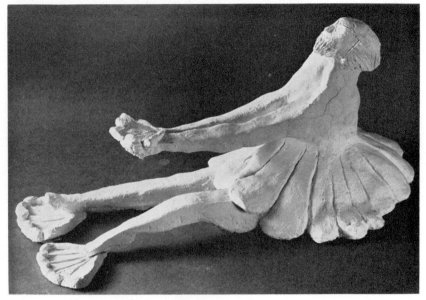

Figure No. 77

"The Figure I saw in the Imagination Tests" (Rorschach test)
My husband came, and then it went all different.
Then I did not want to finish it.
The face suddenly went to a man's face.
It looked like one of the old Pharaohs.
I got very angry about my husband when doing it.
He has spoilt my enjoyment in making these things.
These are oyster shells.
She is offering up the shell.
Just showing the world half an oyster.

It appears that she was striving to make something beautiful in the way of a girl and oyster shells. Her husband comes in to see her. She continues modelling, and the girl turns into the husband. This is the same mechanism as that described as a failed screen model. The result is grotesque.

It has happened in some of her other pieces that she has intended making something nice, but the thought of her husband has come to her, and the piece has turned into something horrible.

Recently the patient has not been so interested in her modelling.

203

She appears to have lost her spontaneity. This may be due to her clinical improvement, and the fact that unconscious material does not seek expression in the same uncontrolled fashion. She experiences considerable guilt in that she is not looking after her two children. She was obviously frustrated by her husband's visit, which ended with her throwing things at him.

CASE NO. 1

Figure No. 78

"Adam and Eve and the Tree of Life"
This is Eve.
This is Adam.
The tree of the two of them, they represent the race.
The length of them represents Time. Time from the be-
ginning of these two to all those on earth now.
The full bosom is Motherhood.
It had to be male and female.
It is not pornographic.
His face has high cheekbones, hers is flat.
He was superior in mind and spirit and physique.

205

The arms represent the branches of the tree, they also lift up to God for guidance.
He knew more about Right than she did.
My father had a terrific chest like this, and a tiny waist.
It might refer to myself.
The male impulse is to dominate, conquer.
The female is the mother, feminine activity, wanting to be sheltered and cared for.
Strange to me because I am a big woman.
It might refer to me and my husband.
I have always had to take the lead with things.
Perhaps I rebel against it.
Like the voice telling me to buy the feminine things.
Like a tree, the roots go all over the world.
The little round things are the nations of people.
I felt I wanted to break it for what has been my own life.
The way he has undermined my self-confidence.

This piece has been under construction for some ten days or a fortnight. During this time, smaller pieces have been begun and finished. It would appear that the patient looked upon it as her magnum opus. It consists of naked male and female figures standing back to back with arms outstretched. In this posture they form a cross. At their feet are a number of small rounded objects. When asked how the idea same to her, the patient is vague. She says she saw it in a dream. Another time she says that she saw it over several days, and it is often in her mind. The same theme has actually appeared several times in her productions.

Although the idea is presented by means of naked figures, the theme does not appear to be sexual. It is rather the idea of creation, of productivity in general.

The superiority of Adam over Eve is worthy of comment. She has taken the model of her father to represent Adam. Some days later she commented, *"My husband always makes me feel inferior to him."*

CASE NO. 1

Figure No. 79

"The Apple."

Have a bite of apple.
Means all I can give someone.
That's what Eve said.

I know that's not the way you should think about a doctor.

There is nothing unusual about the model itself, but it represents an interesting example of a patient's use of a symbol made in psychotherapy, and its adaptation to a reality situation. She makes an apple and offers it to the therapist. If there were any doubt about the meaning of her action, it is made clear by her comments.

The opportunity was taken for psychotherapy around rapport and the transference mechanism.

207

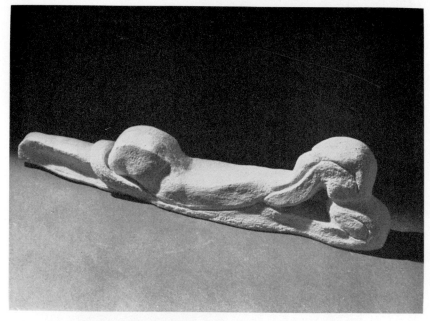

Figure No. 80

"Man's Fulfilment and Botheration."
The hands emotionally in tune make the physical part more perfect.
Not very conscious of the legs.
Except on the woman's part to grasp as much as you can.
The symbol of the circle and the stick. The stick for the male, the circle for the female.
Her legs curling round make the circle.
The whole thing is like a stick.
I was thinking of doctor.
With my husband there is a mental barrier.

The piece represents two figures in intercourse. Their two bodies give the idea of unity. The faces are opposed. The legs are reduced and the arms are absent.

There was no abreaction. From her associations, it is obvious that the piece refers to the transference situation and not to her conflicts. Normally the patient is a rather reserved, almost prudish woman. The open expression of the idea of intimacy with the therapist, with no appropriate affect, is in itself very suggestive of psychosis. Opportunity was taken to further discuss doctor-patient relationship.

CASE NO. 1

Figure No. 81

"The Mermaid."

Just an experiment.
Used to think of myself as a cold fish.
No sexual emotion.
But now I think I might not be a cold fish.
Might be trying to make a beautiful creature out of myself.
Did not think of this when I was making it.
It ought to be a girl's head, but it looks like a man.
I felt I had to make the skin blue and the hair pink.

The piece is an extraordinary looking mermaid with huge breasts and a distinctly masculine profile. She has painted the body blue, and the breasts and hair bright red.

The latent meaning of the strange symbolism is by no means clear. It may be that she thinks of herself as a cold fish, but at the same time the phallic fish becomes the therapist.

Figure No. 82

"A Woman Asleep."

*When you are asleep you are just a head floating round a
    body; no features, no eyes, no mouth, no nose.*
That's the bosom.
That's the body.
Hands around the body, legs curled up.
This is the heart, still beating.
That's the navel.
Buttocks at the back.
Asleep, completely sexless.

The piece consists of a featureless head resting on a disc, which in
turn rests upon a larger disc. On these are traced the outline of arms
and legs.

The patient has attempted an aesthetic work. There is peace and
repose. As seen from the featureless face, the individual has lost her
identity in sleep. We can assume that the figure is in fact feminine, as
she identifies herself with it, and the undue emphasis on the cleft between the fingers, and again between the feet, would seem to be a

symbol of the female, although the patient herself says the piece is completely sexless.

The absence of the body gives expression to the feeling of disembodiment, which is experienced by so many people when they are just on the threshold of sleep.

By the time this model was made, the patient had lost her difficulty in swallowing, which was the original cause of her being sent to hospital. The disturbed state of mind reflected in her models, and her comments about them, was no longer in evidence in her ordinary behaviour. As a result of pressure from the patient and her relations, she was allowed to leave the hospital; and she lost contact with the therapist for a period of some eighteen months. Then her mental state again deteriorated, and she returned to the psychiatric clinic.

CASE NO. 1

Figure No. 83

"A Cat-Woman."

Feel I have had hypnotism or pentothal or something, and
have done peculiar things.
I said I was a raging tiger.
They then said they would let the tiger loose.
It might be a dream, but I feel it's real.
I think I danced to show what a cat does.
A feeling I would make a cat for that means man.
Women's legs because I danced.
I feel it goes stalking, then has an awful fight.
Tears something to smithereens with its claws.
It tears a man to bits, rips him open, bites and snarls.
I'm sure the man is my husband.
The face is half woman and half cat.
Woman's breasts.
Out of this head comes all sorts of painting and song.

Running through this series of models, there are two main themes,
the patient's latent homosexuality, and her hate of her husband. Both
themes find expression in this piece. The cat-woman is both male
and female. The patient says she has a feeling that she would like to

make a cat, for that means man. On the other hand, she speaks of its woman's legs. Its face is half woman, and it has woman's breasts, although they are not shown in the model. By identifying herself with the strange creature, she gives expression to her inarticulate feelings of bisexuality.

In addition to this, the creature, which is she, is fierce. It tears a man to bits, rips him open; and she feels sure that the man is her husband. In this way, her terrible hate is ventilated.

Figure No. 84

"The Devil"

I don't know why I did it.
It came when I mixed the clay that day.
While I was doing it I was thinking of hermaphrodites.

This is the Devil, who at the same time is her husband. He has the horns and cloven hoofs of the Devil, and a leering, mask-like face. His male sex organs are shown, but he also has the large breasts of a woman, and huge flabby buttocks.

The patient has recently accused her husband of being sexually abnormal. The truth or otherwise of this is not known. It may be merely a matter of the psychological projection of the patient's own feeling of bisexuality.

CASE NO. 1

Figure No. 85

"The Two Parts of One Person."
Ability to reason.
The yellow represents intelligence.
That is because of the vision I saw.
The purple is the lowest part.
Impulse and instinct without thought of consequences.
Anger and mean things, this is the red, but still not as low
as the purple.
The little ear on the yellow one is the inward ear that listens
to the inner voice.
There is no ear on the other.
The two are together, because they are inter-related.
The arm that goes across is really part of the brain.
This awful part is in all of us.
A part of split personalities.
The two parts of one person.

The piece consists of two monkey-like figures joined together. One is painted yellow, and the other purple and red.

They are the good self and the bad self. When considered from another point of view, the model expresses the idea of disunity of the individual, a lack of psychic integration. The individual is not a whole, but is two parts. Various expressions of this feeling of lack of unity are frequently found in the models of early schizophrenics, as the forerunners of the more characteristic projections of disintegration.

CASE NO. 1

Figure No. 86

A person asleep.
Half man and half woman.
Impulses that are both male and female.
This part refers to phantasy — the dream world that we
want to believe.
Can go down to this if life is too hard. The dream world
takes over from our intelligence.
The hands are holding these very things to themselves —
holding the phantasy world.
This in the hands refers to sex, and this below is a baby.
The two impulses get mixed up, particularly sex and desire.

This is rather a remarkable model, both as regards its aesthetic value, and its content.

It was difficulty in swallowing that originally brought the patient to the hospital with the provisional diagnosis of carcinoma of the oesophagus. Radiological findings were negative; and in psychotherapy she disclosed that fellatio was forced upon her by her husband. After ventilating her conflicts in this matter, her dysphagia ceased. The

217

present model was made when she was re-admitted to hospital some eighteen months later on account of her disturbed behaviour. It clearly expresses the same conflict. From the psychopathological point of view, the remarkable thing about it is the obvious serenity of the figure. It would seem that this matter, which was very disturbing to her previously, can now be viewed with complete equanimity.

CASE NO. 1

Figure No. 87

The model consists of a poorly constructed seat. Its interest lies in the patient's comments.

> *A Chair.*
> *The chair you were sitting in when I was sitting on your knee.*
> *Or was it you?*
> *It was a room like this.*
> *The day the little gnome went out of the door.*

This serves to illustrate how convincing the delusion of a psychotic patient can be, especially when it is brought into the conversation as a concomitant idea, rather than the central theme. If a patient tells someone that she was sitting on the doctor's knee, the delusional quality of the idea is immediately suspected. On the other hand, when she says, *"This is the chair the doctor was sitting on when I was sitting on his knee,"* the delusional idea is less obvious and more convincing. Her comments also illustrate the fact that, if the patient is allowed to talk freely, something will often be said which shows an earlier statement to be delusional. Thus her talk about the little gnome at once throws

219

doubt on the reliability of her earlier statements.

Her comments, of course, highlight her positive transference with the therapist.

During a previous session, the patient claimed to have seen a little gnome run out the door. She described him vividly as a rather comical character, and was quite at a loss to understand why the therapist had not seen him. The vividness of the visual hallucination and its inconsequential nature had revived the problem of the original differential diagnosis between hysterical hallucinosis and early schizophrenia.

CASE NO. 1

Figure No. 88

What you form of a nation today may not suit in fifty years.
All grows up.
Woman, and a little figure thing comes along.
It all depends really on women for children.
Looks fat and motherly; soft expression.
It represents all women.

The patient's mental condition has improved. She has now come rather to consider herself as an artist, and this piece shows a high standard of technical skill. The Madonna theme is something which nearly all aspiring artists attempt at one time or another. This model could be described as nice or pretty, or even beautiful; but somehow it seems to lack the fundamental strength of some of her earlier, and less well executed pieces. This is characteristic of the modelling of psychotic patients. As their illness improves, there is a general transition to more conventional themes and more conventional symbolism.

221

CASE NO. 1

Figure No. 89

Like a little dog.
Head a mass of ideas about youth and age.
Had a lot of thoughts, but they have all gone away.
Attitude to life.

This well-integrated piece represents some hideous animal. There is great emphasis on the eyes, the tail and the female external genitalia. The tail has the appearance of a huge snake curled up on the creature's back. It would seem beyond doubt that it is a phallic symbol. So the piece must be considered as another projection of the patient's theme of bisexuality.

At the time of making this piece, the patient's mental condition was improving. This is reflected in the degree of integration achieved in the model. It is also shown in the change in character of her comments about the model. In the past, she has openly discussed the psychopathology expressed in the various pieces. Now she can tell us practically nothing. *"Had a lot of thoughts but they have all gone away."* In other words, the repressive mechanism is re-establishing itself. It is interesting to note that repression is now effective at the level of verbal expression, but remains ineffective at the level of plastic expression. Experience in plastotherapy suggests that this principle can be taken as a valid generalization. At the onset of schizophrenia, psychotic material finds expression in plastic form, while repression still remains effective as regards speech; and similarly, as the patient recovers, her speech loses its psychotic quality, but the signs of schizophrenic thought disorder may still be in evidence in the patient's plastic productions.

CASE NO. 1

Figure No. 90

Funny shape, yet I like it.
Like a male and female.
Thinking about what happens to me when I leave.
Penis and sperm.
It made its own shape.
This looks like a woman's buttocks.
Curve of a woman.

The shape has no resemblance to any earthly object, save perhaps some giant sea slug.

In this series of models, the idea of bisexuality has been expressed a number of times. In each case, the idea has been expressed by making a model which relates to one sex, and then giving it some symbol or attribute of the other sex. The woman in childbirth has the phallic legs; the dancing girl with the oyster shells is given a man's face; the mermaid has big woman's breasts, but the face is unmistakably that of a man. The devil who is her husband has the breasts of a woman; the female cat-woman has a distinctly phallic tail. The only exception is the disordered model of the boat-like vagina and the phallic leg. But the present model differs from all these in its mode of symbolization. Here there is no reference to familiar objects. The model itself is abstract, just as is the idea which it expresses. It is an abstraction of the concept of bisexuality.

The patient's psychosis is now remitting, so she is able to integrate the model with some skill; and because of her innate artistic feelings, she produces a piece with aesthetic qualities. There has thus been a transition from the symbolic modelling of a mad woman to the aesthetic modelling of an artist of the modern school. In fact, this piece has a distinct resemblance in character to some well known pieces of modern sculpture. But the most interesting thing about it is that we know so much of the artist, that we know exactly and unequivocally what the piece means.

CASE NO. 2

SIMPLE SCHIZOPHRENIA

The patient was brought to consultation on account of a gradual deterioration in his work record as a university student. He had become increasingly vague. He had rather abandoned any serious academic study, and in its place had become given to long pseudo-philosophical discussions with other students, or with any one who would listen to him. There had been some falling off in his personal habits. His manner of dress had become untidy. Following the long discussions, which would continue for most of the night, he would not get up until midday, and so would miss his morning lectures.

During the clinical interview, his defence was to parry any questioning with pseudo-philosophical observations. His comments always had some relevance to the subject, and by this means he avoided any direct answers. He was not hallucinated, nor did he disclose any ideas of reference.

He was started on deep coma insulin therapy. During the course of treatment, he was encouraged to model, and he was given psychotherapy centered around ideas expressed in his modelling. He developed the habit of modelling faces from the clay, and projecting his thoughts on to the model. In this way, he gives a vivid account of the subjective difficulties of the patient with early simple schizophrenia.

CASE NO. 2

Figure No. 91

The face of Death.
The idea is one opposed to life.
Not Death in the sense of not being in this world.
Not being in action in the normal business of living is death
* in a way.*
In other words, if one has no life at all one is dying, more
* or less.*

CASE NO. 2

Figure No. 92

Ideas of seediness, or squalor, or dullness.
When everything you are used to; when everything you like
goes overboard, you are left with the rueful experience of
getting nowhere.

CASE NO. 2

Figure No. 93

Meant to be a blind man.
He also has a broken nose.
Representation of the general blindness that one feels, the
*   inability to cope with situations.*
Just the state of unseeing.
The broken nose is part of the disorganization.
Disjointed, as it were.
The mouth rather hopeless, and not being able to see clear-
*   ly or sum up situations, as it were.*
Like walking round with a hood over one's head.

229

Figure No. 94

Veiled feeling of happiness or well-being I used to have once.
Just get glimpses of it vaguely.
Just get ideas of what I used to feel like.
Just glimpses.
The genuine happiness of the past seems blighted.
The only way now seems to build up some sort of synthetic
*   happiness.*
The happiness of the past seems blighted as if one's genuine
*   well-being has been permanently ruined.*
I used not even to be aware that I had ever had the feeling
*   of well-being.*
Now I do get glimpses of it.
Perhaps it's the treatment, or something.

Figure No. 95

All rather morbid.

Really a portrait of death which seems preferable to the life
I'm leading at the moment.

Nowhere to escape to at all.

It seems desirable that you can't die without committing
suicide.

Just got to stay alive.

Everything more or less has gone wrong.

What I thought I was going to do was to go back to the
University; instead of that, everything goes wrong, wasted
time and got nowhere.

The gulf between the sick self and the self I thought I could
become has widened.

I don't think I can get back to any equilibrium.

CASE NO. 2

Figure No. 96

Kind of distorted, distorted disjointed representation.
No balance at all.
The gulf between.
(Pause)
So many weird things have happened.
I don't seem to be ill.
I seem to have recovered my own vague identity again.
Seem amazed I could have been involved in these things,
involved with the police.

232

EXCERPTS FROM CASE HISTORIES

Everything exaggerated.
I don't know if things are trivialities or not.
Wandering around the streets at night with some weird people.
The police whizzed up.
It does not seem like me at all.
Another occasion has me more worried.
In company with some woman at the time.
She said she wanted to go home.
I met her mother.
Then we went to her mother's home.
I wandered along.
It ended up she had no business there at all.
Ended up breaking into the house; apparently she was some sort of criminal.
Police arrested her.

CASE NO. 2

Figure No. 97

Meant to be an enigma.
Could call it the face of a saint.
Jesus if you like.
Eyes shut, they don't show anything.
Mouth shut, does not communicate its knowledge.
Relies on faith which does not mean a damned thing.
No scope for the faculty of reason.
Nothing palpable.
Nothing one can focus on for the explanation of the world,
  or of one's self.

234

CASE NO. 2

Figure No. 98

The horror waiting round the corner.
Everywhere you go, everything you do, always some horror
waiting round the corner.

235

CASE NO. 2

Figure No. 99

What it would be like to achieve one's ambitions.
Purity of achievement.
Unsullied by anything, in a world of its own where nothing
*   could touch it.*
No problem could worry it.
Nothing could spoil achievement
Pure integrity about it.

CASE NO. 3

SCHIZOPHRENIA

When she first came to consultation, the patient was a girl of twenty. As a result of a small annuity, she was able to live by herself without working. She avoided any contact with relatives, and actively fought off anyone who would befriend her. She felt that people were looking at her, and sometimes she believed that she could actually hear them talking about her. Her only regular contacts with the outside world were furtive visits to a nearby shop to buy food.

She was given a long course of deep coma insulin therapy, with no improvement. Likewise treatment by E.C.T., narcoanalysis, group therapy and superficial psychotherapy made no change in her condition.

She was subsequently encouraged in painting and modelling; and she was treated in psychotherapy around the material projected in her graphic and plastic productions.

CASE NO. 3

Figure No. 100

I tried not thinking about anything when I was doing it.
Was going to make it a whale then part turned into a man.
He is as dead as can be.
These are the whale's teeth.
But whales don't have teeth.
It must be a shark.
I put eyes in again.
Eyes everywhere.
The fish seems to be eating the man like an anemone sucking
  him up.
It means destruction.
It's all changed now.
There's another person.
This new person seems to be saving the other one.
This is his arm dragging him away.
I was just dreaming when I was doing it.

The model consists of a jumbled mass of clay. It would seem to be a thing without meaning, made in a few moments. In actual fact, the patient took an hour and a half to make it, during which time she was intensely preoccupied with what she was doing. She would move each little piece of clay this way and that. At times she was greatly distressed, apparently by the thoughts teeming through her mind. At other times, she seemed to be frustrated and exasperated by her inability to give her thoughts expression.

Her associations give evidence of her grossly disordered thinking. In her talk about other similar models, she identified the small rounded objects as eyes. They appear in different places all over the model, and are a projection of her ideas of reference.

The idea of one person saving the other one seems to be an unconscious projection of her thoughts about the therapeutic situation.

CASE NO. 3

Figure No. 101

It's nothing.
It does not mean anything.
It's clowns.
They share things.
They share their noses, their eyes and hands.
These are eyes. They share their nose.
This is the mouth of that one.
There are three of them.
The silly one, the sad one, and the happy one.
I did not finish him.
They are one clown really.
They have not any tops to their heads, no brains.
It's not me; it's general.
Looking at it makes me feel more and more hopeless.
I tried to make it not me.

The model was again made in a very painstaking fashion, while the patient was in a state of deep preoccupation and distress.

The figures which she describes as the three clowns cannot be clearly identified. The piece is grotesque and bizarre; nevertheless, there is some evidence of integrative capacity, in that it is reasonably well organised into a whole in the form of a pyramid.

The representation of different facets of the personality of the individual by different persons occurs quite commonly in the modelling of schizophrenics. In these cases, it would seem to be a reflection of the schizophrenic's feelings of disintegration. As such, it is a manifestation of a different mechanism from that which occurs when the artist consciously uses a similar device in the analysis of character in painting or literature.

The patient's associations give evidence of the way in which ideas gain expression in the modelling, in spite of the patient's active opposition. *"It's not me. It's general."* Then comes the pathetic confession: *"I tried to make it not me."*

CASE NO. 3

Figure No. 102

A vampire, only it is half bird and half person.
It alters all the time; it is altering now.
It is one thing, but two parts of one thing.
It's one bird, half human, half bird.
The human and the birds.
That person decides it will fly, this person comes up over the
  wing, and stops him flying.
He is more or less asleep.
This one thinks if he can stop this one flying then he will be
  able to fly.
He is frightened that that one will go away, that's why he
  tries to stop him.
Won't let that one be the leader.
The wing is his face, alive, but it is dead there like a monster
They are just locked there, I suppose they are me, because
  there is nothing else.
I am just having a row with me.
Can't say it in words.

242

I try to work a thing out by blaming someone else.
Now it looks like a leech on somebody.
It was as though it was a leechy type of person.
I think I am a leech.
I feel I am a leech on you and on the Red Cross.
The two figures are a sort of bad and good in me, fighting
for supremacy.

Although the model is equally bizarre, it shows some improvement over the first model. It is bolder in construction, and there is less evidence of the constriction and obsessive preoccupation with detail. Two figures can be seen locked together, one with an arm across the other. It is a plastic representation of two elements fighting within her.

This is the patient's first reference to the bird and its wing. This theme is subsequently developed in symbolic form, and leads to the psychogenesis of the patient's condition. At the edge of the model, the clay is seen to be rolled up. She later uses this effect as a constant symbol for the wing.

CASE NO. 3

Figure No. 103

It has been a lot of things.
It was a bird with three wings.
This is the face of the bird, two eyes.
That was going to be another face, another head.
Here it seems to be getting away from something.
Those two wings just go round.

Here the bird theme is developed a stage further. She says it has three wings.

The model itself has hardly any resemblance to a bird. This might make us suspect that it has some other, altogether different meaning. One of the wings is curled up at the tip, which suggests that the wing is deformed or abnormal in some way.

CASE NO. 3

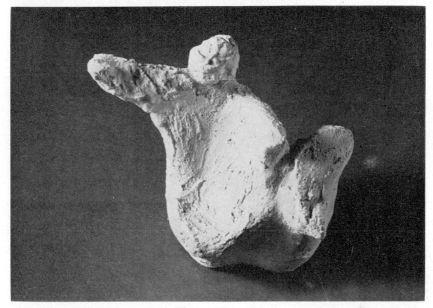

Figure No. 104

The seaman, yet it is the bird also.

Something to do with direction.

Looking up in that direction but leaning in that direction and round the back here too.

This is a sort of nymph thing — it changed and became a wing.

Sort of a wave at the bottom.

An arm too.

The other arm is a wing, it is going that way.

From this direction of the wing, a huddled sort of person.

Why should a person be half a wing and half a wave?

Two symbolic themes are here interwoven in the same piece. In other models, the patient has used the analogy of the turmoil of the sea to express the turmoil of life, and this is what she refers to in her comments.

In this model, the bird or winged creature is further developed. It is shown with a human head. It is unmistakably a person. His arms are outstretched like wings; and at his back is attached another object. This is the mysterious third wing.

245

Figure No. 105

Just don't know.
Same as the last one.
I wish I knew.
Just cry when I make it, for no reason at all.
It's the wings.
It's not a person.
It was a wing — an arm dragging the wing — yet that part went up.
Took hours to do.
Had to get it in the right direction.
Had to be in line with that one.
I don't know. You tell me.
That's a person; head of a person.
This was the head of the bird, the bird person.
Can't get its wings together.
I just don't know.
The wings are frightening, aren't they?
I had the jitters yesterday.
It started off with the wings.

The model again shows the bird person, and the third wing, or the additional appendage which is attached behind.

CASE NO. 3

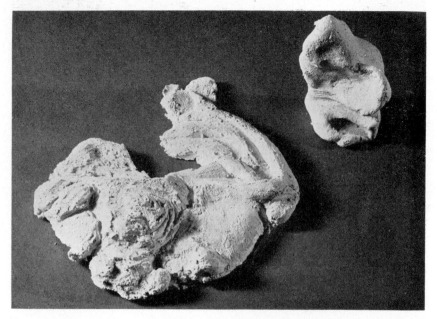

Figure No. 106

This is the denouement. The third wing is shown separate from the bird because the patient realises that it does not belong to it.

The patient's comments about the previous models have been obtained in a non-directive fashion, with the therapist remaining completely passive. The therapist now takes a more active part in the discussion. The patient was very preoccupied with the model, and spoke very slowly. As with other interviews, it was possible to record the conversation verbatim without disturbing her.

> *The two really go together.*
> *I don't know what it is about.*
> *It was a bird, a wing, the people, the sea. All mixed up, all going round.*
> *All mixed up.*
> *A person.*
> *It was just a fin.*
> Therapist: *Could you give the model a title?*
> *A bird being over the sea, or vice versa.*
> *That was going up and up, and I took it off.*

247

Think I had better put it back.

It was a person.

It was looking that way.

Therapist: *This is what has been going to happen in the other models.*

I seem to be lonely for the first time in my life.

No contact with people.

I just miss my mother and father, I think.

If anyone mentions parents, I am off. (Weeps)

Therapist: *Something has been achieved in making the separation, hasn't it?*

Before I couldn't do it. Sounds stupid not to be able to separate a piece of clay.

In reference to previous models, the patient has said that she wanted to leave the third wing off the bird, but had found that she was unable to do so.

The comment that she is lonely for the first time in her life is significant. In the depths of her psychosis, she has been too out of touch to be lonely.

CASE NO. 3

Figure No. 107

If we compare this piece with the early productions, we immediately note a great change. That which was disintegrated has become unified. Chaos has given place to harmony. In fact, the present production is a piece of marked aesthetic form.

> *Don't have to say what it is, do I?*
> *Because I don't know.*
> *Don't know what it is.*
> *God, it's a mess.*
> (Pause)
> *Frightful mood when I did it.*
> *Started off being a bird, then it got smashed up a few times.*
> *Then this wing was all that was left of the bird.*
> *That was a wing too, I think.*
> *Then that was a person.* (points to the head of the bird)
> *And those were two arms* (two furrows)
> Therapist: *Is the bird a person?*
> *Yes, must be. That was an eye.*

249

The person is in bits a bit.
That was a head
(Pause)
That there, like the tree there (looks out the window)
It's a person.
(Pause)
Therapist: *What's this?* (points to the horizontal furrows at the side)
Wing. Looks like the sea.
Used to watch birds a lot by the sea.
Therapist: *How many wings has a bird got?*
Only one.
Therapist: *How is that?*
Don't know. Lost one.
It isn't a dead bird.
Therapist: *You feel the bird lost something?*
Yes, it has only got one eye too.
Therapist: *What about the bird really?*
(Pause)
I don't know.
Could be a lot of things.
Therapist: *Could you talk about them?*
Think it's myself.
Therapist: *This bird has lost something compared with other birds.*
Perhaps not lost it; or never had it; or perhaps never see it.
Therapist: *Tell me about the bird.*
(Shakes her head)
Therapist: *This part that you feel is missing?*
Don't know what it is.
Something other people seem to have.
(Pause)
Therapist: *When did you first have this feeling that some part is missing?*
Have had them a long time.
Therapist: *What about as a little girl?*
Used to think I was peculiar.
Therapist: *Did you feel that something was missing?*
Other people would not play with me.

(Pause)

Having some thing.

B— had it. (Her brother)

Therapist: *What was it really, as a little girl?*

(Shakes her head)

Don't know, just lonely.

Therapist: *Something that B— had and you didn't have?*

(Long pause)

Everybody wanted him.

Should have grown more used to it by now.

Therapist: *Something he had and you did not?*

Love, I suppose. Or is that silly?

Therapist: *No, it isn't silly.*

Do you know what I am talking about, because I don't think I do.

Therapist: *As a little girl there was something that B— had and you didn't.*

Something material, or what?

Therapist: *Might be.*

(shakes her head)

I don't know.

He was sort of on a different planet.

(Long pause)

Therapist: *You felt he had something that you didn't?*

(pause) *Was it something bodily?*

(quickly) *Yes, and something no other little girl has. Felt I wasn't constructed properly.*

Therapist: *The bird with the part missing.*

Well, I started _____, and I got very wound up about that.

Therapist: *Lots of little girls have these feelings.*

Used to get books. Made things worse.

Therapist: *It was all a terrible problem.*

Would not get undressed in front of anybody.

To see if other people were the same or different.

I still have the feeling that I'm different.

Do you get over it?

Therapist: *Yes.* (Pause) *It is the gate to the mountains.*

  (The reference is to a picture which she had just finished).
  You are at the gate. I think you feel it.

251

How can telling someone help?

Therapist: *It gets it straight in your mind. You have been
telling me for a long time in the paintings and models.*

The patient acknowledges her identity with the bird. Then, after
some pressure from the therapist, she admits the phallic symbolism of
the third wing; and openly discusses her castration anxiety as a little girl.

At this point, there was a dramatic change in the patient's manner
and appearance. She had always been restless, agitated and unhappy.
Now, in a matter of seconds, a profound serenity came upon her. This
state of mind remained with her for several days. Her psychotic symptoms remitted, and in four years have not returned; although at times
she has experienced a variety of psychoneurotic manifestations as a
result of her difficulties in adjusting to life after so many years of
schizophrenic isolation.

CASE NO. 4

HYSTERICAL DYSPHAGIA

The patient was referred on account of her complaint that food was sticking in her gullet. Numerous x-ray examinations had all proved negative; but repeated reassurances that there was no organic lesion had done nothing to alleviate her condition. She was openly resentful at being referred to a psychiatrist. She disclosed herself as a highly inhibited young woman, who found any discussion of her private life a near impossibility. During two sessions of formal psychotherapy, she was coldly co-operative and completely unproductive. She was then started on plastotherapy.

CASE NO. 4

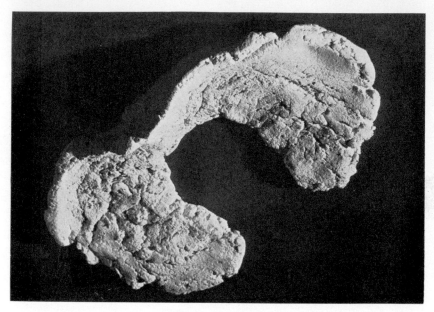

Figure No. 108

Looks like a set of teeth.
Doesn't look like anything.
Just the way my hands made the clay.
Didn't particularly want to make it smooth, left it rough.
Surprised I made anything.
(Pause)
Will have to have my teeth out.

As the model refers to the mouth, it was thought that it might be connected in some way with her feeling of food sticking in her gullet.

Her comment, *"Surprised that I made anything,"* is a reflection of her generally hostile attitude.

The final statement, *"Will have to have my teeth out,"* was added rather as an after-thought. It was at once realized that this was probably a rationalization. If the model were a projection of fear of dental extractions, then the idea would have been expressed in the initial comments, as there is ordinarily no social or psychological barrier to the expression of such a fear.

CASE NO. 4

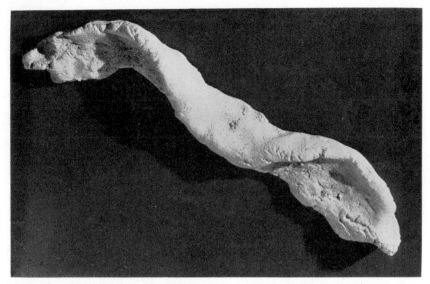

Figure No. 109

Nothing I made has any purpose.
Terrible to be silent when you want me to say things.
All I can talk about is the worry about my throat.
No thoughts.
I am conscious I can't give you any lead.
Had no thoughts when I was making these things.
An anxiety to say something.
(Blocks completely).

The model repeats the "teeth" motif of the first production, although the patient does not identify it as such.

The patient's associations give a good indication of her inhibited nature.

CASE NO. 4

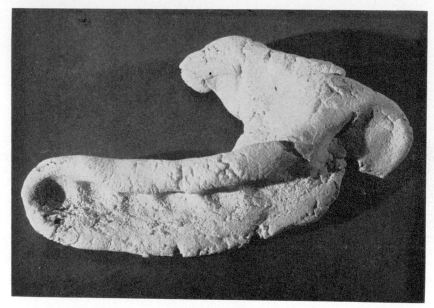

Figure No. 110

Did it when very relaxed.
Doesn't conjure up any thoughts at all.
Feel I am being completely unco-operative, and I don't want
*   to be.*
While I was making this, was thinking of hypnosis.
(Blocks)
Looks like a finger and a thumb.
(Blocks)
Feel I am so dumb.
Don't know why I can't say something.

The patient was very distressed and agitated after making the model. As the patient says, it has some resemblance to a finger and thumb. However, the part which would represent the thumb has the same tooth marks which appear on the two previous models. This suggests a repetition of the same motif. The significance of the part which would represent the finger, and the meaning of the model as a whole, only comes to us by reference to the next production. In fact, this series of models is an excellent example of the gradual emergence of a significant conflict.

over several sessions of plastotherapy.

It is interesting to note that this significant and traumatic idea comes near to expression for the first time when the patient herself says she did the modelling when very relaxed.

The reference to hypnosis comes about through the fact that the patient knew that the therapist practices hypnosis. In a disgruntled way she had said, *"If my throat is psychological, why don't you hypnotise me and cure it?"* Her hostility made her unsuitable for hypnotherapy, so the question of hypnosis had been dismissed on some pretext.

CASE NO. 4

Figure No. 111

The patient declared that she would not do any more modelling; and it was only after considerable discussion that she was brought reluctantly to make an attempt.

> *Find it terribly hard to talk about.*
> (Long pause)
> *Ridiculous, just can't say anything.*
> (Long pause)
> *Must be false modesty.*
> *It's a penis I have made, and a mouth.*
> *Don't know if my mind wanted it.*
> *My husband always wanted me to be more passionate than I am.*
> *Just a thought.*
> *Not that he insists on anything.*
> *Feel I am lacking in responsiveness.*
> *He wanted me to consult a gynaecologist about my lack of desire.*
> (Blocks)

258

Therapist: *Just talk about it, the penis and the mouth.*
Suppose it is just the idea that, if I should ever have to kiss my husband in that way, I could never do it.
Can't say any more.
(Long pause, patient very distressed).
Therapist: *Just let yourself talk about it.*
Feel ashamed when I think about things like that.
Other people can laugh and joke about sex, but it never seems very funny to me.
Feel more upset today than I have in the past.
(Later, when about to leave, she says)
Tremendous effort to talk about things you never have before.

CASE NO. 4

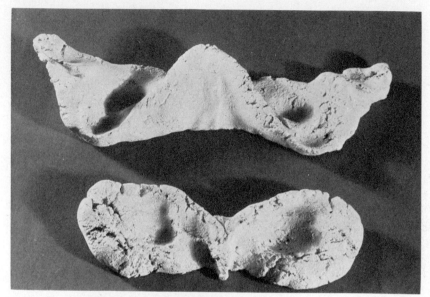

Figure No. 112

I made these two things, but they are not connected with what
I was thinking when I made them.
Masks — eyes and nose.
Was thinking of my marriage.
Thinking perhaps I have cheated a little.
Never really madly in love with my husband.
Perhaps I don't rise up to expectations.
Always feel quite happy except when arguments.
Don't know if it's normal, if you feel you just loathe a person.
It frightens me.
After seven years, seems a bit late to delve into it, to see if
you did the right thing.

There has been a change from ideas concerning the mouth to an expression of open hostility towards her husband. This is really a logical transition from the conflict concerning fellatio expressed in the previous model.

The associations illustrate the way in which the modelling stirs up the patient emotionally. The patient is so inhibited and proper, that in formal psychotherapy she denied all conflicts with her husband; whereas now she speaks of loathing him.

CASE NO. 4

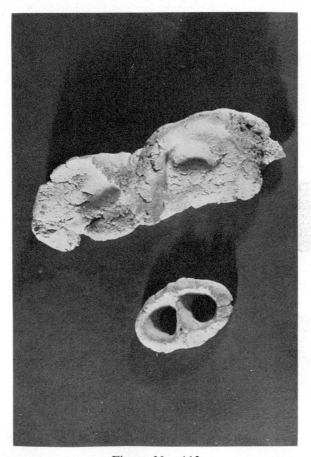

Figure No. 113

For the first time, the patient volunteers improvement in symptoms. She is easier and much less hostile.

> *Mask.*
> *May represent my husband.*
> *Was thinking about death.*
> *Have morbid thoughts about death.*
> *Think about it more than any normal person.*
> *Dread the day my father should die.*
> *Wonder how he feels, knowing he has not long to live.*

261

This is meant to be a part of a skull.

The juxtaposition of the mask representing her husband, and the skull representing death, must surely be an unconscious expression of a death wish. The associations about her aged father are in the way of an easy rationalization. The patient was not considered sufficiently advanced in psychotherapy to accept an interpretation without anxiety, so the matter was not discussed.

CASE NO. 4

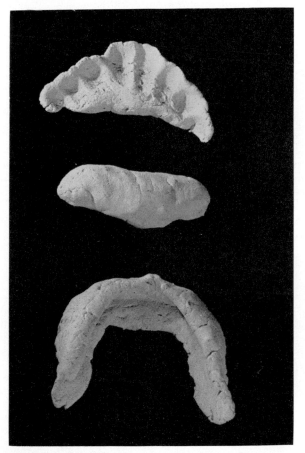

Figure No. 114

It is three weeks since the last visit. There is an obvious change for the worse in the patient's appearance. She says her symptoms have returned worse than ever, *"which only goes to prove that they were not psychological."*

It transpires that her husband has made her tell him all that has been going on in psychotherapy, although the patient had been warned not to discuss these matters. The patient told her husband of her thoughts of fellatio. He reacted emotionally, and blamed her on account of her pre-marital sex experience. The patient has been depressed and has been

263

thinking of leaving her husband.

Just go on making the same thing.

A mouth.

(Pause)

Just made it, didn't think about it.

Then did a set of teeth.

Then (speaks very softly) *another penis.*

Without any thoughts about making them.

(Pause)

Does it matter that I keep making the same things all the time?

Therapist: *No, it means they are significant to you, doesn't it?*

The husband's interference has caused a relapse of symptoms, and this in turn has been reflected in the return to the significant theme in the modelling.

CASE NO. 4

Figure No. 115

Really couldn't model anything today.
Top half of the face.
Tried to make a perfect nose.
Wished I had a nose like that.
I was rather light-hearted, I am afraid.
(Smiles and laughs lightheartedly in a way she has not done
    before. The patient by her manner indicates that she is
    sure she has made a model of no psychological significance.)
Therapist: *Who could it be?*
Suppose it's me.
Spent most of the time trying to model the nose.
(Long pause)
Therapist: *Just let yourself talk about it.*
Nothing I can say.
Therapist: *The face has not got any mouth.*
(With obvious surprise) *No, it has not.*
Don't know why.
Didn't even think about it.
(Long pause)

265

Therapist: *Just talk, you're all relaxed and easy; just let
yourself talk about it.*
Have been analysing my own character.
Feel childish.
Always seeking reassurance from people.
(The patient talks of irrelevancies which are omitted from
the record).
Therapist: *You have made yourself without any mouth.*
Yes.
Therapist: *Can you talk about it?*
Don't think about it.

The model and the patient's associations together demonstrate a
number of psychodynamic processes of plastotherapy. The patient was
quite free from the tension and anxiety which have been obvious during
her other sessions of modelling. From her behaviour, it was clear that
she believed she had made a model with no unpleasant implications.
The reader may well be surprised at this. The most obvious feature of
the model is the absence of the mouth, which for her is known to be the
psychologically significant area. Yet the patient does not see this. There
is a psychological scotoma. In this way, the model is a good example
as to how a conflict may achieve plastic expression, without the patient
being aware of what is happening.

At the conclusion of the plastotherapy, the opportunity was taken for
further enquiry about the patient's experience of fellatio. On previous
occasions, she had been either so distressed, or so inhibited, that no real
information had been elicited. At these times, it had seemed that
persistence in the questioning would only precipitate the patient into
an acute anxiety reaction. So it was not known whether her psychological conflict about fellatio was one of phantasy, or one of actual experience. Now when asked about it, she first claims an amnesia, and
that she cannot remember anything about it; then she says that she had
never thought of it until she came to consultation. Later she says that
she had heard some women friends talking of it; and finally she says,
"It must have been when we were first married".

CASE NO. 4

Figure No. 116

Lower half of him.
Thinking about my unsatisfactory sexual desires.
Worries me that I don't seem quite normal in that respect.
Hardly ever feel the need for it.
I cannot love my husband enough.
Would not like to believe that.
That side of things does not seem important any more.
(Pause)
Eyes and nose. Did not make a mouth.
Did not know I made it at all. It just seemed to happen.

The patient is getting better. The basic conflict is now expressed in a more typically psychoneurotic fashion. This is shown in the change to a more conventional type of symbolism. The lower half of the male figure represents the sexual part of her husband. She does not make a mouth to her own face, because that is the significant thing when it is considered in relation to the sexual part of her husband. In other words, she has no mouth for the sexual part of her husband.

The patient's last comment is worthy of notice. *"Did not know that I made it at all. It just seemed to happen."* This is very typical of the way in which conflicts gain expression in plastotherapy without the full awareness of the patient.

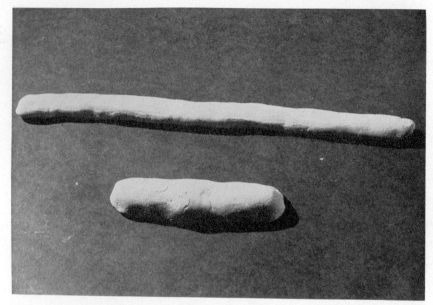

Figure No. 117

First one, no idea.

Second one, penis.

Wondering if the idea of the penis in the mouth is the only cause of this trouble.

Horrified when I came to you, and disclosed this thought was in my mind, embarrassed and ashamed.

Don't want to make love as much as most people.

Wonder if that had anything to do with it.

Just something about sex which seems distasteful.

Feel I must be inferior to most women.

Just like to know the reason.

(Pause)

Therapist:*Just talk, talk about the models.*

(Pause)

Therapist: *About this first one.*

No idea what it is meant to be.

Felt it had to be perfectly round when I was making it.

Felt it was some symbol of oesophagus or penis.

Therapist: *So the two things are associated in your mind.*

The idea is still repulsive to me.

In her earlier models the patient had expressed her conflict. In this model, she clearly relates her conflict to her symptoms.

CASE NO. 5

PRE-PSYCHOTIC SCHIZOPHRENIA

The patient is a shy, sensitive, introvert young man whose presenting symptom is that he feels that he must glance sideways at people. Five illustrations of his models are shown in order to demonstrate how deeply unconscious psychopathological material may be projected in plastotherapy.

CASE NO. 5

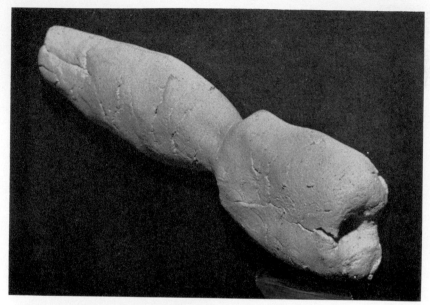

Figure No. 118

Could be a penis.
Don't know.
(Voice becomes inaudible. Long pause, becomes rather restless)
Yes — well —
When I used to masturbate used to sort of think up new ways to masturbate.
(Fondles the model with his hand)
Used to worry.
Putting my penis into an old lavratory roll.
(Keeps fondling the model)
Think if I am still tensing up —
Think if I meet people, might glance down at their penis.
(Pause)
Chap was showing me pictures of people on the beach.
I would have been embarrassed there.
(Destroys the model, apparently absent-mindedly.)
(Long pause)

270

Therapist: *Would you make the clay again like you had it, and just talk about it.*
Feel I want to smile a bit.
(Enthusiastically) *Feel it is helping me.*
Therapist: *Just let yourself talk.*
(Patient blocks)
Therapist: *It has a hole at the other end.*
Mmmm . . . . couldn't work that out.

The significant feature of this phallic shape is the carefully hollowed out hole in the base. The patient can give no explanation for it. On account of the combination of the phallus and the hollow, the model was provisionally regarded as a symbol of bisexuality. This interpretation was confirmed in a subsequent session, when the patient stated that he often had the feeling that he was growing a vagina in the perineum.

CASE NO. 5

Figure No. 119

Yes — well — a penis.
(Pause)
Don't know what it means.
Not frightened at all.
(Mumbles inaudibly)
Now just feel hazy in the head.
(Pause)
When I was making it, held it in my hand, reminded me of
masturbation.
(Pause)
This haziness in the head.
(Pause)
Therapist: *Just let yourself talk.*
(Pause)
Thinking about the feeling of being effeminate.
Tense up when meeting people.
Look down at them (meaning he looks down at the genital
area).

Makes me frightened.

(Pause)

Therapist: *Let yourself talk.*

Remember the first time I got this looking to the side, saw a woman secretary, she had her legs crossed.

Think she thought I was a bit mad.

I was glancing across at her.

Started to think I was seeing sex in everything.

I didn't know the meaning of pervert, homo, all those things.

Was getting into my head I was the sort of person who might commit sex crimes, children, or anything like that.

Dirty mind or what.

If anyone mentions anything, feel I apply it to sex.

(Patient had been talking in a rather distressed fashion, with a good deal of pressure of ideas. He now comes to a stop as if he has suddenly run down.)

In another session of psychotherapy, the patient mentions a constant worry that his penis is too large. Although it is not mentioned in the present associations, it would seem that the model is a projection of this idea.

CASE NO. 5

Figure No. 120

First one I made — don't know — unless it's a penis again.
  Might be a knife.
Second one, could be the top of a penis.
Talking to you now, I don't feel they mean so much, like
  they used to. (i.e., he is not so disturbed by sexual
  thoughts.)
(Pause)
On Monday masturbated in my sleep.
(Pause)
Therapist: *What about the second one?*
Don't know, could be top of a penis, could be a woman's
  vagina.
(Pause)
Therapist: *It could be a woman's vagina.*
Yes (said very readily)
(Pause)
Therapist: *So it's a man's sexual organ and a woman's sex-*
  ual organ?

274

One time thought I was growing a vagina at the back of the penis there.

He again makes a phallus with a hole in the base. The explanation of the hole is found in his comment about growing a vagina at the back of his penis, although he did not refer his remarks directly to the model. The association of the other shape with the top of a penis must again be a projection of his anxiety about the large size of his organ; but at the same time, it is such an unrealistic association that it immediately suggests a psychotic process.

CASE NO. 5

Figure No. 121

This could be a vagina.
Then I made this, it could be a penis.
Then I thought, "It would not fit."
Then I thought, "You have no worries about that now."
When I was making this, made a hole at the top, and a hole at the bottom.
(Mumbles inaudibly)
With this one, just pushed a hole in and raised it up round the edges.
(Long pause)
Somebody once said to me when I was at school that a vagina was like a small behind, like a small hole.
(Pause)
Therapist: *Just let yourself talk.*
I know a bit better now what a vagina is like.
Have held her a bit.
(Voice trails off inaudibly)
Nothing worries me about it now.

(Pause)

Except I did feel I was growing a vagina sort of underneath. Don't think this means anything.

Remember jokes a fellow made about a penis being too big.

These two shapes are really a repetition of the same ideas which were expressed in the previous illustration.

CASE NO. 5

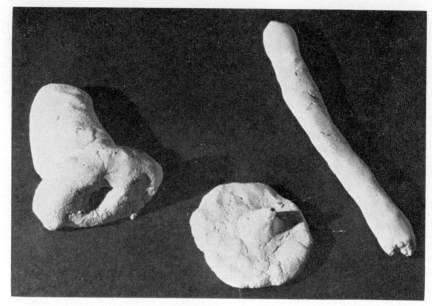

Figure No. 122

When I first picked up the clay, didn't know what I was going to make.

Thought of making a person, then stretched the clay out rolling it backwards and forwards.

Then made this, and this one.

When I was making this I was thinking about the way I look down. (He had said that when he is talking with people he feels a compulsion to look at their genitals.)

Perhaps compare them with mine.

This looks like the same thing I was making the other day, a vagina.

Did think of something.

When I was away on a job, went out late one night, masturbated, next day terrible headache, went to work and had to knock off.

(Pause)

Therapist: *Just let yourself talk about these things.*

Just now feel a bit headachy.

(Pause)

Therapist: *Just let yourself talk about these things.*

(Pause)

This long one here does not mean a thing.

Therapist: *What about this one?*

Dullness all over me.

Masturbation was a terrible thing to me.

(Pause)

They just look like models now, hat or something.

Therapist: *You said it was like a vagina.*

No, not today.

Therapist: *And this?*

It is a penis.

Therapist: *Whose?*

Mine, I suppose.

Therapist: *How do you know it is yours?*

Just felt it was mine.

Therapist: *And this?*

Doesn't mean anything.

(Pause)

Feel a dull pressure all over me.

Therapist: *What's this?* (pointing to the conical projection)

Could be a hat.

Then I thought it could fit in there (Points to the hole at the base of the penis.)

The symbolism of the modelling has become more complex. From what we already know about the patient from his previous models, it would seem that the shape on the right represents a normal penis; whereas the shape on the left is his own penis. He has expressed concern about the large size of his organ, but has also said that he felt that he was growing a vagina. The hole in the base of this shape would seem to be a projection of this phantasy.

The question, *"How do you know it is yours?"* was an invitation to the patient to identify the organ as his own, on account of the hole; but he did not do this, and merely said that he felt that it was his.

The shape in the centre has no resemblance to a vagina; he says that it looks the same as the model of a vagina which he made on a previous occasion. It would seem likely that the conical projection is somehow associated in his mind with the clitoris.

279

The patient says that the conical projection, which we identify as a clitoris, would fit into the hole at the base of the penis, which is his phantasy vagina. This would seem to be a deeply unconscious expression of his homosexuality.

The five illustrations shown here were made over a period of six weeks. During this time, the patient has shown quite marked clinical improvement. It is felt that his improved condition results from the concomitant therapeutic processes of plastotherapy, rather than from insight.

Another interesting aspect of this case it that, although the models show a gross disorder of psychic function, the patient has been able to continue at work in a responsible professional capacity.

XIII

EVALUATION OF PLASTOTHERAPY

DISADVANTAGES

A TECHNIQUE HAS BEEN DESCRIBED in which modelling is used as a vehicle for dynamic psychotherapy. As a conclusion to this account, it would seem proper to offer some sort of evaluation of the merits and demerits of the method.

There are obvious disadvantages. It requires equipment which formal psychotherapy does not require. Unless it is competently arranged, the procedure can become cumbersome and messy. However, the necessary arrangements would be a small price to pay for more effective and speedier psychotherapy.

More important is the practical disadvantage that many patients are inclined to reject the procedure without proper trial, or more often without any trial at all. A common reason for such rejection is that the patient feels that modelling with clay is silly. He feels that it is childish; it is beneath his dignity, and out of this prejudice he turns down any suggestion of treatment by such a method. In this respect, it must not be forgotten that other forms of psychiatric treatment are often rejected by the patient out of prejudice, even when there is good clinical reason for believing that the treatment would be of great help to the patient. For instance, this applies to electro-convulsive therapy. Because of public prejudice against this form of treatment, psychiatrists have learned to be circumspect in their dealings with the patient and his relatives when advising E.C.T. A little time spent in explaining the treatment and its results almost always dispels the prejudice. Similar considerations apply to plastotherapy. Now that the author has a better understanding of the importance of these matters, rejection has become quite rare, whereas in the early stages of the work it was quite common.

There is another real disadvantage to plastotherapy which might easily escape the reader. This is the occurrence of acute anxiety reactions. Such reactions are to be avoided in consulting room practice when the patient has to return home after the session. Treatment with plastotherapy undoubtedly involves a much greater risk of acute anxiety reactions than does formal psychotherapy. However, with experience in plastotherapy, the author has become more aware of situations which may lead to these acute reactions, and now they are a much less common occurrence than formerly.

ADVANTAGES

The foregoing account of plastotherapy offers abundant evidence that significant psychological conflicts, which have been suppressed by the patient, find rapid expression through modelling. There are many examples in which the traumatic material has been withheld during considerable formal psychotherapy, only to be ventilated in two or three sessions of modelling. Case No. 4, the patient who had difficulty in swallowing as a result of conflicts concerning fellatio, is a good example. The most important mechanism in such cases is that in modelling the patient is denied, to a great extent, the use of habitual verbal defences.

In a similar way, deeply unconscious repressed material may find easy expression in plastotherapy. In this case, the means of expression is different. The repressed conflicts find expression in individual and universal symbolism. The expression of the patient's homosexual drives in the bisexual symbols of case No. 1, and the expression of the castration phantasy in the bird with the phallic wing in case No. 3, are both good examples of this process.

The relatively informal and unstructured setting of plastotherapy makes it easier for the therapist to make purposive variations in the doctor-patient relationship. The therapist is allowed greater freedom of behaviour. He communicates with the patient through his behaviour, and by this means is able to vary his emotional relationship to the patient according to the needs of the therapeutic situation. As this takes place at a non-verbal level, it is not recorded in the account of the patient's associations, and the reader may easily under-value the importance of this aspect of plasto-therapy.

With the disturbed patient, modelling may become a means by which he can communicate with the therapist. Verbal expression has failed, but he can still fall back on the more primitive plastic symbol as a means of communication. This occurs with the psychotic patient. It is seen in case No. 4. When the therapist finds out the meaning of these plastic symbols, he can use them together with verbal symbols, to convey ideas to the patient.

Plastotherapy is of value in diagnosis. It may be a particular help in the diagnosis of early schizophrenia, which is often so difficult and so important. The means by which plastotherapy is effective in these circumstances are that, in the development of a psychosis, the defences concerning plastic expression fail before the defences concerning verbal expression. As a result, a patient may disclose disordered thinking in his modelling, while his conversation in clinical examination still remains normal. The patient who made the bizarre model of a mouth is a case in question.

A further advantage of plastotherapy over formal psychotherapy is that it promotes in the patient a much higher degree of tolerance of the disturbing conflict. The patient may express some traumatic idea in words; but his habitual defences come to his aid, and the idea is soon removed from consciousness. But when it is expressed in modelling, it is there before him, and he learns to develop a tolerance to it.

There are other considerations. Non-verbal communication plays an important part in any form of psychotherapy. The circumstances of the usual verbal interview are somewhat set and fixed. There is a certain rigidity about the situation. The behaviour of both the patient and the therapist is limited by culturally accepted patterns, so that it is expected of the patient that he will discuss his symptoms and problems, and it is expected of the therapist that he will question the patient about his past life. In other words, the set-up of the interview is essentially arranged for the verbal communication of ideas. This situation does not make for the easy use of non-verbal communication, which is so important and effective in psychotherapy. It is too rigid to allow the therapist

much scope to communicate to the patient by means of his behaviour.

On the other hand, once a transition to modelling is made, the
therapist is no longer bound by the rather rigid conventions of the
interview. He is much freer. His behaviour need not conform to
any fixed pattern. He can sit at the other side of the room, and
leave the patient in emotional isolation. He can take some of the
clay in his hand himself, and mould it with the patient. The therapist and the patient are doing something together, and this in itself
works to establish a warm emotional relationship. He can show
his concern for the patient, and his understanding of the patient's
difficulties. It is a situation in which the therapist is able to communicate much more freely. He is no longer bound by the conventional rules of an interview, as understood by the patient and
accepted by himself.

Thus the tempo of the patient's anxiety, which is such an important factor in psychotherapy, is more effectively regulated when
the patient is modelling. Too great anxiety inhibits the patient and
tends to work against the ventilation of suppressed material. It is
easy to move closer to the patient physically. The therapist can put
a hand on his shoulder, or he can take some of the clay himself.
No word is spoken. But the closer emotional relationship achieved
by this non-verbal communication reduces the patient's anxiety.

On the other hand, in the absence of sufficient anxiety, the
patient is too composed, and lacks the motivation to ventilate
suppressed material. The patient's anxiety is mobilized by direct-
ing his attention to anxiety-producing conflicts, by indicating that
one's problems are expressed in modelling; at the same time,
emotional support is withdrawn by physically moving away from
the patient, or actually leaving him in the room by himself. Of
course, in the ordinary interview, the patient's anxiety is mobilized
or allayed, according to the moment to moment requirements of
the interview situation; but in modelling, the greater flexibility of
the situation allows greater play of non-verbal communication, and
so the control of the patient's anxiety is easier and more effective.
In this respect, the management of the interpersonal relationship

between patient and therapist during modelling resembles the situation during the physical medical examination of the patient, which gives the physician the opportunity to exploit these mechanisms for the benefit of the patient.

That type of short-term psychotherapy which depends for its therapeutic effect upon the manipulation of the emotional relationship between patient and therapist is known as relationship psychotherapy. The emotional interchanges of this type of therapy, the symbolic giving of love and the withdrawal of love, are very much dependent upon non-verbal means of communication. This in turn is much easier in an unstructured, flexible millieu, rather than in a rigid conventional one such as an ordinary interview.

Considerable emphasis has been given to the differences between plastic and verbal expression. Perhaps some comparison should be made between plastotherapy, and the use of painting and drawing as a means of expression in psychotherapy. Some of the author's experiences in this latter field have been published in book form under the title, "The Door of Serenity." Most of the psychiatric literature in this field tends to deal with the bizarre quality of schizophrenic art rather than with its use in treatment. In the author's experience, modelling is a much more effective medium for the elicitation of suppressed and repressed conflicts than is painting or drawing. This applies particularly to the psychoneurotic. Modelling seems to be much more dynamic in its effect on the patient than is painting. The patient becomes more emotionally involved and more distressed in modelling; and in the author's experience, the acute anxiety reactions of plastotherapy are rare when painting is used in a similar manner in psychotherapy. The way in which the changing shape of the clay in the patient's hands becomes associated with ideas in the patient's mind may be a factor in this. The primitive nature of moulding, as compared with the more sophisticated nature of painting, may have some effect; or it may be that moulding, which is characteristically an activity of childhood and infancy, may do something to initiate some kind of regressive mechanism. These are matters of mere speculation; the consistent clinical observation is that modelling is more effective

285

than painting as an aid in psychotherapy.

The reader is again reminded that plastotherapy is not a form of treatment in its own right. It is merely a technique in psycho-therapy, and as such must be integrated into the general programme of treatment.

It seems beyond doubt that plastotherapy speeds up the general process of psychotherapy. In this respect, it must be emphasized that the speeding up is not confined to the attainment of insight by the projection of suppressed and repressed material in the modelling, but it also extends to those other less clearly defined aspects of the therapeutic process, in which are included both the experience of emotion and the toleration of conflict.

As regards the acutal use of modelling in this way, two facts have remained matters of wonder to the author. The first is the way in which non-psychotic patients, who maintain a complete composure during a psychotherapeutic interview, become so easily disturbed in modelling. The second matter of wonder is that many non-psychotic patients, who are of such reserved disposition that they cannot bring themselves to talk of intimate matters, should openly model the likeness of a penis or a breast. It would seem that the explanation of these matters must depend on the different psychodynamics of plastic, as opposed to verbal expression.

Figure No. 123

It still remains a matter of wonderment to the author that inhibited patients will often make a physical likeness of those parts of the body which they are quite unable to discuss in words.

A highly intelligent, introvert girl of twenty-one was brought to consultation on account of increased withdrawal, and a falling off in her work record as a University honours student. The patient would talk freely and easily on inconsequential matters; but as soon as the discussion would be led to herself, she would become inhibited, and she would defend herself with a long intellectual consideration of the subject, such as students commonly do in formal debating. During four sessions of psychotherapy, she maintained an emotional isolation, and parried any attempt at enquiry by an intelligent, logical, but pseudophilosophical discussion of the questions put to her. Any open discussion of her personal or intimate life seemed quite beyond her. On the fifth visit, she was given the clay. She promptly made this phallic shape. Her associations demonstrate a number of important psychodynamic aspects of plastotherapy.

Yes.
(Pause)
Well

(Blocks)

Therapist: *Just let yourself talk.*

Was not thinking of making anything so — much —

Experiencing the feeling of the clay.

Rather self-conscious.

Felt I had to let myself go.

Thought for some reason you might have expected something sexual.

Don't know why.

Think that's what that object is.

Therapist: *Just let yourself look at it, and let yourself talk what comes into your mind.*

Feel rather than see.

When you came in, my first reaction was to hide it or break it.

(Blocks)

Feel I did what was expected of me.

Probably quite silly.

(Blocks)

Therapist: *Just let yourself talk.*

(Pause)

Therapist: *Just look at the object you have made and let yourself talk.*

Extremely ugly form of clay. (Sighs)

I don't know.

Therapist: *What are the thoughts it suggests to you?*

Oh —

(Blocks)

Really don't like saying.

Therapist: *Just let yourself talk.*

(Patient gives a nervous laugh)

Things which one is not generally expected to talk about.

Hard to break that down.

(Pause)

Well, don't see the point in breaking down a barrier.

Seem to rebel.

Make a sex organ, that's what I was thinking when I made it.

Where do you expect me to go from there?

Therapist: *Just let yourself talk.*

Have expended all my energy in overcoming my embarrassment.

288

Am now outside the experience of making it.
(Pause)
Therapist: *What comes to your mind?*
Well — er — well — (suddenly says) *Why should people talk about these things with anyone else.*
Therapist: *It may be a help in getting better.*
I don't know.
Suppose these are excuses to myself to justify my reticence.
Feel it's rather unnatural.
Therapist: *It is unnatural?*
Don't like having things put over me, so to speak.
Feel I like to — just like to see where I am going and why.
Know I am protecting myself in some way.
Something to be gained by the unpleasantness of talking to you.
(Patient defends herself by engaging in irrelevant conversation).
Therapist: *Tell me the thoughts the shape suggests to you.*
Yes I would — yes — think of —
(Pause)
Think of two men whose sex organs I have handled in the way I did that clay.

A young woman, who is so inhibited that she is quite unable to discuss her personal life at all in four sessions of psychotherapy, makes a penis as soon as she is given the clay. Instead of debating with the therapist as a kind of game, she is now emotionally involved, as can be seen from the nature of her associations and her thought blockage.

She rationalizes that she felt that it was expected of her to make something sexual. It would be equally true to say that it was expected of her that she would talk of her personal life during the formal interviews; but for four sessions she successfully parried every oblique and direct enquiry in these matters.

She says, *"My first reaction was to hide it or break it."* This represents a sudden panic when she fully realizes what she has made; and she experiences the urgent desire to defend herself by denial.

Later, she makes the comment, *"Don't like having things put over me, so to speak. Feel I like to — just like to see where I am going and why."* This is a clear expression of the patient's feeling of lack of control of the situation in plastotherapy, as compared with the ease with which she could parry verbal enquiry in an ordinary interview.

PART II

HYPNOPLASTY

Modelling as a Technique in
HYPNOANALYSIS

XIV

HYPNOPLASTY — INTRODUCTION

ORIGIN

J UST AS MODELLING CAN BE USED TO ADVANTAGE in the psychotherapy of the waking patient, it can also be used with the hypnotized patient. Hypnoplasty is the name given to the therapeutic use of modelling with the hypnotized patient. The present study has developed from the author's earlier work on the use of hypnotic painting as a technique in hypnoanalysis. These investigations were published in book form under the title, *"Hypnography."* However, it is felt that there are sufficiently significant differences in the psychodynamics of plastic and graphic expression as to warrant a separate description of the use of modelling in the psychotherapy of the hypnotized patient.

Hypnoplasty is not a method of psychiatric treatment in itself. It is purely a technique in hypnoanalysis, which itself is a procedure in the general psychotherapy of the patient. Hence it is always important that any treatment by hypnoplasty should be adequately integrated into the general programme of psychotherapy.

PURPOSE OF HYPNOPLASTY

In the same way as modelling is used with the waking patient for the purpose of shortening the time of psychotherapy, hypnoplasty is used for the purpose of shortening the time of treatment in hypnoanalysis.

It has been shown that one of the important effects of modelling in the waking state is the way in which it aids the expression of suppressed and repressed material. In these circumstances, the patient has full use of speech, but he is unable to ventilate the conflict in words, as the expression of the ideas is inhibited by the psychological mechanisms of suppression and repression. The situation with the hypnotized patient is rather different. The effect of the suppressive and repressive mechanisms is greatly reduced on account of the hypnotic state. The ideas are ready for ventilation. However, they are often held back by another factor. Many patients do not talk readily when hypnotized. Hypnoplasty is of particular value with these patients, as the suppressed or repressed ideas can be given expression in modelling. The ventilation of the idea in modelling is usually accompanied by the expression of a good deal of emotion. This leads the patient into unverbalized phonation by way of grunts and groans. This in turn soon leads to the explosive utterance of emotionally charged adjectives and nouns. His emotion brings him to blurt out phrases and comments. In this way, the expression of the idea in modelling arouses the appropriate emotion, and soon brings the hypnotized patient to express himself in words, in a manner which might be achieved only after many hours of orthodox verbal hypnoanalysis.

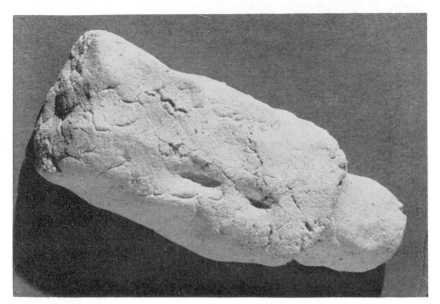

Figure No. 124

In the great majority of cases, the hypnotized patient models the likeness of some object which is connected in some way with some suppressed or repressed psychological conflict. It usually comes about that it is directly or indirectly related to his present illness.

Thus a young woman came to treatment. She suffered from distressing frequency of micturition of several years duration. She had undergone a great deal of medical and surgical investigation and treatment. When hypnotized, she makes this rough model of a car, and she gives the following associations.

> *A car.*
> *In a car that I first got the bladder trouble.*
> *Sitting on one chap's knee.*
> *Car full.*
> *Mother and father in front.*
> *My sister sitting beside another sailor.*
> *Noticed sailor's buttons undone.*
> *Nothing I could see.*
> *But felt embarrassed.*
> *Shortly after that my bladder wanted to go.*
> *Same all the way home.*
> *Dad had to stop three or four times for me.*
> *Sailor came out to live with us.*
> *Was rather keen on my sister.*

TYPE OF PATIENT

The models made under hypnosis discussed in this section concern only psychoneurotic patients. This has been occasioned by the nature of the author's medical practice, which is private extramural psychiatry. With the exception of a minority of patients who had short periods in a general hospital, all the patients lived at home and attended the author's professional rooms for consultation. In such circumstances, it is felt that hypnosis would be unwise with pre-psychotic or psychotic patients, so the present work on hypnoplasty deals only with psychoneurotics.

In most cases, hypnoplasty has been used with patients who were being treated with hypnoanalysis, and who showed difficulty in talking under hypnosis. There have been a few cases who talked readily enough under hypnosis, but who still retained effective powers of suppression and repression. With these patients, the modelling functioned in a way very similar to that described in reference to the waking patient. A few other patients were treated with hypnoplasty because it was thought that the plastic expression of the conflict itself would be beneficial, as the permanence of plastic expression, as opposed to verbal expression, tends to condition the patient to better tolerate a reality conflict. With some other patients, if for any reason, such as rigidity of personality or basic insecurity, it was felt that they could not be introduced to modelling in the waking state, they were hypnotized and treated in hypnoplasty.

XV

SOME GUIDING PRINCIPLES IN HYPNOSIS FOR HYPNOPLASTY

THE MEANING OF BEHAVIOUR

T HE PROBLEM OF BRINGING the hypnotized patient to express unconscious material in modelling might at first seem rather complex. However, in actual fact, the project has not produced so many technical difficulties as had been anticipated. It would seem that success or otherwise in this work is very much dependent upon an appreciation of the meaning of hypnotic behaviour, both as a means of communication and as a means of psychological defence.

Sometimes in hypnosis the patient appears to be acting. The fact is that the hypnotized patient does act. An understanding of this is essential for work in hypnoplasty. In the past, this tendency of the hypnotized patient to act has led many observers to doubt the reality of hypnotic phenomena. They have been misled into believing that hypnosis was nothing more than an elaborate form of simulation. We must remember that behaviour in general, besides being directed to some purpose in reality, is also used as a means of expression. The child, when asked to do something which he does not desire to do, will perform the act in such a way as to let the observer know that it is done under protest. The child's behaviour is thus used as a means of communication. So also, adult behaviour is consistently used to communicate subtleties of meaning to those nearby. In this way there is normally a certain quality of acting with our ordinary everyday behaviour.

This same process operates in hypnosis, but it operates in a highly exaggerated form. As the patient often does not speak readily in hypnosis, he is largely deprived of his usual means of communication. As a result, he relies more and more on his behaviour as a means of expressing himself to the therapist.

In hypnoplasty, this tendency of the hypnotized patient to express himself in his behaviour is more marked than in most other situations. There are two reasons for this. In the first place, the patient in hypnoplasty feels a great need to communicate because of the threat of the ventilation of unconscious material. Although the patient is hypnotized, the ventilation of unconscious material is always likely to become a threat to him, on account of the varying and fluctuant nature of the depth of hypnosis in hypnoplasty. Added to this, the situation in hypnoplasty is rather different from other hypnotic procedures. In suggestive therapeutics, the hypnotized patient just sits or lies down, and listens to the suggestions of the therapist. Likewise in ordinary hypnoanalysis the patient just talks. But hypnoplasty demands constant motor activity in the hypnotized patient, and this in itself makes it easy for the patient to use his behaviour as a means of communicating with the therapist.

When first starting the work on hypnoplasty, and before I fully understood this process, I can well remember being quite baffled by the patient's obvious acting. A patient would do things, such as taking a piece of clay between the thumb and the little finger, instead of using the full grasp of the hand. I remember thinking that the patient was not properly hypnotized, and that he was merely simulating. My bewilderment only increased when I tested him in other fields of activity, and found him to be deeply hypnotized. It is now quite clear that such behaviour, obvious acting, is a means of expression. The patient was only expressing the idea, "You can see I am hypnotized; a hypnotized person cannot model." In this way, he was using the hypnotic situation as defence against the ventilation of traumatic material.

Figure No. 125

Because of the hysteroid quality of much of the behaviour of the hypnotized patient, it is easy to be misled into believing that the patient is simulating, when in reality he is deeply hypnotized.

In hypnoplasty, the patient quite frequently experiences vivid hallucinatory phenomena. These hallucinatory experiences are usually accompanied by appropriate affect. However, this model and the accompanying associations serve to illustrate an extremely vivid hallucinatory experience which is accompanied by a labile and somewhat inappropriate affect. This, and the impression of childish acting which the associations give, might lead one to suspect simulation. But the genuineness of the phenomena is shown by the way in which tears come to the patient's eyes. The tears cause his nose to run, with the result that tears and mucus run from his nose and drip, unheeded by the patient, onto the table. The matter is all the more convincing in that the patient is a man of fifty who is controlled and reserved in his normal conversation.

> *Piles of money.*
> *I can see them, silver and gold on a red velvet, shiny.*
> *Stacks of coins, stack after stack, all shiny.*
> *Stacks and stacks of coins.* (Mumbles inaudibly)

299

Piles of money.
It's not mine.
That's what I should have.
Twenty-five years (Nose dribbles on the table)
But I am happy. (Mumbles)
Lousy. (Mumbles. The therapist takes the patient's hand-
    kerchief out of his coat pocket and wipes his nose, which
    is dribbling on the table. The patient takes no notice, and
    his hallucinations continue).
Can see cheque butts in front of me, Bank of — (Laughs)
It's got wings on it.
The money's going, there's nothing there, just a blank table.
At the next session, a week later, the patient made another pile of
money, and gave the following associations.
Dark
Just little piles of money.
Fat man there.
It's me.
Funny
Watching it disappear.
It's me, it's me.
Therapist: *Tell me about the fat man.*
See myself.
No clothes on.
See the appendix scar.
It's me, just watching it.
Therapist: *What is he thinking?*
Can't keep his hand on any money.
Can't keep it.
Therapist: *What sort of man is he?*
Fat like me (with extreme emotion) *like me.*
Putting his hands out to stop it disappearing.

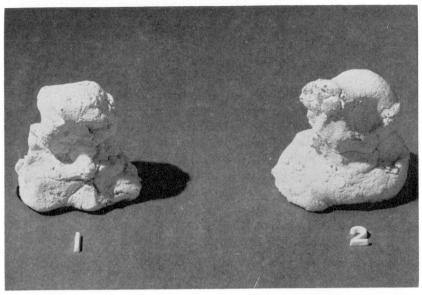

Figure No. 126

Sometimes one can learn a great deal from the patient's behaviour. By what he does, rather than by what he says, the patient may let us know how he feels towards some person who is concerned in his past or present psychological conflicts. By his behaviour, the patient may communicate his moment to moment reaction to the therapist. Sometimes these communications would appear to be clearly purposive; at other times it would seem that they are merely reflections of the patient's changing mood, and are made without any reference to the presence of the therapist.

The patient makes two primitive figures. The first one he identifies as his mother. He speaks of her as soft, loving, tender. As he speaks, he caresses the model gently with his fingers.

He identifies the second figure as his father-in-law. The patient speaks of him as hard, tough and hateful. As he speaks, he angrily grasps the model around the neck as if in the act of strangulation.

THE DYNAMIC CONCEPT OF HYPNOSIS

The expression of psychic material by modelling in the hypnotic state first necessitates the induction of an adequate depth of hypnosis. Any detailed description of hypnotic phenomena, or any comprehensive account of methods of induction of hypnosis is beyond the scope of the present work, in which the primary aim is the discussion of the processes governing the plastic expression of psychological conflict. Nevertheless, it would seem wise to state some general principles of hypnosis which are particularly relevant to hypnoplasty, as well as to give some brief account of techniques for the induction of hypnosis which are especially suited to this type of work.

Success with hypnosis for the expression of psychological conflict by modelling is very much dependent upon the therapist's own concept of the hypnotic state. Since the last world war, there has really been a great change in informed medical opinion as regards many aspects of hypnosis. Until then, Bernheim's views found general acceptance. The therapist simply overwhelmed the patient. His use of authority became more and more irresistible until the patient was mastered; and when his mastery of the patient was complete, he added therapeutic suggestions for the relief of symptoms. The ruthlessness of such an approach allowed little scope for the subtleties of psychodynamics. But now, with the use of passive methods of induction, and the advent of hypno-analysis, all this has changed. Informed medical opinion no longer regards hypnosis as a static mental state, in which the subjugated patient automatically accepts suggestions. Hypnosis is looked upon as a highly dynamic psychological condition which is constantly varying, and in which all the ordinary psychological mechanisms of the waking subject are operative; only they are modified and disguised by the hypnotic state. Such a concept of hypnosis is essential for success in hypnoplasty. This is so because hypnoplasty evokes various forms of behaviour which can be understood only when they are regarded as defences against the expression of traumatic material. When regarded in this light, the apparently odd, purposeless behaviour of the hypnotized patient becomes meaningful.

In the past, hypnosis has been regarded as a fairly static mental state. This type of thinking is reflected in the great number of references in the literature to description of levels of hypnosis. The present work has made it quite clear that the idea of different levels of depth of hypnosis is valid only for the particular individual when considered within the limits of a constant psychological situation. The giving of therapeutic suggestions is such a situation. However, the therapist who uses hypnosis in the continually varying psychological situations of hypnoplasty will very soon realize that this concept of constancy in the hypnotic state is no longer tenable. In the hypnotized patient, the threat of ventilation of psychological conflicts still evokes various defensive reactions. The nature of these reactions varies continually according to counter moves by the therapist. These varying psychological reactions of the patient cause continual fluctuations in the depth of hypnosis. Furthermore, the expression of the conflict itself usually calls forth some degree of abreaction in the hypnotized patient. This abreaction in turn causes variations in the depth of hypnosis. There are further complications. The therapist working in hypnoplasty will frequently observe that the patient appears to be deeply hypnotized in some areas of activity, yet at the same time, in other areas of activity, the patient is only very lightly hypnotized. In other words, the patient can manifest different levels of hypnosis in different areas of ego function at the same time. Accordingly, the therapist who would practice hypnoplasty must abandon the old idea of definite levels of hypnosis, and in its place he must come to regard hypnosis as a highly dynamic and constantly fluctuating state of mind.

Figure No. 127

When hypnosis is used in a dynamic psychotherapeutic situation such as hypnoplasty, the classical concept of levels of hypnosis is no longer valid. This follows from the fact that some patients who are sufficiently deep to fall asleep on the appropriate suggestion, are still not deep enough for hynoplasty; while other patients who are deep enough for hypnoplasty are still not deep enough for hypnotic sleep.

The same principle is demonstrated in this model and the following associations.

> *Girl, that's what I have in my mind.*
> *Frightened of sex.*
> *Girls always worried me.*
> *Only want sex.*
> *Never seem to be interested in anything else.*
> *Conflicts with my morals.*
> *Seem to have no other interest in them.*
> *I am happiest if I can't get serious.*
> *I don't feel happy with them.*
> *Someone else's girl and it is easier.*
> *Always a conflict between wanting sex and my morals.*
> *No interest in girls other than that.*

The poor production of the model, the lack of symmetry, and the general disorganization would suggest a moderate depth of hynosis. On the other hand, the associations, for the most part, are given in normal grammar and syntax, and show none of the disorganization which is seen in the model. In other words, it would seem that the modelling and the speaking functions of the psyche are functioning at different depths of hypnosis.

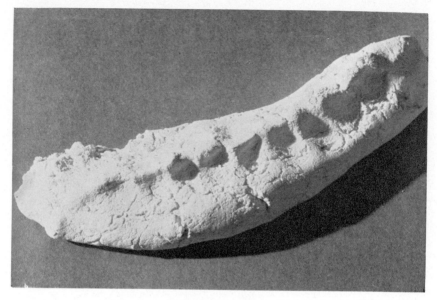

Figure No. 128

The highly dynamic and constantly fluctuant nature of the hypnotic state in hypnoplasty is demonstrated in the associations to this model. The patient is a man in his middle forties, suffering from spasmodic torticollis. The model represents a loaf of bread.

> *Food.*
> *Bread.*
> *Biscuits.*
> *Boy waiting for the baker.*
> *Waiting for bread.*
> *One week everything.*
> *Pictures, everything.*
> *Next week nothing.*
> *No butter, no light.*
> *It doesn't matter, and spend it.*
> *What of the future.*
> *Don't live to work.*
> (Pause)
> *Quickly, get the doctor.*
> *Get the doctor.* (emotion)
> *Catch your death of cold.*

Bogey man coming.
Two shillings.
Rich.
Got two shillings.
Hide Jim.
Hide behind the door until father goes.
Play outside.
(Pause)
Might get V.D.
Careful.
Look out.
Look out Jim.
Frightened.
You might get this.
You might get that.
Wash your hands.
Don't walk on the bathroom floor, you might get something.
(Pause)
Fear.
Silly.
Silly fears.
(Pause)
Do I want to get better?
Wonder do I.
Misery.
Got to get better.
But to face up to all those fears again.
Don't have to with a neck.
Excuse.
(Pause)
Going to get better.

The associations were given spontaneously, and were continued without prompting.

At first the patient talks of his childhood poverty. They have money one week and none the next. There is a pause. There is no communication from the therapist, either verbally or non-verbally. Suddenly he shouts out, *"Quickly, get the doctor."* He is re-living some past experience. It would seem clear that the depth of hypnosis has increased since he first started to talk. He continues in deep hypnosis and calls out, *"Hide Jim,"* and later, *"Look out Jim."* There is a pause, and he then talks of *"Fear, silly fears."* The abreaction of the emotion in his re-living of these past experiences has reduced the depth of hypnosis. He is now no longer re-living an experience; he is looking back on it, commenting about it. There is another pause, and he reflects upon the present-day reality situation. *"Do I want to get better?"* Finally hypnosis is quite light, and he expresses his resolve, *"Going to get better."*

The important consideration from the point of view of the practical management of the hypnotized patient is that these changes in the depth of hypnosis have come about without any suggestion, verbal or non-verbal, from the therapist. These fluctuations in depth come in response to dynamic forces within the psyche. It can be seen how the process of association leads the patient to the re-living of past experiences with a consequent increase in depth of hypnosis. The abreaction which this entails lightens hypnosis. This in turn has its effect on the ideational content, which becomes more realistic.

EFFECT OF PATIENT'S PRECONCEIVED IDEAS

To a large extent, the manner of behaviour of the hypnotized patient is determined by the subject's preconceived idea as to how a hypnotized person does behave. These preconceived ideas really act in a similar way to the suggestions of the therapist. There is abundant evidence of this. Mesmer's patients believed that the magnetic fluid would throw them into a convulsion, and in fact they were convulsed. Braid's patients equated hypnosis with sleep, and they went to sleep. Other patients associate hypnosis with the Svengali-Trilby type of phenomena, and they exhibit various manifestations of somnambulism. This principle is important in relation to hypnoplasty. It is clear that there will be difficulty in getting a patient to perform the co-ordinated motor activity of modelling, if he has the firm belief that one goes to sleep in hypnosis. Accordingly, when discussing hypnosis with the patient prior to treatment, it has been found wise to give emphasis to the idea of automatic motor activity. *"For medical hypnosis you just let yourself go. You will find that you can let yourself go so completely that your body works automatically. You will find that you can do things automatically as if you were in a dream. At the same time your body works easily and normally."* When the actual induction is commenced, these ideas can be given further emphasis. The important factor is that the patient who is going to be treated in hypnoplasty should not be allowed to harbour preconceived ideas equating hypnosis with sleep, nor should he be subject to any inadvertent non-verbal suggestion to this effect from the therapist.

This principle applies in the selection of the type of method to be used for the induction of hypnosis. In general, hypnosis by suggestions of relaxation and sleep is best avoided if the therapist is contemplating treatment by hypnoplasty. Methods such as arm levitation, the induction of repetitive movement, or the dynamic method, which involve the patient in motor activity from the very start, are more suitable for hypnoplasty. On the other hand, if the patient's personality structure is such that he is easily hypnotized by suggestions of relaxation, and it is difficult to hypnotize him by active methods, then a return can be made to these methods after the patient has been first hypnotized by suggestions of relaxation.

CONDITIONING THE PATIENT

When hypnosis is used for any medical purpose, the patient always needs some kind of preparation. This may take the form of reassurance and a brief description of hypnotic phenomena and procedure. When it is a matter of suggestive therapy, it is easy enough to emphasize ideas of relaxation, drowsiness and sleep. For verbal hypnoanalysis, the therapist can bring into the conversation such ideas as talking when in a very relaxed state, or talking as if it were in a dream. But the motor activity of modelling in hypnoplasty requires a rather different approach.

Until recently, the therapist has traditionally adopted an authoritative attitude towards the patient. He commanded the patient, and he used all the devices of prestige to make his commands more powerful. Thus, in this situation, the therapist was active and the patient was passive. The patient obeyed suggestions; he remained inert, and started no activity of his own initiative.

Now, the situation in hypnoplasty is practically the reverse of this. The therapist is passive. There is no recourse to authority, no blatant use of prestige. The patient is shown how he can allow himself to drift into hypnosis. The patient is not lying down inactive, but is actively modelling the clay. More than this, the patient has to take the initiative as to what he makes. The therapist suggests to him that his hands will make something from the clay, but the patient has to decide, either consciously or unconsciously, what is to be made.

This type of activity comes more easily to the hypnotized patient if he is gradually conditioned to these ideas prior to the actual induction of hypnosis. From the beginning, the therapist remains passive. During the interview, the patient is led into the way of letting himself go. This facilitates the abandonment of the self in passive hypnosis. The patient can be introduced to the feeling of automatic movement by the repeated leisurely elicitation of the tendon reflexes during the physical examination of the patient.

It is essential that the whole of the procedure of hypnosis be orientated towards the idea of movement. In talking about hypnosis to the patient, and in explaining it to him, the idea of activity is casually, but repeatedly brought into the conversation. *"You let yourself go so completely that your body works automatically. Your arms and legs just work automatically. Your hands and fingers can do things. All you do is let yourself go."* The ideas can be expressed in different terms, appropriate to the social and educational background of the patient.

The interview is structured so that the patient is allowed to keep a good measure of initiative. This seems to make it easier for the patient to retain the degree of initiative in hypnosis which is necessary for hypnoplasty. It is seen that the approach to the patient is vastly different from the classical concept of suggestive therapeutics, when everything possible is done to increase the therapist's authority so that his mastery over the patient might be nearly complete.

MOTIVATION FOR HYPNOSIS

With hypnoplasty, as with any form of treatment which involves hypnosis, the matter of motivation is of great importance. It is widely recognized that insincere or perverse motives often prompt patients to seek psychiatric treatment. Thus, hysterics may come to consultation with no desire for relief of their symptoms, but rather as an excuse for the continuation of their condition. Guilty persons may come for treatment when they really seek to be hurt or humiliated. These perverse motives are much more common, and much more important when treatment is by hypnosis. Persons frequently ask to be treated by hypnoanalysis, when it is quite clear that they are going to resist hypnosis all they can. Another patient may seek treatment by hypnosis because he unconsciously hopes to satisfy his need for dependency in the hypnotic situation. Women patients may be led to ask for treatment by hypnosis, not so much for the relief of their symptoms, but rather because they unconsciously wish to satisfy their masochistic yearning by being overpowered in hypnosis. Patients of either sex may seek hypnosis

311

on account of the intensity of the emotional relationship, which they experience as disguised eroticism. Pre-psychotic schizophrenics often seek treatment by hypnosis in the vague belief that it will ward off their ill-formed ideas of influence.

It is clear that, before commencing the induction of hypnosis for hypnoplasty, the therapist must be sure of the patient's conscious reasons for seeking treatment. More than this, in the light of the patient's personality structure, he must also make an estimate of the unconscious motivation. If there is evidence of perverse motivation, it is usually wisest to defer the question of hypnosis.

XVI

INDUCTION OF HYPNOSIS
FOR HYPNOPLASTY

CHOICE OF METHOD

THE READER IS REMINDED that there is no attempt to give a general account of the induction of hypnosis. Such information is available elsewhere. The present chapter is to be looked upon merely as a commentary on procedure when hypnosis is to be induced for the purpose of hypnoplasty.

The active nature of hypnoplasty demands that hypnosis should be induced by a method which involves some motor activity on the part of the patient. There are three techniques — arm levitation, induction of repetitive movement, and the dynamic method, each of which can be used very satisfactorily.

The choice of the method to be used is determined in the following manner. During the physical examination of the patient, the tendon reflexes are tested in the usual way. The knee jerks are elicited in a very leisurely manner. During this procedure, the patient is given a few casual suggestions of relaxation. *"While I test the reflexes, you let your legs go loose. They are quite loose, loose and relaxed. Your legs are loose. You are relaxed and comfortable all over."* The patient interprets these suggestions in relation to the elicitation of the tendon reflexes, and he does not associate them in any way as a test for hypnosis. Thus the therapist is able to obtain valuable information about the patient's suggestibility, without the patient being aware that he is being tested in this area. The nature of the patient's response to these suggestions determines which particular technique will be used for induction. As the suggestions are given, some patients respond by becoming progressively more relaxed. These are persons who would ordinarily be induced by suggestions of relaxation and sleep. But this is not desired when hypnoplasty is contemplated; so these patients are induced by the initiation of repetitive movement of the arm.

Other patients respond to the suggestions of relaxation by becoming progressively more tense. These are often nervous, anxious, apprehensive persons. This type of patient is well known to every physician. His muscles share the tension of his mind. In the extreme form of this condition, the patient's thigh muscles become so tense that his heels are lifted off the couch when the physician places his arm beneath the knees when about to test the reflexes. These patients are easily hypnotized by arm levitation. The flexors of the elbow joint share in the general tension of all the somatic muscles. This greatly facilitates the lifting up of the arm in response to suggestion.

This increase in tension in these patients in response to suggestions of relaxation must not be confused with negativism. It is due to quite a different mechanism. It is purely the somatic result of anxiety. Patients who exhibit negativism are not suited for induction by arm levitation. When given suggestions of lightness of their hands, they invariably lean forward and push their hands down on the table, and the process of induction is brought to a stop. On the other hand, patients exhibiting negativism are easily hypnotized by the initiation of repetitive movement of the arm.

A third group of patients shows little or no response to the suggestions. As a general rule, these are the more difficult persons to hypnotize. With them, it is usually best to use the dynamic method.

There is an exception to these general rules of procedure. Occasionally one meets patients who make such a completely positive response to the few suggestions of relaxation that it is immediately obvious that they would be extremely easy to hypnotize by this method. Sometimes these patients are rather difficult to hypnotize by an active method on the first occasion. In this case, the patient may be hypnotized by suggestions of relaxation, and while hypnotized he is given suggestions of activity in hypnosis. On the next occasion, he is hypnotized by an active method. He must be taught to be hypnotized by an active method before commencing hypnoplasty.

THE INDUCTION OF HYPNOSIS BY ARM LEVITATION

This is the method of choice for tense, anxious patients in whom tension is a feature. The muscle tension of anxiety always has the tendency to partially flex the patient's arms. This is seen in the stance of the anxious patient, in whom the arms are characteristically bent up, in contrast to the flaccid hang of the arms in the relaxed person. This muscle tension is utilized for the induction of hypnosis.

The method is well described by Wolberg, and the following is merely an outline of the procedure. The patient sits down with his elbows and forearms resting on a table. His palms are downwards, and his fingers extended. He is directed to look closely at his finger tips. *"Your eyes look at your fingers, your eyes look at your fingers. Your fingers begin to tingle. You feel the tingling in your fingers."* Suggestions of this nature are continued. It is inevitable with a tense patient that some slight involuntary movement will occur in one of his fingers. This calls for immediate comment. *"Your finger moves. It moves. It is tingling and light. It feels light. Your whole hand is light."* Further spontaneous twitching movements can be anticipated. *"More little movements; little movements come in your fingers. Twitching movements; one finger twitches, then another."* Once the involuntary twitching is established, suggestions proceed to lightness and levitation. *"Your fingers twitch. They tingle. They are light. They are so light that they lift up. They are lifting up into the air. Your whole hand is light. Your hands are lifting up, right up into the air."*

The success of the method depends on the correct selection of patients. Relaxed persons are generally not suitable. It is quite contra-indicated for negativistic patients, who merely push down on the table. It is easy and effective with the tense and anxious; and has the advantage of quickly producing a deep hypnosis, which at the same time allows the motor activity necessary for hypnoplasty.

With this technique, there is a point in management which is worth comment. As with any medical use of hypnosis, it is essential that rapport should be fully established with the patient,

315

prior to inducing hypnosis. Usually, as rapport is established, anxiety is allayed, and there is a general tendency for muscle tension to be lessened. A reduction of muscle tension is no help to arm levitation. So steps are taken to gain rapport, but at the same time the patient's tension is allowed to continue. Because of one's natural desire to help the patient to feel more comfortable, there may be some reluctance on the part of the therapist to do this. He feels that he wants to reassure the patient and so put him at ease. But this is obviously not in the best interests of the patient. More than this, on occasion it may be a real advantage to take active steps to increase the patient's tension just prior to the first induction by arm levitation; but once the patient has been hypnotized on one or two occasions, these precautions become unnecessary.

THE INDUCTION OF HYPNOSIS BY THE
INITIATION OF REPETITIVE MOVEMENT

This method is particularly suitable for patients who are going to be treated in hypnoplasty, as the patient is accustomed from the very beginning to the idea of automatic motor activity. It is used for hypnoplasty with those patients whom one would ordinarily hypnotize with suggestions of relaxation and sleep. One proceeds in the classical manner, with graded suggestions of relaxation. *"You are just lying there. You let yourself go. Everything lets go. You are calm, and warm, and comfortable. There is an easy, nice, relaxed feeling. Everything lets go. While you are here nothing matters. You feel the muscles of your legs. You feel them relax. They let go. It is all through you. Everything lets go. All your body, all your mind lets go. You are calm, and comfortable, and easy. The relaxation of it is all through you. The heavy, drowsy relaxation of it."* At this stage, if we were continuing in the classical manner, the idea of sleep would be introduced. *"The heavy, drowsy, relaxation is all through you. You feel the heavy, drowsy, sleepy, relaxation. Your eyelids are heavy with the sleep of it. Your legs are heavy with it. It is all through you, the deep, heavy, sleep of it."* But instead of suggesting sleep in this way, when the

316

patient is fully relaxed he is told, *"Everything lets go and your body works automatically. Your whole body works automatically. I take your arm but it does not disturb you. I take your arm and it goes back and forth, back and forth, back and forth."* So saying, the patient's arm is taken loosely by the wrist, and raised, leaving the elbow resting on the couch. It is moved back and forth in time with the verbal suggestions. In this manoeuvre, it is an advantage if the patient's arm is moved by pulling on the cuff of his sleeve rather than by actually holding the wrist. This permits the forearm to wobble about, which allows the initiation of spontaneous movement to come more easily. The movement of the arm by pulling on the cuff, and the verbal suggestions, are continued until the forearm takes on repetitive movement of its own. Challenges are then introduced. *"Your arm goes back and forth, back and forth automatically. You do not move it. It moves itself. It moves itself, and you cannot stop it. It goes back and forth, back and forth automatically."* It is then suggested that the patient open his eyes, and his gaze is directed to the movement of his hand. *"Your eyes open, but you do not wake up. Your eyes open but you do not wake up. Your eyes look at your hand. Your eyes look at your hand. It goes back and forth, back and forth automatically."* The observation of hypnotic phenomena in the self always has the effect of increasing the depth of hypnosis. This is an extremely easy and effective method of inducing hypnosis, and it is suitable for a wide variety of patients.

The method is of particular value in the hypnosis of negativistic patients. These patients are often difficult to hypnotize by other methods. The patient is recognized by the fact that he responds to suggestions in the opposite way to that which is suggested. The reaction can be seen most clearly if arm levitation should be attempted. The patient sits with his hands on the table. When suggestions of lightness of his hands are given, his hands are actually pushed down on the table, as is seen by the flattening of the finger pulps. The important factor about this reaction is that, although the patient's reaction is the opposite to that which was suggested, it nevertheless signifies that the patient is in fact highly suggestible.

It is merely a matter of using an appropriate technique, and the patient can easily be led into hypnosis. With these patients, when the method of repetitive movement is used, it is found that the patient pulls his arm back on the suggestion of forward movement, and pushes it forward on the suggestion of backward movement. The result is that a back and forth repetitive movement is soon established. This is allowed to continue for a few minutes, and the patient quickly drifts into hypnosis.

THE DYNAMIC METHOD OF INDUCTION OF HYPNOSIS

This method is used with those patients who are more difficult to hypnotize. It is described elsewhere by the author in some detail.*

The dynamic method utilizes the following principle. The patient may be fully co-operative, and may consciously desire to be hypnotized. Yet unconscious defences prevent him from allowing himself to go into hypnosis. These arise if the abandonment to hypnosis, with its consequent loss of control, is regarded as a threat to the ego. The defences commonly take the form of various manifestations of restlessness, sleep, negativism, or simulation of hypnosis. The significant feature is that the patient is unaware that his behaviour is directed to ward off the onset of hypnosis. In the dynamic method, these defences are incorporated in the suggestions; so that the defences are either circumvented, or are actually turned against the patient, and used in the inductive process.

In this method, the actual nature of the initial suggestions is of no importance. The success of the technique rests on the correct interpretation of the patient's response, and its immediate use in the next set of suggestions.

For example, a start may be made with suggestions of relaxation. It may be observed that the patient fidgets, or shows some other form of restlessness. This is regarded as a defence against the abandonment of the self in complete relaxation and the threat of loss of control in hypnosis. So the suggestions are switched from

*Medical Journal of Australia, 1:18:644, 1955.

relaxation to movement. *"Your hand moves. You see your hand moves. It moves again."* If the movement is maintained, a transition can be made to the initiation of repetitive movement. The patient's arm is taken by the cuff and he is told, *"Your arm moves. It moves back and forth. It moves back and forth automatically,"* etc. If, on the other hand, the restlessness is not maintained, a further change must be made. If it appears that the patient is becoming calm and relaxed, a return can be made to suggestions of relaxation. If there is no increase in relaxation, a change to arm levitation may be made. When this is done, it is quite likely that the patient will defend himself with negativism, by actively pushing his hands down on the suggestion of lightness. When this happens, hypnosis can often be induced by switching to the induction of repetitive movement, because the patient's negativistic defence can be used against him in establishing a back and forth movement of his arm. However, at this stage the patient may change his defence to sleep. When an attempt is made to establish repetitive movement, the patient is found to be unco-operative because he is half asleep. The suggestions are now switched to relaxation and sleep. This process of changing the suggestions according to the particular defence of the moment is continued until the patient is eventually hypnotized.

The successful use of the dynamic method demands from the therapist a state of mind quite different from that usually advised for the giving of suggestions. In the hypnosis of the difficult patient, it used to be advised that the therapist should continue to repeat a set stock of suggestions over and over again. The ideas could be expressed in different form, but any abandonment of the particular suggestion before it was fulfilled was regarded as defeat. In the dynamic method there is no set pattern of suggestions. The nature of each suggestion is determined by the patient's reaction to the previous suggestion, and the areas in which the suggestions are made are under constant change. The essence of this method is the making of quick changes in the nature of the suggestions, according to the particular defence which the patient is using at the moment.

XVII

THE TECHNIQUE OF HYPNOPLASTY

THE PRELIMINARIES

J UST AS MODELLING IN THE waking state is used as a special technique in psychotherapy, in the same way modelling in the hypnotic state is used as a special technique in hypnoanalysis. One of the common difficulties in hypnoanalysis is that some patients do not talk readily when hypnotized. Hypnoplasty has proved a significant factor in the treatment of some of these patients. Instead of using words, the patient gives expression to the conflict by plastic means. In this way, the difficulty of talking in hypnosis is circumvented. But there is more to it than this. It is found that the expression of a conflict in modelling somehow facilitates the subsequent expression of the conflict in words. Thus a patient may be hypnotized, but treatment may be held up by the patient's difficulty in talking in hypnoanalysis. But after the expression of the conflict in modelling, it often happens that the patient will talk quite freely in hypnosis.

Plasticine, or any of the materials commonly used for modelling, are suitable media for hypnoplasty. The models illustrated in the text were all made with a proprietary modelling compound which consists of Plaster of Paris mixed with some other material to delay the setting time. It allows the patient about three-quarters of an hour before setting. It finally sets absolutely hard and rigid. This is an advantage for research purposes, as the models may be kept with no chance of their losing shape. The disadvantage is that the material has to be mixed with water. It is rather messy, and is inclined to stick to the fingers. The result is that the hypnotized patient is likely to soil his clothes from contact with his fingers. For ordinary therapeutic purposes, as opposed to research, it would seem that plasticine is a very suitable medium.

It has been the custom not to tell the patient that he is going to be asked to model. In fact, precautions are taken to see to it that the patient has no forewarning of what will be expected of him. For instance, the modelling materials are brought into the room only after the patient has been deeply hypnotized. The reason for these precautions has been the belief that the patient might consciously elaborate ideas for modelling, which might interfere with the spontaneous production of unconscious material. In actual fact, experience suggests that these precautions are unnecessary. If conscious elaboration were an important factor, it would be expected that there would be significant differences in the character of models made in the first session, compared with those made in subsequent sessions. Differences of this nature have not been observed, even though the patient may have no amnesia of the previous session.

THE CRITICAL DEPTH

Hynoplasty requires a certain critical depth of hypnosis. If hypnosis is too light, when the patient is given the clay and it is suggested that he model, he is likely to exhibit anxiety and wake from hypnosis. There is no certain test for adequate depth of hypnosis for modelling, but it has been found that the maintenance of repetitive movement of the arm with the eyes open, in the face of direct challenges to stop the movement, is a reasonably reliable guide. In fact, it would seem wise not to attempt hypnoplasty with any patient unless this criterion is fulfilled. It usually works out that the patient has had at least two sessions of hypnosis before commencing hypnoplasty.

In coming to a decision as to whether or not a patient is adequately hypnotized for hypnoplasty, the condition of the patient's eyes is often a useful guide. When repetitive movement of the arm is induced, the patient almost invariably closes his eyes. He opens his eyes again in response to the suggestion, *"Your eyes open but you don't wake up. Your eyes open but you don't wake up."* The patient opens his eyes, and invariably looks away from his moving arm. It is as though he does not wish to witness movements of his body which are beyond his control. In looking away, he defends himself by dissociation. He does not own his unruly member. His gaze is then directed to his arm. *"Your eyes look at your hand. You don't move it. It moves itself automatically, and you can't stop it. You can't stop it. You can try what you like, but you cannot stop it."* If the arm falters in its movement, this is immediately seized upon. *"There, you tried to stop it, but you could not. You tried to stop it, but could not."* The patient is likely to defend himself further by spontaneously closing his eyes as if he were going to sleep. His gaze is again directed to his hand. The deeply hypnotized patient usually develops a glassy, unblinking stare, with the eyelids widely open. This is a sign of adequate depth for hypnoplasty. Any tendency for the eyes to blink usually indicates that hypnosis is not so deep. If his gaze wanders around the room, it is probable that the patient is not sufficiently deeply hypnotized for hypnoplasty. The estimation of the depth of hypnosis in these terms is not just a theoretical exercise. It is a matter which requires a definite decision each time hypnoplasty is contemplated, as it is usually unwise to try a patient with modelling unless there is every reason to believe that he will fulfill the appropriate suggestions. It is unwise because failure may precipitate acute anxiety reactions.

THE INITIAL SUGGESTIONS

With the patient sitting at a table, repetitive movement is induced, and he is challenged to stop it. He can then conveniently be put into an hypnotic sleep while the modelling material is brought in, and placed on the table in front of him. He is told, *"I take your hand, it goes back and forth, back and forth automatically. Your eyes open. Your eyes look at your hand. Your eyes look at your hand. It goes back and forth automatically."* The movement is allowed to continue for a while, and he is told, *"Now I take your arm. It flops down on the table. Now your eyes look at this clay. It is modelling clay. It is for modelling things. Your hand takes up the clay. You take the clay in your hand."* While these suggestions are being given, the therapist can take some of the clay in his own hand, and mould it with his fingers in front of the patient. This is a non-verbal suggestion for the patient to do likewise, and it serves to introduce him to the plastic possibilities of the clay. At this stage, the therapist can offer the clay in his hand to the patient. The patient invariably takes it, and the suggestions continue. *"Your hand takes the clay. Your fingers mould the clay. Everything lets go. You do not wake up from it. It is all through you. Your fingers mould the clay. Both hands work on it. They make something. They make something out of the clay. Something in your mind, deep in your mind. Your fingers make something, something to do with the thing in your mind."*

THE PROCEDURE IN HYPNOPLASTY

Patients respond to this series of suggestions in different ways. With a surprising number, there is practically no delay. They immediately set about moulding the clay in a purposive fashion. This contrasts with the usual behaviour of psychoneurotic patients in the waking state, when there is almost invariably some delay in making a start at modelling. Furthermore, in the waking state, the patient almost always shows some signs of anxiety when he is first asked to model; but the hypnotized patient rarely shows this initial anxiety.

The clay may be taken in one lump, and worked into some relatively large object, or little pieces may be broken off and each moulded into some significant shape. With many patients, one of the most noticeable features has been the prompt start on the modelling, and the purposive nature of their behaviour from the very beginning. Because of this purposive quality, and the obviously reasoned approach to the problem, it was at first thought that these were the less deeply hypnotized subjects. However, subsequent experience has proved that this is not always the case, and reasoned purposive activity may be quite a characteristic of the deeply hypnotized patient in hypnoplasty. Some patients keep on moulding the clay with their fingers. The process becomes rhythmical. They are absolutely intent upon it. Their eyes maintain an unblinking gaze on the changing shape of the clay. Sometimes it would seem that the patient would continue in this fashion indefinitely. Sometimes the intensity of his preoccupation suggests that he is obtaining some erotic satisfaction from this rhythmical fondling of the clay. There is no sign of boredom or fatigue; it would seem to go on and on without end.

When this state of affairs develops, it is clear that some active intervention is necessary. Further suggestions are given. *"Your fingers make something. They make something. No matter what it is, your fingers make something. They make something, something to do with the thing in your mind."* With variation and repetition of these suggestions, the patient eventually moulds the clay into some definite shape, a shape which has meaning to him, although its meaning may not be clear to the therapist.

With other patients, the process is rather different. They seem to fiddle with the clay until some spontaneously occurring shape suggests something to them. This shape is then purposefully structured into a better likeness of the object in mind.

Sometimes the patient will take the clay when it is offered to him, but will make no move to model it at all. He just holds it in his fingers, and remains steadfastly looking at it. He is utterly without movement; he becomes a kind of living statue. This is the catatonic state, which is not infrequently seen in hypnosis. Suggestions of modelling go unheeded, and the patient may continue thus for a long period. When first encountered, the condition may be quite alarming, because the therapist is likely to feel that he is losing touch with the patient. The answer to this problem, as with nearly all the problems of hypnosis, is found in seeking the meaning of the patient's behaviour. Why has he become statuesque like this? The reason is obvious. He has become like this to avoid disclosing himself by modelling the thing which is in his mind. The proof of this is that the suggestions of modelling may be repeated and repeated, and their form changed and changed again, and the patient will not make the slightest response; yet he will invariably accept suggestions which are not concerned with modelling. An easy way of meeting this catatonic denial of suggestions is to return to the initiation of repetitive movement. The patient's arm is taken by the sleeve. *"Your arm goes back and forth, back and forth," etc.* Because these suggestions do not threaten the patient with the disclosure of hidden conflicts, they are accepted. The patient is conditioned with other inconsequential suggestions. The idea of dissociation is now introduced, and emphasized more and more. *"You do not do it, your hand does it."* Then a return is made to the clay. *"Your fingers pick up the clay,"* rather than *"You pick up the clay."* The suggestions continue, *"Your fingers hold the clay. Your fingers squeeze the clay. They squeeze it again."* By this means, the patient is brought around to shaping the clay without any suggestion which could be interpreted as a threat of disclosure of psychic conflict. The patient is allowed to become thoroughly accustomed to shaping the clay. Then the idea of shaping it into some object is slowly introduced, and all the time the emphasis is maintained on the dissociation. Sometimes the dissociation can be further increased by bringing in the idea of sleep. *"Your fingers do it. They do it in a sleep. Your fingers do it in a sleep, and you do not wake up from it."* The idea of movement, of doing something, must be kept to the fore; otherwise the patient may use the suggestion against the therapist, and defend himself by escaping into an hypnotic sleep. If this happens, the patient's behaviour can be interpreted to mean, *"You told me I was in a sleep. I am asleep. You can see that I cannot model."* This situation can be met by again inducing repetitive movement of the arm, and getting the patient to open his eyes and watch the movement of his hand. He is then brought back to the clay, and emphasis is placed on the fact that his eyes remain open.

Sometimes the patient makes some shape, and then starts stroking it very carefully and very gently. The action soon develops the quality of fondling or caressing. When the shape is recognizable as a human figure, or part of it, the sexual nature of such fondling is obvious. But it often happens that the model is meaningless without the patient's associations. When this was first encountered, it was not known how to interpret the patient's behaviour. In these cases, the patient has always given sexual associations to the model; so when this behaviour occurs now, it is immediately recognized as a sexual equivalent.

A number of patients who were treated by means of hypno-plasty had previously been given some sessions of hypnotic paint-ing. As a general rule, it seemed that a session with the simpler technique of expression by hypnotic painting with black paint on white paper tended to make it easier for the patient to start the rather more complicated business of modelling. On the other hand, those who were not given any prior experience in painting were all still able to adapt themselves to modelling without any great difficulty. There has been considerable variation in the ease with which patients have taken to modelling, and variation in the psychological significance of the models; but no patient has failed to produce a model of some kind.

There is often a tendency for the patient to continue fiddling with the model, even after he has completed it. He wants to keep chang-ing it. It does not seem quite perfect enough for him. Then some other idea comes to his mind. He destroys the model, and starts making something new. This leads to practical difficulties. When it appears that the patient has completed something which might be related to some psychological conflict, the model is taken from him so that he will not mutilate it, and so that his associations to it can be obtained. He is told, *"I take it. I put it over here."* With these words, the model is taken and placed in front of the patient, where he can see it, but at the same time where it is just out of his reach.

Short of actually demonstrating the hypnotized patient in the process of hypnoplasty, it is difficult to show how the moulding of the clay brings the patient to the expression of significant conflicts.

An unmarried woman of thirty is hypnotized, and is given the clay. She moulds it slowly with her fingers. At first she makes it into a table, and spontaneously recalls an incident at meal time. She is a child. She says something pert, and everyone laughs. She is embarrassed. She continues to mould the clay, and she lapses into silence. The appear-ance of the clay seems to suggest something to her. She makes the rough likeness of a face.

> *Something I do not want to talk about.*
> *Chap used to drive me home.*
> *Is in love with me.*

But is married.
Feel too weak to hold out against him.
He is a lot older than I am.
It frightens me if I should get well, what I might do.

She then smooths out the face, and for purposes of record it is lost. However, the account of the associations gives some idea of the way in which the moulding of the clay helps to bring the hypnotized patient to express the conflict in words.

From the point of view of treatment, her last comment, which came rather as an after-thought, is most significant. *"It frightens me if I get well what I might do."*

The persistence of her symptoms is a defence. She must be given insight into the nature of this, and helped to a more direct way of facing her problem.

XVIII

THE MODELS MADE IN HYPNOPLASTY

Description Of The Models

AT FIRST SIGHT, nothing could seem more meaningless than a collection of clay models made in hypnotic trance. Some of them can be recognized as objects of everyday life — a house, an animal, a human figure. In general, they are a very poor likeness of the object which they represent. They are more like the chance products of children playing with clay than the work of intelligent, though neurotic adults. But the majority of these models would seem to have no meaning at all. They can be looked at from this angle or from that angle, and they still appear nothing but random rubbish. There are still other models, to the observer just as meaningless as these, but they are seen to have been shaped with care. Though seemingly senseless, it is clear that they are no wanton products, but the result of care and thought. These are the careful likenesses of things that never were. They are but the phantasies of reality, yet at the same time they are the reality of the psyche.

By the patient's verbal associations to these models, we learn that they are each connected in some way to some deep-seated conflict in the patient's mind. A human figure represents some particular person whom he loves or hates. A house is the place where some incident took place which has become a matter of psychological conflict.

The conflict to which the model refers may belong to any part of the life span of the patient, or to his phantasy of the future. As he is making the model, it is not possible to tell whether it refers to some everyday reality problem of the present, or whether it refers to some remote event of childhood. In this respect, it was at first thought that grossly disorganized models probably represented some spontaneous regression to a childish pattern of behaviour.

However, subsequent experience has shown that in hypnoplasty the disorganization of the model is little guide to the presence or absence of regression. Some patients, who are clearly not regressed, make very disorganized models referring to present-day conflicts; and other patients, who disclose by the nature of their spontaneous comments that they are in fact regressed, often make quite well integrated models.

Many of the models represent the human figure. The construction is often very primitive. Two blobs of clay, one for the head and another for the body, and four appendages for the limbs will usually suffice. The arms may be omitted altogether if they are not connected in any way with the idea which is to be expressed, just in the same way as the limbs are omitted in some forms of modern sculpture. Although the figure may be very rudimentary, the sex may be clearly indicated in an obvious manner. This may be by way of dress, or some symbol such as a pipe or long hair, or more commonly by the uninhibited modelling of the genitalia or breasts. When the idea expressed in the modelling has a sexual significance, it does not matter how rough the general execution of the model may be, it is almost always sexually differentiated. When a number of models is examined, it will be seen that the process may assume great subtlety. For instance, when expressing ideas about his father as his father, the patient makes the figure clearly male. On the other hand, if he is expressing ideas about his father as a source of authority, then the model may be large, but of undisclosed sex. The mother and the loved one are sexual forms, but some person at work whom the patient hates is asexual.

As one would expect, the models of hypnoplasty show a significantly greater degree of disorganization than those made by psychoneurotics in the waking state. Some of this disorganization is due to a real loss of motor ability in hypnosis. But experience suggests that this, in fact, is probably only a minor factor in the disorganization. There are at least two other very active mechanisms. It would seem that the patient's motor ability is very much influenced by his preconceived ideas of behaviour in hypnosis. This tends to modify the way in which the models are produced,

329

in much the same way as direct hypnotic suggestion. In the actual modelling process, it would seem that this mechanism may become elaborated into a defence. The patient fulfils the suggestion to make a shape connected with something in his mind, but he sees to it that the model he makes is so disorganized that the horrible secret connected with it will not be disclosed to the therapist.

Another factor concerning the greater disorganization of the models made in hypnosis, as compared with those made in the waking state, is the ease with which the hypnotized patient drifts into hallucinatory experiences. It may be that a hypnotized patient makes a very disorganized human figure. From what he says about the model, it is often clear that he sees it, not as a disorganized mass of clay, but as something well formed, with a distinctive shape of its own. The patient may adjust a shapeless blob of clay which serves to represent the head of the figure. As he does so, he may make some such comment as, *"A lovely face."* When this type of behaviour was first encountered, it was thought that the patient must surely be playing some kind of elaborate game. But this is not so. The extreme intensity of the patient's preoccupation, and perhaps an unheeded tear, are evidence that the patient's behaviour is genuine. It seems clear that the patient does in fact see the shapeless mass as her beautiful face. This process may become still further developed. It is not the shapeless model that he sees as a beautiful likeness of his loved one; he actually sees her, in all the vividness of hypnotic hallucinatory experience.

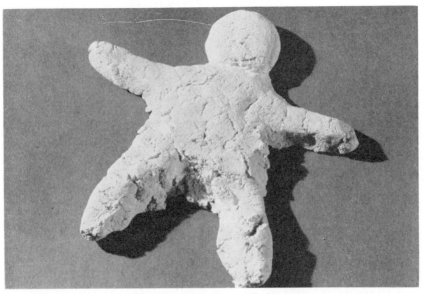

Figure No. 129

The models made by hypnotized patients resemble the shapes made by children at play.

This figure of a man has quite a childish quality about it.

The patient gives the following associations.

A man.

Not any man in particular.

Just someone to love.

Just someone to love me.

That is all I have ever wanted.

This makes it clear that the model is not just some random shape of a man without any particular meaning. It is something which is directly related to a basic psychological conflict.

In her ordinary conversation, and in a formal interview, the patient is very inhibited. Her defences are such that in the waking state she would not openly express such an idea as this.

Figure No. 130

Disorganization is a prominent feature of the models made in hypnosis. However, the degree of disorganization varies very considerably, not only with the general depth of hypnosis and the nature of the particular ideas being expressed, but it also varies with the individual patient.

This illustration shows four models of houses. They are made by different patients, but each was hypnotized to approximately the same depth, and in each case the models were used to express rather similar ideas; nevertheless, the models show very great differences in their degree of organization.

1. This neat and well executed model was made by a young man who was really quite deeply hypnotized. Before the modelling was commenced, rigidity and automatic movements of the arms had been induced, and had been maintained in face of direct challenges. When it was seen that he was making such a well integrated model, it was thought that hypnosis had probably become lighter, so automatic movement of the arm was suddenly suggested to him. The suggestion was accepted, and the movement of the arm was continued in spite of direct challenges to stop it. From this it was assumed that the patient had

not become lighter in hypnosis, and that he was in fact making a well integrated model though quite deeply hypnotized.

The patient was suffering from a severe anxiety state which troubled him most when he was under pressure to do things in the company of other people. He uses the model to represent a house in the country where he feels that his symptoms would be less disturbing.

Country, not the city.

City life too fast.

Too much rush.

2. This is a typical example of conventional plastic symbolism. There is the rough shape of a cottage surmounted by a chimney.

The patient, a man of fifty, gives the following associations.

House used to live in when a small boy.

Cut my hand very badly.

Lot of stitches.

Man next door kept birds.

Maid called Alice.

Go for walks.

Girl I used to play with.

Man next door used to frighten me.

3. This model shows greater disorganization. It is only very roughly shaped, and there is no chimney. It is doubtful if it would be recognized as a house without the patient's associations. She is not as young as she was; she is lonely, and she fears that her chances of marriage are fading.

Supposed to be a house.

The one I would like.

Would have liked to have been an architect.

Just like having someone to love; a house of my own.

The comment about being an architect would seem to be an attempt at defence by introducing an irrelevancy; but the defence peters out of its own accord, and the significant idea is given expression.

4. This model shows still greater disorganization. The shape is not recognizable as a house. We learn from the patient's associations that the three projections are chimneys. This gives the model a bizarre quality, as we do not ordinarily look down on a house. It is the type of model one might expect of a psychotic who was modelling in the waking state. However, the patient was a man in his middle forties suffering from writer's cramp, and he presented no signs of psychosis

333

whatsoever. It would seem that in his mind three chimneys represents a large house, the type of house which it is his ambition to own.

> *It's a house.*
> *Mine.*
> *The one I would like to have.*
> *Three chimneys, brick.*
> *I am looking at it.*
> *Outside, perhaps I want to be inside.*
> *It's my own.*
> *Must be mine.*

Figure No. 131

This model of a house shows really gross disorganization. The patient is a man in his middle forties. He has married a woman who is his social superior, and who comes from a much wealthier family. He is unable to support his wife and children in a way comparable to her former style of living.

> *House.*
> *House with a fireplace.*
> *Somewhere to live.*
> *Don't do it very well* (i.e., making the model).
> *Not a big house.*
> *Just for all of us to live in.*
> *Got to get better.*
> *Get better.*
> *Make it up to my family.*
> *They have stuck to me.*
> *Getting around like I am.*
> *People say I can't get over it.*
> *I have not got the guts.*
> *She helps me.*

Live with my family.
They pity me.
People say it is imagination.
Nothing wrong with me.
Still frightened.
Fear.
Must get right.
Must get right.
Help myself.

Besides the disorganization, there are other interesting facets to this model. The patient obviously pictures a house as something hollow, something that one can get into. Clinically, he is a very inadequate person, and in his ordinary life, when he is confronted with some difficult problem, he has developed the habit of leaving his office and going home to get what comfort and support he can from his wife. In hypnosis he makes, as it were, the house of his dreams; but he makes it as a kind of rabbit burrow where he could go and hide from the stresses of the outside world.

There is another problem about the interpretation of this model. The patient, in his associations, refers to it as a house, but it would seem possible that at a deeper level of psychological integration, the model may have a frankly sexual connotation. It has the characteristic shape of a female sexual symbol. Moreover, the house itself is a common female symbol. Furthermore, we know that the patient's habitual defence in face of stress is to retreat home, perhaps not so much to the physical security of his house, but rather to the emotional support of his wife. While making the model, the patient became very preoccupied with poking his finger into the hollowed out part of the model. The present reality situation is that his wife is no longer giving him the support which he craves. These factors would tempt one to add a deeper sexual interpretation; but we must be mindful of the fact that the deeply hypnotized patient gave no sexual associations to the model.

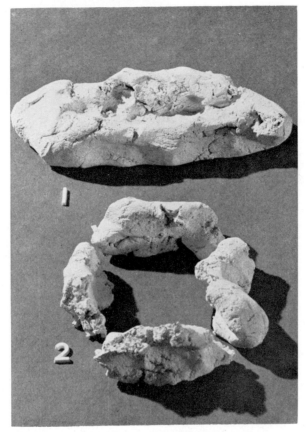

Figure No. 132

This illustration serves to show the gross disorganization which sometimes occurs in the models made by hypnotized patients.

1. This is the canoe which he once had when a child.
2. This is the living room where various dramatic incidents occurred.

337

Figure No. 133

These two figures were made by the patient on different occasions. They have been placed side by side only in order to be photographed. There is an extreme simplicity about the figures. There is just the suggestion of a face. There is no neck, and a slight division of the clay at the other end serves to indicate the legs. The arms are completely absent. In spite of this simplification, the figures are clearly identified as male. The patient's basic condition was latent inversion. In his associations he made it clear that one of the figures was his father and the other was himself.

SPECIFICITY OF THE MODELS

This leads to what is clinically the most significant feature of the models made in hypnoplasty, that is their specificity. A human figure always represents some particular person. It is never just a man, or just a woman. If the patient gives non-specific associations such as these, it means that he is defending himself by denial. Further enquiry, *"You look at it. Who is it? You can see. Who is it? Your voice speaks out,"* will invariably disclose the real indentity of the figure. This is a contrast to what is found with psychoneurotics in the waking state, who occasionally produce non-specific figures as a defence. In hypnosis, this happens only on extremely rare occasions, and that when the patient is only very lightly hypnotized. Similarly, a house is never just a house; it is always the house where some traumatic incident took place. A tree is not just a tree; it is always some particular tree which is associated with some psychologically significant idea in the patient's mind.

Many of the shapes produced in hypnosis are quite unrecognizable by the therapist, and they would remain meaningless without the patient's associations. The difficulty in recognizing the meaning of a model arises from at least four different sources — the poor craftsmanship, the oddness of the things represented, the symbolism, and not uncommonly from a purposeful distortion of the model.

In spite of these complicating factors, the specific identity of the model can almost always be determined by careful elicitation of the patient's associations.

There is, however, a group of models in which the specificity is of a rather different character. Thus, a model may refer to some specific class of things, rather than to a particular individual. There are also models which do not refer to the actual thing which is modelled, but to some specific abstract idea, the meaning of which is conveyed by the model.

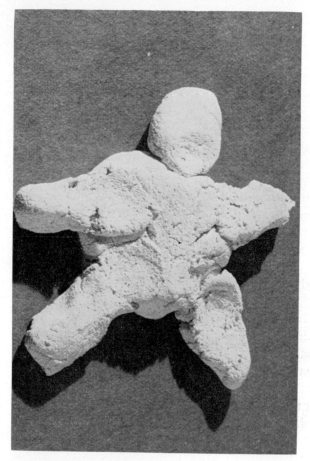

Figure No. 134

Some of the models made in hypnosis refer to some particular class or group of things, rather than to some particular individual object. This is still consistent with the general principle of the specificity of the shapes made in hypnoplasty.

A young man, who has great difficulty in his interpersonal relationships, makes this figure. While still under hynosis he explains that it it is *"Young people."* Thus the single figure represents a specific group of people, the young people, those with whom he has such difficulty in social contacts.

PLASTIC SYMBOLISM IN HYPNOSIS

The hypnotized patient uses representational, conventional, individual or universal symbols, as described in the modelling of the waking patient.

The essential feature of the representational symbol is that it is a likeness of the object which it represents. This is the simplest form of symbolism. The difficulty with representational symbols in hypnoplasty is that the likeness is so often very poor. This leads to confusion of representational with conventional and individual symbols. A point which may be used to distinguish the poorly constructed representational symbol is that it is often given some peculiarity which serves in the patient's mind to identify it with some particular individual object. Thus, a woman who has conspicuously long hair is symbolized in a figure which is mostly hair; or a particular house which has a large chimney may be symbolized in a model which is mainly chimney. These individual characteristics of representational symbols are likely to be missed by the therapist, as he is not usually familiar with the object symbolized.

In hypnoplasty, patients commonly use conventional symbols. A man is a head and a body with two arms and two legs. A house is a cube with a chimney on top. These conventional symbols are always specific, so that in fact they represent some particular man or house. The patient gives them this specificity in his own mind; but it is not shown by any particular feature of the model, as in representational symbols.

The individual symbol is the plastic neologism. Like the verbal neologism, it is both individual to the particular patient, and has the characteristic of being frequently repeated. Like the verbal neologism, the individual symbol is often bizarre, and at the same time it is often peculiarly apt. Because of the bizarre quality, and also because of the patient's difficulty in explaining the symbol, or even giving comprehensible associations to it, it is often difficult to determine the meaning of such symbols. They are a feature of pre-psychotic and psychotic modelling, as well as of hypnoplasty, but they occur only rarely in the modelling of psychoneurotics in the waking state.

The universal symbols are the well known shapes of Freudian psychopathology. For the most part, they are the primitive expression of male and female sexuality. They usually occur in deep hypnosis, and it is often clear that the patient has no awareness of their significance.

As compared with the models made by patients in the waking state, the models of hypnoplasty are ill-formed and often disorganized. As far as the models are concerned, it would seem that the hypnotized patient has greater power of imagination. By phantasy, or even by active hallucinatory processes, he fills in the structural shortcomings of the models. He sees the model with different eyes from those of the waking therapist. This mechanism has the effect of rather obscuring and confusing the nature of the symbolism of hypnotic modelling.

In hypnoplasty, there is always difficulty in estimating the patient's degree of awareness of what he is doing. A patient may make a model of a human figure, and say, *"My wife, I hate her."* It would seem that, at the time, the patient must have been aware that he was making some likeness of his wife, and also aware of his feelings towards her. When the session is over, some patients will volunteer that they knew all the time exactly what they were doing, and what they were saying. Other patients have a complete amnesia. Yet at the same time, within the limits of the hypnotic state, it would seem that many of these patients know what they are doing in hypnoplasty. With others, it would seem that dissociation mechanisms are more active. The patient makes a model in a purposive way, but all the time the meaning of it is dissociated from his consciousness. His fingers do it. He does not know anything about it. His voice makes comments about it, but he does not comprehend the significance of the words which he uses. With universal symbols, this process is carried still further. In the hypnotic state, his fingers make a shape, which in the language of the unconscious has meaning, but his voice can tell us little about it, because the symbol belongs to a language which he does not understand.

Figure No. 135

Most of the models made by hypnotized patients are conventional symbols. However, the model is usually disorganized so that the conventional symbolism is not readily recognizable without clues from the patient's associations.

My father at Sydney High School.
Took me away and put me to another school.
Ask him why and he said, "You are a failure, that's why,"
    and I lost heart.

Without the patient's associations it might be hard to recognize this model as the likeness of a man. But now we know that it is the patient's father, we can discern the head and arms, although the legs are lost in the general disorganization.

This is a typical conventional symbol of hypnoplasty. It was made by a man in his middle forties, and refers to an incident in his childhood.

343

Figure No. 136

The patient was a schizoid youth in his late twenties. He came to consultation on account of a distressing psychic dysuria. The condition took the form that he could pass his water only in the toilet of his own house. Anywhere else he was simply unable to micturate. As a result, he could only take work which was offering near his home, so that he could return home in the lunch hour. He was cut off from any real social life.

The patient was basically a latent invert. He made this strange "boomerang" symbol on several occasions in hypnosis. On each occasion he gave similar associations.

> *Babies.*
> *Boy and girl baby.*
> *Might be me, not sure.*
> *Dad wanted a girl.*
> *Don't know.*
> *Might be me.*
> *Don't know.*
> *Just a girl — no name.*

It is now seen that the model consists of two figures joined together by their heads. The figures are very much reduced so that there is no clear demarcation of the parts. The patient says that they are a boy and a girl baby. He also says, *"Might be me."* From the way in which the patient spoke, not only on this occasion but also on other occasions when he made this symbol, it seemed clear that the whole model, and not just part of it, referred to himself. In other words, he is part baby boy and part baby girl. In this way the symbol expresses his latent psychosexual inversion.

The model is now seen to be a classic example of the individual symbol. It is something which is used only by the particular, individual patient. It is frequently used by him, and is always used with the same meaning. It communicates an idea which is ordinarily difficult to express. In fact it is a plastic neologism.

Figure No. 137

Sometimes it is difficult to be sure as to which particular grade of symbolism is actually being used.

This model was made by the same patient who made the homosexual individual symbol. These were the only associations which could be obtained.

Man.

Must be me.

Feel cold, somehow.

There is no doubt that the model represents a human figure. However, it is a matter of theoretical interest to discuss the nature of the symbolism. Is the model a much reduced conventional symbol, or is it in fact a universal phallic symbol?

With the hypnotized patient, as distinct from the patient in the waking state, poor construction of conventional symbols is usually due, either to the general disorganization of work done in the hypnotic state, or to the purposive distortion which is sometimes used as a defence to obscure the meaning of a model from the therapist. The reduction in form of the present model does not appear to result from the general disorganization of the hypnotic state, which characteristically produces a rough, untidy, poorly finished model. This production, on the other hand, would seem to be quite carefully finished. This would lead us to suspect that the omission of the arms is purposive. But the purpose of the omission can hardly be to disguise from the therapist that the model is in fact a human figure, as the head and nose are shown, and the patient immediately acknowledges it as a man in his associations. It would therefore seem likely that the arms were purposely omitted, in order to convert the figure into a phallic symbol.

There is other corroborative evidence. On two or three occasions, the patient made a model to represent his mother. Each time he used a conventional symbol which took the form of a roughly disorganized female bust with large breasts. Whereas each time he made a model to represent himself or his father, he used this phallic or pseudophallic type of symbolism. When we bear in mind that the model was made by a latent invert, it becomes easier to understand how it is that the patient unconsciously wishes to feature himself as phallic.

Figure No. 138

There is often a process of condensation in the plastic symbolism of the hypnotized patient. The symbol comes to express two different ideas simultaneously. This is seen in those models which can be interpreted at more than one level of psychic integration. Such models commonly have one meaning in virtue of their conventional symbolism, and at the same time convey a deeper sexual meaning in virtue of an underlying universal symbolism.

However, this model is an example of another type of condensation. It represents two different objects at the same level of psychic integration.

The patient envies his more successful business associate. This model is his friend's big car and also his boat. The model represents the two separate objects at the same time.

RELATION TO DEPTH OF HYPNOSIS

In the study of hypnotic modelling, it was at first thought that the shapes which were a better likeness of some object were in reality the product of lighter hypnosis. This is not the whole truth of the matter. Many a patient who has undoubtedly been very deeply hypnotized has produced a well integrated likeness of some object. On the other hand, some patients who did not appear very deeply hypnotized have produced profoundly symbolic material. A difficulty in this approach is that we have no single criterion as to depth of hypnosis. This is what we would expect if we regard hypnosis as a dynamic, fluctuant condition, rather than as a static psychological state. The depth of hypnosis will vary, not only from moment to moment, but it will also vary in different areas of activity at the same moment. These variations in depth are often determined by the patient's interpretation of the significance of the particular activity. Nevertheless, it would seem that there is some co-relation between the depth of hypnosis and the degree of disorganization of the model. This may be seen in patients who complete a series of models in one session of hypnosis. It often happens that the patient becomes progressively more deeply hypnotized as the session proceeds. In these circumstances, the series of models may show a graduated disorganization and disintegration.

XIX

THE ASSOCIATIONS TO THE
HYPNOTIC MODELS

THE ELICITATION OF THE ASSOCIATIONS

F ROM THE POINT OF VIEW OF THERAPY, the verbal associations
which the patient gives to the model are equally important as the
model itself. In fact, in many instances, if it were not for the
patient's associations, the meaning of the model would be completely lost to the therapist. It is only through the verbal associations that the material expressed in the modelling can be used in
psychotherapy with the patient.

An idea which has been expressed in modelling becomes more
easily ventilated in words. This principle is in fact the main
rationale for the therapeutic use of hypnotic modelling. When the
patient has completed a model, and while he is still hypnotized, he
is asked about it, and his associations to it are obtained. Care is
taken to see that an adequate depth of hypnosis is maintained. A
practical point in management arises here. With the hypnotized
patient, it is sometimes difficult to know when he has finished the
model. He may go on and on changing it all the time. It would
seem that the partial failure of the repressive mechanism due to
hypnosis allows a continual surge of repressed and suppressed
material to the threshold of expression. In these cases it has been
found best, when the patient pauses for a moment, to take the model
and place it out of the patient's reach, and then proceed immediately to ask him about it. If the patient is left with the model,
he usually continues to fiddle with it, and it is more difficult to
bring him to talk about it.

Not infrequently, the patient gives the associations quite spontaneously while he is at work moulding the clay. When this

happens, they come in the way of a man talking his thoughts aloud. He is completely preoccupied with the matter in hand. The ideas are often accompanied by a good deal of emotion. Sobbing and bursts of anger are common. Primitive ideas are expressed in primitive fashion. Verbal phrases of ordinary life give way to unverbalized phonation, the language of groans and grunts. Once the patient has started in this fashion, it is usually an easy matter to lead him on into giving expression to his thoughts in words. The therapist can communicate with the patient in his own language. Unverbalized interrogatory grunts invite the patient to say more about the matters in his mind. An interesting point arises here. It has often seemed that the patient has been so completely preoccupied with the model and the stream of thought that it evokes, that he would be quite oblivious of any interrogatory grunt. However, in spite of the intensity of his preoccupation, the patient still remains sensitive to this type of communication from the therapist. This comes about, of course, through the way in which hypnotic rapport sensitizes the patient to all that the therapist does.

If the patient does not start to talk spontaneously, he is given suggestions after this manner. *"You can talk and you do not wake up from it. Your voice talks and you do not wake up from it. What is this that your fingers have made. Your voice talks and you do not wake up from it."* Many patients who previously refused to talk in hypnosis will now talk quite freely.

As a general rule, the associations are given in disjointed phrases, each of which contains a single idea. There is no ordinary use of syntax. The phrases consist mainly of verbs, nouns, and emotionally coloured adjectives.

The fragmentary and disjointed nature of the associations in hypnoplasty is in contrast to the more logical and more grammatically expressed type of associations obtained in the waking state. The neurotic patient in the waking state usually gives a lengthy series of associations which are expressed in his usual use of language, and with normal grammar and syntax. The associations rarely have the completely disjointed character seen in hypnosis. In the waking state, pre-psychotic schizophrenics and psychotics may have great difficulty in explaining the ideas expressed in their modelling, but for the most part they use normally constructed sentences, rather than the verb-noun-adjective phrases of hypnosis.

Sometimes there is difficulty in obtaining the associations. This must be accepted for what it is — a defence against the expression of distressing ideas. Emphasis on dissociation often helps. It is the patient's voice that speaks these awful things, not the patient himself. When there is a complete refusal to talk about the model, it is best to get the patient speaking first of psychologically inconsequential matters. Then he can be brought back to some unimportant aspect of the model, and finally to the real meaning.

When the model has been made in response to a good deal of dissociation, it is not uncommon for the patient later to incorporate this into a defence. When he is asked about the model, he merely says, *"I do not know what it is."* When he is taxed further, *"You made it. You know what it is,"* he answers,*"My fingers made it. I do not know what it is."* It has been found that the best way to proceed in these circumstances is to abandon the present model without further comment, and to proceed with another. Once one model has been made, even if a very complete dissociation was necessary to get it made, it has been found that subsequent models can be made without dissociation. So the patient's own responsibility is now stressed. *"You do it. You know what it is. You make it yourself."* By this means, the patient is robbed of his defence by denial by dissociation.

Now, in retrospect, on looking through the recorded associations which patients have given to various models, it would seem in many instances that they are very incomplete. One cannot help gaining the impression that with a little more time and persistence, much more valuable material might have been forthcoming. There are several reasons for this. Probably the most important is my own inexperience. It was very much a matter of making cautious progress over new ground, with very little in the way of psychological signposts for guidance. There was always the feeling that any too active enquiry might wake the patient from hypnosis, and so run the risk of his gaining a sudden awareness of very disturbing repressed material. In other cases, the associations are incomplete because it had become clear that the patient's defences were particularly strong in the particular area in question. In some few cases, the elicitation of the associations had to be curtailed by the practical difficulty of private psychiatric practice, which necessitates some limitation of time with an individual patient. However, as a general rule, enquiry for further associations has been stopped only when the patient has communicated by non-verbal means either that he is definitely finished, or that he is becoming too distressed by the enquiry.

THE MEANING OF THE MODELS

The meaning of the model becomes known to us only through the patient's associations. In plastotherapy with the waking patient, we may learn a lot about the model from the patient's non-verbal communications and from his reaction to the model. With the hypnotized patient, these matters are much more difficult to interpret; so we come to rely practically entirely on the patient's verbal associations.

The ideas expressed in the models of hypnotized patients are the ideas of basic human conflict. There is nothing superficial or shallow about them. There is none of the pretence of ordinary convention. Psychological defences may still be active, but there is none of the conscious evasion which is so often a feature of waking psychotherapy.

The ideas expressed in hypnoplasty are by no means always repressed material. Reality problems of everyday living which the patient has already ventilated in waking psychotherapy may be expressed in hypnotic modelling. There is no doubt that sometimes the hypnotic state merely provides the patient with an excuse to express ideas which are clear in his consciousness, but which, for shame or other reasons, he has been unable to bring himself to express. He may still be unable to speak of them in hypnosis; yet they may find ready expression in modelling.

The ideas expressed in the modelling are in fact quite often found to have been suppressed rather than repressed. An example of this category was a man who had suppressed all ambivalent thoughts about his wife, but which were expressed in all their hatred in hypnoplasty.

Other material is truly unconscious. The repressed memories of childhood traumata are given expression, and so also are profoundly unconscious ideas of sexuality and bisexuality.

The subject matter of the models is often so odd that one would have no hope of guessing what the model means without the patient's associations. A strip of clay represents the path in the woods where he seduced the girl. A rounded blob is the stone on which the young couple sat and made avowals of eternal love.

Figure No. 139

The models made in hypnoplasty are of such an unpredictable nature that it is often quite impossible to discern any meaning in them without the patient's associations. This strip of clay represents the track down to the beach where he had seduced the girls some twenty years previously.

Beach track.
Used to go and sleep with them.
Lovely girls.
Get up and have a swim, and I was happy.
Nothing ever happened to them, I was always frightened it might.
(Pause)
I'm out with another woman.
Talking to another woman.
She wants me to be intimate with her, but I am married.
I'm too frightened.
(Pause)
I see Joan (his wife)
Sometimes I want to be abnormal with her.
Do things differently with her.

355

Do things abnormally.
Touch her breasts with my private part.
Turn her over and do the act the wrong way.
Sometimes I want to do that.
Sometimes I want her to kiss me.
Kiss me on my private parts, but I have never done it.
That worries me.
Worries me.
(Pause)
See John (his son) *standing there looking at me.*

The model and the associations illustrate the way in which the hypnotized patient makes the likeness of some object which is directly connected with some disturbing conflict. He talks about the model, and ventilates the conflict; but he soon rambles on in his associations, and comes to give spontaneous expression to related conflicts.

Figure No. 140

The model is often quite meaningless without the patient's associations. An unhappy, lonely woman makes this shape. She says it is a building in Singapore. She had been there for a trip some years previously. She had made friends there. She was happy and had a good time. She now thinks longingly of this state of affairs, which is such a contrast to her present lonely isolation.

ABREACTION

Some patients abreact spontaneously while they are modelling the clay. With others the situation is different. The patient makes a model of some object which is directly connected with some significant conflict. While he is making the model, he is very preoccupied with what he is doing. He appears remote and starry eyed. There is no display of emotion. However, when he is asked about the model, and he gives associations to it, he commonly loses his starry eyed abstraction. He becomes animated; and as he continues to give associations, he expresses greater and greater emotion.

The reason for this common sequence of events is not clear. When the patient is making the model, the disturbing conflict must be in the patient's mind; yet it is only when the ideas are given verbal expression in the associations that there is any abreaction. Another interesting aspect of this phenomenon is that it is not influenced by the hypnotic state. It would seem to occur very much the same way in both the waking and the hypnotized patient.

When he is giving the associations, either spontaneously or in response to suggestion, the patient often becomes extremely worked up about it. He identifies the model as the real object. The model often represents a person. If the patient has ambivalent feelings towards this person, and he expresses his hate or his anger, he will often injure the model as if he would cause hurt to the real person by the mutilation of the image. There is a danger in this type of abreaction that the patient may become lighter in hypnosis. This may reach a stage at which the patient suddenly becomes aware of what he is doing. This sudden surge into consciousness of highly traumatic material may produce a very acute anxiety reaction in the patient. The severity of such reactions must be seen to be believed. If such an untoward reaction should occur, it calls for immediate deepening of hypnosis; or if the patient has actually returned to the waking state, he should be immediately re-hypnotized. He is then given suggestions of calm and ease, and is put into an hypnotic sleep, and allowed time to recover.

Figure No. 141

The patient often makes a model with an air of abstraction, in an apparent emotional calm. But when he starts to give associations to the model, it would seem that his emotions become freed, and he abreacts.

At his first session, a fifty year old man makes this model, which apparently represents his wife.

> *Something to do with being loved by a woman.*
> *Always wanted to be loved by a woman properly.*
> *I know exactly what I am saying, it is all queer.*
> *There is a good deal of sex in it.*
> *Difficult to talk about.*
> *For years unsatisfied, frustrated, tensions.*
> *Always have been like that at home.*
> *Never been in step at all.*
> *Sex, it should not matter, sublimated or something.*
> *Look elsewhere.*
> *Feel I should not want to be comforted, should rise above it.*
> (Weeps)
> (Mumbles inaudibly)
> *No more thoughts.*

When the patient had been wakened, and he was preparing to leave, he volunteered, *"It is very unlike me to cry. I cannot understand it, but I feel calmer somehow."*

359

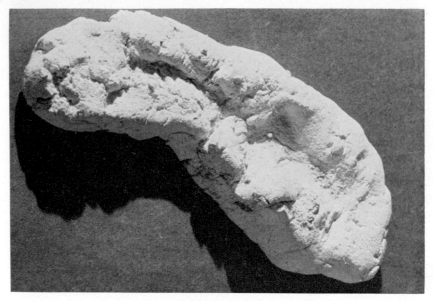

Figure No. 142

Sometimes the abreaction takes the form of the expression of emotion during the reliving of some disturbing event of the past. The patient experiences again the emotions which he felt at the time of the incident. The hypnotic state readily allows the function of this mechanism in hypnoplasty. It does, however, occur occasionally in plastotherapy with the patient in the waking state. When it does occur in these circumstances, it is very much more disturbing to the patient, as in the absence of hypnosis, the incident is experienced in full consciousness.

The patient has had some previous sessions of hypnoplasty. He takes the clay and models spontaneously. As he moulds the clay, he talks without any intervention from the therapist. The model apparently represents the lounge in the patient's sitting room.

> *Lounge at home.*
> *Living room where the boys are.*
> *Resting, talking to the boys.*
> *Being able to relax.*
> (Pause)
> *Respect you.*
> (Pause)
> *Joan bought it out of her own money.*

(Pause)
Told me so too, hundreds of times.
She had the place painted.
Her money not mine.
I make money, to forty pounds a week.
I will do it.
Sixty, seventy pounds a week.
(Pause)
Oh. the phone.
Tell them I am not in.
(Pause)
Share and share.
Share and share alike, that's it.
(Pause)
Everybody is good to me.
How do you feel Bob.
I am getting better.
Get better.
Bob looks bad today.
Oh you will never get over this.
Joan thinks I will.
Does not matter about your neck Bob.
Just carry on.
(Pause)
Got to be at the meeting.
(Pause)
Bill and Bert (his sons) *watching me all the time.*
Cannot understand what has happened to Daddy.
(Pause)
Take your arm down from your face.
Doctor said nothing wrong with you.
(Pause)
Stay with me Bill.
I am going for a swim, cannot help you Dad.
(Pause)
Don't argue with Mum, it upsets her.
(Pause)
Have to get better.

Figure No. 143

This model and the associations illustrate a rather different form of abreaction. The patient gives vent to the emotion appropriate to a present-day problem from which in the waking state he remains emotionally aloof.

A forty year old man complains of impotence. In an ordinary interview he discusses his problem without emotion or distress. When hypnotized, he makes this figure, which he identifies as his wife.

> *Body.*
> (Pause)
> *Wife.*
> *It's my wife in bed.*
> *She is waiting for me and I can't.*
> *Waiting for me.*
> *In bed.*
> *I am not much use.*
> *Waiting for me in bed, but I do no good to her.*
> (Weeps)
> *Never feel I satisfy her.*
> *She is not cold.*
> *Just can't.*

I feel that I have never got to her.
(Hypnosis not so deep)
Good wife.
Does not ask me for anything.
(Pause)
Can't seem to get to her in bed.
(Weeps)
Know it's me.
It's her in bed.

XX

THE PATIENT'S DEFENCES
IN HYPNOPLASTY
NATURE OF DEFENCES

I T MAY BE that the traumatic conflict is suppressed rather than repressed. The patient, motivated by the distress of symptoms, feels that he wants to ventilate the matter. Nevertheless, he is held back by conscious evasion because he finds it hard to face the humiliation and shame of expressing his weakness and his guilt; and he is also held back by the unconscious defence mechanisms which work to save the individual from any hurt of body or mind. When the traumatic material is really repressed, similar, but unconscious, mechanisms are at work. Hypnoplasty is essentially a technique to help the patient, by preventing these defences from interfering with effective treatment. It aims to achieve this by two means — the use of the hypnotic state as opposed to the waking state; and the use of plastic expression as opposed to verbal expression.

With psychotherapy in the waking state, conscious evasion almost always functions to some extent; sometimes it is very active, sometimes it is minimal. The hypnotic state reduces the activity of conscious defences. However, the old idea that the hypnotized patient is robbed of all conscious and unconscious means of psychological defence is quite irreconcilable to the observed facts of hypnoplasty. The point which is often overlooked is that these defences take different form with the hypnotized patient. In light hypnosis, there is often clear evidence of the operation of conscious defences. This applies particularly to verbal hypnoanalysis. One of the factors which helps to make this possible is the varying depth of hypnosis in different areas of psychic activity. Thus, when tested in one area, the patient is deeply hypnotized; yet in another area he is able to evoke conscious defences in much the same way as he would in the waking state. The matter is made more complicated by attempting to define, in too absolute a fashion, what is conscious and what is not. This is difficult enough with the waking patient. In hypnosis it is even more difficult. It is clear that the same defence may be used by different patients with different degrees of awareness; and the same defence may be used by the same patient on different occasions, with different degrees of awareness.

In hypnoplasty, it would often seem more useful to consider the defences in the light of varying degrees of awareness, rather than as conscious or unconscious.

Figure No. 144

The way in which a patient's defences operate is often disclosed in his modelling.

1. A young man is only lightly hypnotized. He makes a ship. In his associations, he expresses the idea that he wants to sail away from all his troubles. This is not quite a screen model, but the superficial idea which it expresses acts as a defence of the patient against the expression of more significant and more painful ideas.

2. The same patient, in rather deeper hypnosis, makes a bed. By means of the model, and his general behaviour, he signifies that he is hypnotized and wants to go to sleep. He thus uses his behaviour as a means of communicating with the therapist; and at the same time, it acts as a defence against the expression of disturbing conflicts.

DEFENCES AGAINST HYPNOSIS

The patient wants to be rid of distressing symptoms. He accepts the advice of the therapist that hypnosis will help him in this respect. He is agreeable. He states clearly that he will co-operate in the induction of hypnosis. Without this degree of co-operation, it is unwise to attempt hypnoplasty. However, many patients state that they want to be hypnotized, but at the same time they retain certain doubts and misgivings which they do not voice. In fact, they are ambivalent in the matter, in that they simultaneously hold opposing attitudes to the same proposition. At a logical level, they wish to be hypnotized in order to get well; at the same time they do not wish to be hypnotized because of the innate, biologically determined fear of losing control. This latter provides the motivation for conscious and near-conscious mechanisms to avoid hypnosis. It often happens that these doubts do not come to the fore until the induction process has actually started, and the patient feels himself threatened by the impending loss of control. A similar process works at a clearly unconscious level. If the ego regards the loss of control as a threat, then unconscious mechanisms, quite outside the patient's awareness, come into operation to prevent loss of control in hypnosis.

The reader who is not familiar with the techniques of hypnosis is reminded that hypno-analysis requires a passive type of induction of hypnosis, as opposed to the authoritative type of induction which was formerly used for symptom removal by suggestion. The passive approach allows the patient a great deal of freedom. He is thus in a position to use defences in a way which is not possible in authoritative hypnosis, in which the patient is simply overwhelmed by the prestige and authority of the therapist.

Restlessness may be manifested in many diverse forms, which all have the effect of preventing or delaying the onset of hypnosis. This applies particularly when the induction is by suggestions of relaxation and sleep. The patient cannot get comfortable. He fidgets. He wriggles about. The pillow is too high; or the blanket is too heavy. Sometimes the purposive nature of this restlessness is even more obvious. When the therapist starts giving verbal suggestions, the patient may ask some unimportant and irrelevant question. The hypnotic process is thus halted, and a new start must be made. The same effect may be brought about by a sudden desire to use the handkerchief. The patient is not really aware of the purposive nature of these matters, although the true purpose of his behaviour is quite obvious to the therapist or to any observer. Coughing may come to be used in a similar way. A patient who has no sign of respiratory infection, and who has had no recent cough at all, may develop a tickle in the throat. This necessitates an occasional cough to clear his throat, which in turn makes hypnosis by suggestion of relaxation very difficult, or impossible. In actual practice, these defences are easily circumvented by switching to induction by arm levitation or the dynamic method.

Sleep is another means of defence against hypnosis. The patient may feel that if he goes to sleep he will not hear any suggestions, and will thus escape being hypnotized. This defence is effective in arm levitation, but can easily be countered by changing to induction by suggestions of relaxation.

Negativism is also used as a defence. The patient feels that he will avoid hypnosis if he does the opposite of what is suggested to him. But this very defence can be used against him, and he is led into hynosis by the method of repetitive movement.

Simulation of hypnosis is also used as a defence. This is obviously much more of a conscious process than the other defences. It seems that the patient is agreeable to letting himself be hypnotized; then at the last moment he changes his mind. He believes that if he consciously does all that is suggested to him, he will not be hypnotized, as he is acting of his own free will. This situation is most easily managed in arm levitation. It is recognized by the immediate response of the patient to suggestions. He responds too quickly. In ordinary circumstances, when induction is by arm levitation, the arms are raised only slowly, and with a good deal of tension and tremor. At the same time, the patient's gaze becomes fixed and unblinking. On the other hand, the patient who is defending himself by simulation raises his arms promptly and easily in response to suggestion, and his gaze does not take on the appearance which is so characteristic of the hypnotized patient. This situation is met by allowing the patient to continue his simulation. He moves his hands up and down at the slightest suggestion. The patient is acting, to lead the therapist to believe that he is hypnotized; and the therapist acts, to lead the patient to believe that the therapist believes that the patient is hypnotized. If the therapist can manipulate the situation so that this state of affairs continues, the patient, unbeknown to himself, drifts into real hypnosis. In leading the patient on in this way, any challenges must be avoided, for the patient is likely to accept a challenge and bring the whole process to a halt. He simply puts his hands down; and the therapist is faced with a failure of induction. An easy method of assuring the patient's continued simulation is to let him be flattered about the way in which he thinks he is misleading the therapist. This method of combatting defence by simulation is most effective if it can be spread over two or three short sessions before the patient is finally challenged, and thus brought to awareness that he has in fact been hypnotized.

DEFENCES AGAINST MODELLING

In general, the hypnotized patient takes to modelling much more easily than does the patient in the waking state. Usually there is little or no delay in taking up the clay and kneading it with the fingers. At first, this kneading process may not be purposive, but in the majority of cases, it very soon comes to be done in a manner which indicates that there is some clear object in view. In contrast to the waking patient, there is rarely any evidence of anxiety when it is first suggested to the patient that he should model something.

Nevertheless, patients do at times use various defences against modelling. Sometimes when the hypnotized patient is given the clay, he defends himself by simply doing nothing. When he is offered the clay, he makes no response; it appears that he does not see it. This refusal to see the clay is of course quite purposive. The patient will often maintain his gaze fixed on some other object, or just staring into space. He is using the hypnotic situation as a

369

defence. By his behaviour, he communicates with the therapist. *"You can see that I am hypnotized. A hypnotized person cannot model clay."* First the patient's gaze is directed to the clay. *"Your eyes look at the clay. Your eyes look at the clay."* It is then easy enough to proceed with some degree of dissociation. *"Your hand takes the clay. Your hand takes the clay."* This is more effective than, *"You take the clay."* The suggestions are continued. *"Your fingers mould the clay."* There is usually not much difficulty in this, because looking at the clay, taking up the clay, and moulding the clay are not psychological threats. It is only when the clay is to be moulded into a shape with reference to something in the patient's mind that the process becomes a psychological threat. As long as adequate depth of hypnosis is maintained, it will not be long before the changing form of the mass of clay comes to take on a shape which is associated with something in the patient's mind, and he comes to make some likeness of it.

On a few rare occasions, patients have wakened from hypnosis when they have been offered the clay. This has happened only in the earlier work in hypnoplasty, and in retrospect it seems clear that these incidents happened when modelling was attempted with inadequate depth of hypnosis. Waking in this way is a situation to be avoided, as it may precipitate an acute anxiety reaction. If this occurs, the patient should immediately be re-hypnotized, and given suggestions of calm and ease.

Sleep is a not uncommon defence. The patient is offered the clay, and he just slumps forward in a deep sleep. The situation is met by initiating automatic movements of the arm, with the patient's eyes directed on his hand. The suggestions then proceed with emphasis on the eyes being open and watching what he is doing. *"Your eyes are open. You see the clay. You see the shapes that your fingers are making with it."*

The patient may purposefully make a poor likeness of the object. The suggestion to model something connected with the thing in his mind is fulfilled; but at the same time, the model is made in such a way that the nature of the thing in his mind will not be disclosed to the therapist. In many cases, this process accounts for much of the disorganization of the models. One is not able to determine the presence of the mechanism by inspection of the model. The evidence for the operation of this mechanism lies in the manner in which the model is made. A patient may make a model which in actual fact is quite a good likeness of the object. He may then proceed, carefully and deliberately, to alter the model, to distort it, so that the likeness is destroyed and only a shadow of the likeness, as it were, remains. When this defence was first noticed, it was thought that the probable explanation was that the traumatic material was approaching the threshold of awareness, as a result of loss of depth of hypnosis. Subsequent experience has clearly shown that this is not the whole explanation. This defence by purposive distortion of the model may be used by patients who from most criteria would appear to be really deeply hypnotized.

Instead of distorting the model as it is made, and so attempting to disguise its meaning, the patient may make a model, and then add embellishments to it which have the effect of making the essential shape less obvious. This is defence by camouflage. The patient fulfills the hypnotic suggestion to make something which is related to the thought deep in his mind, but he then camouflages it in order that the therapist may not recognize what he has made. The process has a childish simplicity about it. Nevertheless, it is a defence which is quite often used by intelligent and sophisticated patients in the course of hypnoplasty. This defence is most commonly found when the patient makes some sexual symbol, and the mechanism represents an attempt to deny what he has done.

If the traumatic ideas are nearing consciousness through hypnosis becoming lighter, the patient may react to defend himself from such awareness, by impulsively destroying the model which brings such awful thoughts to his mind. If this should happen, it is an immediate indication to the therapist to increase the depth of hypnosis, as the patient is on the verge of an acute anxiety reaction.

As a defence against making something significant, screen models occur only very rarely in hypnoplasty. This is in contrast to the modelling of the psychoneurotic patient in the waking state. When screen models have been made in hypnoplasty, it has always transpired that the patient was not as deeply hypnotized as he was at first thought to be. In fact, this would seem to be a defence which can be used only in light hypnosis. All other models would appear to have a specific reference, and to be of some psychological significance.

DEFENCES AGAINST VERBAL ASSOCIATIONS

The patient may have allowed himself to be hypnotized without defending himself, and he may have fulfilled the suggestion to make something from the clay, but when it comes to talking of what he has made, his defences may become very active. Any situation may be interpreted by the patient as threatening, or not. It seems that this is the factor which determines the particular stage in hypnoplasty at which psychological defences are called into play. The patient's insecurity may call the defences into play at the onset of hypnosis. It may be that the hypnotized patient feels that the actual making of a shape discloses his inner conflict to the therapist; accordingly he defends himself against modelling. On the other hand, the making of a model may not be regarded by the hypnotized patient as disclosing himself to the therapist, in which case there is no occasion for psychological defence. At the same time, he may feel that talking about the model discloses his innermost self in a way which he cannot tolerate even in hypnosis. It is probable that this statement of affairs is a gross over-simplification of the processes which determine what defences will be evoked, but some such mechanism is probably the basis of this process.

The patient may defend himself by refusing to talk about the model. Questions are repeated over and over again in different form, but he makes no response at all. The situation is met by getting him first to talk about some object which is of no psychological significance. When he is accustomed to talking, he is brought back to the model. If necessary, dissociation may be suggested. *"Your voice talks about the model,"* rather than *"You talk."* An emphasis on the dream-like quality of the situation may help. *"It is all a dream, and your voice talks. It talks all in a dream."*

Instead of a refusal to talk, the patient may talk, but he does so in such a low voice as to be inaudible. He just mumbles. This would seem to be a really childish attempt at defence. It might suggest that a very lightly hypnotized patient was merely playing with the therapist, or alternatively that the patient had undergone spontaneous hypnotic regression, and was in fact functioning at a childish level. However, experience has shown that this defence may occur in deeply hypnotized patients who show no other evidence of regression.

In other cases, the patient may talk quite readily, but he denies any knowledge of the model. This defence by denial occurs most frequently when the model has been made in response to a good deal of dissociation. The patient indicates, *"My hand made it. I do not know what it is."* Once a patient has made one model, he will usually make another without dissociation. So he is brought around to making another model. This time, emphasis is placed on his own responsibility. *"You do it. You make it yourself."* By this means he is robbed of the use of defence by denial, when it comes to talking about the model.

The patient may defend himself in the associations by trying to deny the specificity of the object he has made. When asked what the model is, he says, *"A man."* When asked, *"What man?"* he counters with, *"Just a man."* The patient is then told that he can see quite clearly who it is, and usually with very little pressure from the therapist, he discloses the specific identity of the model.

It is rare for patients in treatment by hypnoplasty to allow themselves to be hypnotized, to model the clay, and then to talk about the model, without calling into play some of these defences. With some patients, almost every suggestion that is given evokes some defensive reaction. At the same time, there is no doubt that the patient is deeply hypnotized. From these considerations, it is clear that the old concept of the hypnotized patient being quite defenceless and completely in the power of the therapist is quite untenable in hypnoplasty.

Figure No. 145

When he is hypnotized, a man of forty-five smooths out the clay, and makes marks like writing on it.

Letters.

Letters asking for money.

He goes red in the face, and appears to be very angry. He suddenly disfigures the model, and screws it up.

His action amounts to a defence. It is defence by denial. He thrusts the remains of the model away as if to deny that he ever received such letters.

(The model was straightened out again to be photographed. None of the other models has been altered in any way).

374

XXI

SOME PSYCHODYNAMICS
OF HYPNOPLASTY

VENTILATION OF CONFLICTS

Hypnoplasty facilitates the ventilation of psychological conflicts in a number of different ways.

When a patient is so driven by shame or guilt as to consciously withhold relevant material, it often happens that the significant conflict is promptly ventilated in the first session of hypnoplasty. In these circumstances, it seems that the strange subjective feeling of hypnosis, coupled with the unaccustomed activity of modelling, really provides the patient with an excuse to unburden himself. In the absence of hypnoplasty, the same material would eventually have been disclosed in ordinary psychotherapy, but it might have taken some considerable time. The continued voluntary withholding of material usually has a harmful effect on psychotherapy, not only on account of the time wasted, but also on account of the fact that the patient who is allowed to continue to voluntarily withhold material for any length of time becomes secure in his defences, and is likely to develop an increasing contempt for the therapist. The judicious use of hypnoplasty puts an end to this situation.

In other cases, hypnoplasty facilitates the ventilation of conflicts by the way in which it allows, for the patient's benefit, the full exploitation of the dissociation of the hypnotic state. In purely verbal hypnoanalysis, it is often difficult to make full use of dissociation. It is difficult for the patient to dissociate responsibility for his voice. The patient may be given the suggestion, *"Your voice talks, you do not talk, but your voice talks."* Such a manoeuvre usually requires fairly deep hypnosis. However, in hypnoplasty it is a much easier matter to induce a satisfactory dissociation as regards the action of the hands. *"Your hands do it, you don't do it, your hands make the thing in your mind."* The modelling thus comes to have the effect of fully utilizing the therapeutic advantages of the hypnotic state, which are otherwise not fully exploited in simple verbal hypnoanalysis.

In hypnosis, just as in the waking state, modelling aids the expression of conflicts in virtue of the fact that the patient's habitual defences are circumvented. Every patient whom we see, whether he be young or old, has had the experience of his whole life in developing psychological defences in conversation. The modelling places him in a completely different situation, in which his habitual defences are, for the most part, inapplicable.

In another way, the very process of moulding the clay helps to bring about the ventilation of the conflicts. The hypnotized patient characteristically keeps his gaze fixed on the changing shape of the amorphous mass in his hands. Shapes spontaneously arise, which become associated with ideas in his mind which are seeking expression. It would seem that this process occurs more readily in hypnosis than in the waking state. With the disorganization of the repressive mechanism in the hypnotic state, the significant conflicts are already on the threshold of expression, and easily become associated with shapes in the clay. By this means, the ideas are brought to ventilation in a way to which there is no counterpart in a purely verbal technique.

Through the effect of the hypnotic state, this process may proceed a step further. Instead of the patient purposefully making some object through the medium of dissociation, or instead of associating spontaneously occurring shapes in the clay with pressing unconscious material, the patient may fill in the gaps, as it were, by active hallucinatory processes. This type of hallucinatory experience is not uncommon in hypnoplasty. It seems to occur at two levels. Sometimes the patient will take a completely unshaped piece of clay and name it as some object. It may be that it has been suggested that he will make something which is connected with the thought deep in his mind. He takes a shapeless piece of clay and calls it his wife. He talks about his wife, and at the same time he keeps looking at the piece of clay. His manner of speech and behaviour make it clear that he regards the piece of clay as some likeness of his wife, in just the same way as another patient will make a female figure and identify it as his wife. In the case under discussion, it seems that the hypnotized patient actually sees an hallucinatory model of a human figure.

In the other type of spontaneous hallucinatory experience, the process is developed still further. To continue with the same example, the patient looks at the shapeless clay and talks of his wife. However, from what he says, it is clear that it is not a clay model of his wife which he sees; instead he sees her as a living person.

In these cases, the modelling is the catalyst which suddenly crystallizes the patient's conscious or unconscious thought into a vivid visual experience. This contrasts with the commonly used screen technique of inducing visual hallucinations in ordinary verbal hypnoanalysis.

Figure No. 146

The models made in hypnoplasty may refer to conflicts of any period in the life span of the patient or his phantasy of the future. These three models made by the same patient in a single session refer to quite different periods of his life.

1. This is his father. He talks of an incident in childhood when his father humiliated him.

2. This is the trunk in his office. In it are stored copies of papers for taxation purposes. He is worried that they may be required by the taxation authorities.

3. This is his phantasy of the future. It represents a house in the country where he would be away from doubtful business enterprises, leading an honest life.

Figure No. 147

The conflicts which are ventilated in the modelling show different grades of psychological content.

1. *A Symptomatic Model.* The patient is a young man suffering from a chronic anxiety state. He enjoys social gatherings, but when he goes to take a drink, his hand shakes so much that his nervousness is obvious to those around him. He is likely to spill his drink. He feels embarrassed, humiliated and ashamed of himself.

In hypnosis he makes a model of a glass. This is merely a way of describing a symptom of his present illness. A true symptomatic model is thus not connected with causative factors in the patient's illness, and hence is of no value in treatment. Symptomatic models are usually made only in light hypnosis. They have occurred very occasionally in the present study.

In actual fact, as the patient continued to give associations to the model of the glass, he came to talk of an incident in childhood when he had been scolded for upsetting a tray of glasses. It seemed that this incident was a factor in determining the particular way in which the patient's anxiety state was manifested.

2. *A Reality Problem.* The patient is a man in his middle fifties who

379

owns a sheep station. He has an anxiety state as a result of domestic conflict. In rather light hypnosis he makes this model of a rabbit. This serves to express a reality problem in that he is worried about a plague of rabbits on his sheep station. It has no causative relationship to his illness, other than that it aggravates his condition as an additional cause of anxitey.

3. *A Suppressed Conflict.* The patient suffers from disseminated sclerosis. She has been referred for psychiatric investigation, in the belief that there may be a functional overlay to her organic illness.

She makes a model of the dam in which she had found her child drowned some months previously.

> *Nothing goes on in my mind.*
> *A dam.*
> *It is meant to be a dam.*
> (Pause)
> *It is hard not to see that beautiful son of mine.*
> *Had to discipline my mind.* (Weeps)
> (Pause)
> *Must not know what it is like.*
> *Must not know what it is like for the other children.*
> (Apparently refers to her crippled condition on account of the disseminated sclerosis.)
> (Pause)
> *All you see are those lovely eyes.*
> (Apparently refers to her drowned child.)
> *So you go on.*
> *Cannot even pick up handkerchief if you drop it.*

4. *A Repressed Conflict.* The patient recalls a situation when she was five years old. When her parents went out at night, they would leave her at a neighbour's house, and she would be put to bed in the same room as their little boy aged nine. The model represents the boy; and in hypnosis she recalls how he used to expose himself to her. *"To show me what little boys are made of."*

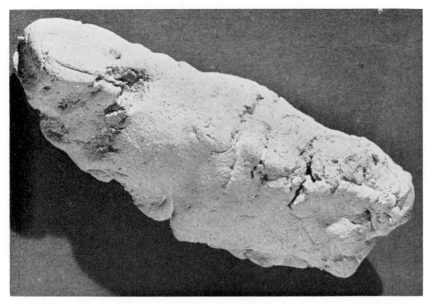

Figure No. 148

The ventilation of the conflict is often accompanied by vivid hallu-cinatory experiences so that the patient sees the shapeless mass of clay before him as a clear likeness of some object which is related to some conflict in his mind.

A man of fifty, who had been suffering from a minor hysterical tic for forty years, took the clay and started moulding it in his hands. He then stopped as if he had completed what he was doing.

Cow.

Used to frighten me when I was a little boy.

Very frightened.

Cow used to frighten me.

EMOTIONAL PARTICIPATION

The control of the patient's emotional participation is an important and sometimes difficult aspect of any form of psychotherapy. As a general rule, any session of any form of psychotherapy in which the patient is not emotionally involved is of little or no therapeutic value. In fact, emotional isolation is not only a common defence, but it is often a defence which is particularly difficult to counter. Defence by intellectualization is a good example.

This emotional isolation from the matters under discussion may be maintained even in the hypnotic state. It would seem that dissociation plays an important part in this. In fact, this defence, whether in the waking or the hypnotic state, is basically a dissociative phenomenon. Hypnosis, with its facilitation of dissociation, may aid the patient's emotional isolation in this way.

It is an unmistakable clinical observation that modelling in the hypnotic state increases the patient's emotional participation in the therapeutic process. It is probable that the mechanism which brings this about is the permanence of the plastic symbol, as opposed to the transience of the verbal symbol. The patient can isolate himself emotionally from the problem when it is expressed in words, but it would seem that he is unable to defend himself in the same way when he is continually faced with the plastic expression of the conflict. This greater emotional participation brings with it greater therapeutic effect for each particular session of treatment.

In this way, emotional participation in the therapeutic session is initiated. The next problem of technique is the control of this participation. In the waking state, this may be quite difficult. The therapist can vary the patient's emotional participation by reassurance, or by moving closer to him emotionally. In hypnoplasty, the hypnotic state allows easier and more effective control of these mechanisms. Because of the degree of rapport innate in the hypnotic situation, the therapist can communicate effectively with the hypnotized patient by means of unverbalized phonation. This language of *"Um"* and *"Ah"* and grunts can be used to convey degrees of emotional tones in a way which is not possible with the logical use of words in formal syntax.

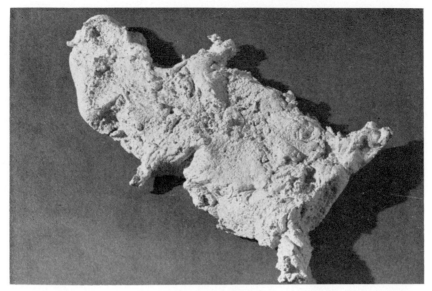

Figure No. 149

The initiation and control of the patient's emotional participation is an essential part of any effective psychotherapy. The middle-aged man who made this model was characteristically reserved and restrained in an ordinary interview. In hypnoplasty, he can no longer maintain his emotional isolation.

> *Figure.*
> *Figure of somebody* (Almost inaudible).
> *Don't know, man or woman.*
> *Somebody.*
> *It's* — (Inaudible)
> *Think it's a woman.*
> *Could be my mother.*
> Therapist: *What is she doing?*
> *Had a* — (mumbles)
> *Can't see any other woman.*
> *In hospital.*
> *Don't think that is it.* (loudly)
> (Pause) (Weeps, nose dribbles, therapist wipes his nose without disturbing him.)
> *Good woman.*

Always did her best for me.
Tried to help her.
(Pause)
She is always right.
(Pause)
Therapist: *What is happening now?*
(Patient becomes disturbed)
Both — possessive.
She says things I am not to say to anybody.
(Weeps)

MODELLING FACILITATES VERBAL EXPRESSION

It is a consistently observed clinical fact that modelling brings many hypnotized patients to talk, when previously they would either not talk at all, or would talk only very little, or with great difficulty. This statement is made in reference to deeply hypnotized patients, as distinct from patients in light hypnosis and hypnoidal states. In this respect, it is well to note that much of the recent literature in hypnoanalysis refers to work done with patients in very light hypnosis. The published records of such cases often show the patient speaking in a controlled manner with an appropriate use of syntax and grammar. It would seem that the hypnosis of many such patients is so light as to be little more than a deep reverie. In this type of light hypnosis, the patient can usually be induced to talk quite easily if rapport with the therapist is satisfactory. In fact, in this type of situation, success depends very largely on the degree of rapport with the waking patient prior to hypnosis.

The situation with the more deeply hypnotized patient is different. His ability to talk is very much influenced by any preconceived ideas as to the nature of hypnosis. If, in spite of what he is told by the therapist, he really believes hypnosis to be a form of sleep, then he is likely to have difficulty in talking in the hypnotic state. It would seem that one effect of hypnoplasty is that the induction of the patient into manual motor activity facilitates a transition to vocal activity. The barrier to speaking seems to be broken down. If he can do things with his hands, then there is no reason why he should not talk.

Another very important mechanism works to the same end in leading the patient to speech. This comes through abreaction. In hypnoplasty, the plastic expression of the conflict leads the patient to feel the emotion concerning the ideas which he is ventilating. The expression on his face, and his manner of handling the clay, reflect the mounting emotion which he feels. We can often see him getting more and more worked up. He starts to grunt and groan. This unverbalized phonation then drifts into the spontaneous mumbling of words. These are emotionally charged words

385

appropriate to the heightened feeling which he is experiencing. Then these emotionally charged words become connected together into short phrases which are full of feeling. At this stage, a little participation on the part of the therapist leads the patient into expressing his conflict in words, and the deeply hypnotized patient is brought to talking, when previously he may have made no response to questions.

HYPNOPLASTY AFFECTS THE STATE OF HYPNOSIS

It follows from our basic concept of hypnosis as a highly variable state of mental functioning, that particular activities on the part of the hypnotized patient are in turn likely to influence the state of hypnosis. This is seen to be so in hypnoplasty.

As a general rule, there is a definite increase in the depth of hypnosis when the patient starts modelling the clay. This occurs independently of any verbal suggestions of increased depth. In fact, provided that the patient has first reached the critical depth to enable him to model, then hypnoplasty is an effective way of increasing the depth of hypnosis. An exception to the general rule occurs when the too lightly hypnotized patient is introduced to modelling. He is unable to achieve the necessary dissociation. He becomes lighter, and may experience signs of anxiety.

The abreaction which so frequently occurs in hypnoplasty has its effect on the state of hypnosis. Moderate abreaction increases the depth of hypnosis, but severe abreaction often has the opposite effect. Hypnosis becomes lighter, and if the patient becomes really very angry, and gives full vent to his feelings, he may suddenly wake from hypnosis.

Regression and hallucinatory states not uncommonly occur spontaneously in hypnoplasty. This of course may happen in any form of hypnotic treatment; but the impression is that both regression and hallucinatory experiences occur spontaneously more commonly in hypnoplasty than in purely verbal techniques of treatment. When they occur, they have the secondary effect of further increasing the depth of hypnosis.

The practical significance of these matters is that the therapist must be constantly watching the depth of hypnosis. One of the dangers of hypnoplasty is that the patient may suddenly wake himself from hypnosis by the violence of his abreaction. If the patient is seen to be getting too light, he is given suggestions of greater depth. *"It is all through you. You feel it. It is all through you. You feel the heaviness. The heavy drowsiness is all through you."* When the patient seems to be going too deep, he will often become lighter if the tone of voice in which the suggestions are given is changed. A more natural conversational tone seems to have the effect of bringing the patient back to closer contact with the reality of his environment.

Figure No. 150

The hypnotized patient may talk about some incident of childhood. Sometimes it is clear that he is merely recalling some forgotten or half forgotten memory of the past. In other cases, it would seem that the patient is there in person, watching this incident which has taken place in the past. In still other cases, it would seem that the patient has really regressed in time. He is no longer just an observer; he is actually reliving the incident of childhood, and experiencing again the emotions which he felt on the original occasion.

The model is grossly disorganized, but it can be seen that it represents the bust of a large-breasted woman.

> *Mum, I think.*
> *Just Mum.*
> *Warm, comfortable.*

The associations would suggest that the patient is a child, as an adult would not ordinarily refer to his mother as *"Warm, comfortable."* The patient is actually a schizoid youth of thirty years. It would seem that he has spontaneously regressed in hypnosis, and is reliving his childhood feeling for his mother.

TOLERATION OF CONFLICT

The idea of toleration of psychological conflict has both theoretical and practical implications. Present day psychiatry is so taken up with the reductive method of psychiatry, and so orientated towards an analytical approach, that the student is liable to believe that the only effective way of helping the patient is the analysis and resolution of each and every conflict. Even in formal psychoanalysis, this is not really possible. In short-term psychotherapy, it is neither practicable nor desirable. In areas of minor significance, the patient is, in fact, going to be left with unresolved conflicts. Hypnoplasty, used as a technique in short-term psychotherapy, can often help the patient to better tolerate such conflicts. This of course applies particularly in the field of reality conflicts.

The effective mechanism in this process concerns the permanence of plastic expression, as opposed to the transient nature of verbal expression. Repeated expression in words of a painful idea, over a number of sessions of psychotherapy, brings the patient some tolerance of the conflict. He can now think of the matter without becoming upset, whereas formerly any thought of it would greatly disturb him. This happy state of affairs only comes about slowly. The reason for this is that the expression of the conflict in words takes only a few seconds, and the patient's attention is soon on to some other matter. This, of course, is aided by psychological defences aiming to save the patient the hurt of dwelling on the painful conflict. In plastotherapy, on account of the more permanent quality of plastic expression, this does not happen so readily. The patient remains faced with the conflict. He is thus forced into tolerating the unpleasant idea in a way which does not obtain with the spoken word.

This toleration of the conflict also comes about with the hypnotized patient. As a general rule, patients who ventilate their distress about some reality conflict in a number of sessions of hypnosis, develop a tolerance of the distressing situation. This process is correspondingly more effective with the permanence of plastic expression. Strangely enough, it still has some considerable effect even when the patient has a complete amnesia for the session or sessions.

During this work on hypnoplasty, it has been observed that a number of patients have made a degree of symptomatic improvement which could not be attributed either to insight or to direct suggestion. Most of these patients had reality conflicts of some magnitude. It was thought that their clinical improvement was largely the result of better tolerance of the conflicts, brought about by this mechanism. Sometimes it would seem that the tolerance of the conflict proceeds a stage further, and it is really a matter of better psychic integration. This does not necessarily imply better insight. It would seem rather that the continued exposure of the patient to the plastic expression of the conflict has done something to facilitate the function of those mechanisms which normally work to preserve psychic homeostasis.

XXII

ANXIETY REACTIONS IN HYPNOPLASTY

ANXIETY FROM SUDDEN AWARENESS OF HYPNOSIS

PRIOR TO TREATMENT, time is taken to explain hypnosis thoroughly to the patient. Queries are invited; and doubts are allayed. In order to avoid any question of rushing the patient into treatment without giving him full opportunity to consider the matter, no start on hypnosis is made until the next visit. The patient desires treatment. He is going to do what he can to co-operate in the induction of hypnosis. In spite of this attitude of co-operation, and the therapist's assurances that anyone who really wishes to be hypnotized can, in fact, let himself go into hypnosis, there are still many patients who really believe that they will not be hypnotized. This belief that one will not be hypnotized is not to be confused with the patient's unconscious defences against hypnosis. In as much as the patient believes that he will not be hypnotized, he enters the induction phase with an air of confidence, and a complete absence of anxiety. The suggestions are continued. It does not matter what method of induction is used; a time eventually comes when the patient suddenly becomes aware that he has in fact been hypnotized. There is a sudden change in the patient's appearance. His earlier confidence has left him. Tightening of the lips, frowning and grimacing are almost invariable. He may become pale, and sweat profusely. Restlessness is common. By unverbalized phonation, he may communicate his distress to the therapist, and thus ask for help.

A patient distressed in this way needs help; and it is quite easy to give it to him in the form of reassurance. *"Good. You let yourself go and your body works automatically. That is good.*

Good that you are letting yourself go. You are calm and easy; calm and easy and comfortable. It is good; good that your body works automatically. You just let yourself go with it. It is easy, calm and comfortable. You feel the calm. It is a heavy, drowsy, peaceful clam. You are calm, and secure. It is easy."

Anxiety reactions of this type are usually precipitated by the first serious challenge given the patient by the therapist. In challenging, the patient is given a suggestion, and is then challenged not to fulfil it. If the patient refuses the challenge, he automatically drifts a little deeper into hypnosis, so he can then be given a slightly more difficult challenge. In successful induction, if the patient accepts the challenge, he finds that he is unable to perform the act which he is challenged to do. He tries, but his muscles do not work. He experiences some anxiety, and becomes more deeply hypnotized. Challenging is thus an important technique for increasing the depth of hypnosis. The practical point is that the patient must be closely observed, particularly during the initial challenges, so that the therapist can quickly move in to reassure the patient if there are any signs of mounting anxiety.

In actual practice, the most severe reactions occur when the patient has been defending himself by simulation of hypnosis. The usual situation is that the patient was consciously prepared to co-operate in treatment. However, at the last minute, he feels frightened of the idea of abandoning himself to hypnosis. He defends himself by pretending to be hypnotized, and he consciously fulfils all the suggestions given to him. The therapist avoids challenges until the patient is actually hypnotized. He is then challenged to put his hands down, or move his arm, whatever the case may be. He finds he cannot do it. He suddenly realizes that he is, in fact, hypnotized. He is filled with anxiety, which may reach the proportions of acute panic.

One naturally does what one can to avoid anxiety reactions, on account of the distress caused to the patient. Practically the whole of the work of the present study has been done in consulting room practice. In this type of practice, another factor has to be considered. The patient must not be allowed to become so disturbed during treatment that he is unable to go back to his place of work after treatment, or unable to return home. This means that there must be a constant watch for signs of undue anxiety, so that appropriate action can be taken at the first signs of any untoward situation developing.

ANXIETY FROM SUDDEN AWARENESS OF
REPRESSED MATERIAL

As a result of the hypnotic state, and of the circumvention of the habitual defences through plastic expression, repressed material is ventilated. This comes first in the modelling itself, and then verbally through the associations. Much of this repressed material is extremely traumatic in nature. Repressed ideas of illicit love and unnatural hate are given expression. Still more deeply unconscious ideas, thoughts of incest and homosexuality, may pour forth. From the practical point of view, the important factor in hypnoplasty is that the expression of these ideas does not unduly disturb the patient, provided an adequate depth of hypnosis is maintained. These ideas, which would be devastating in their effect on the waking patient, may be discussed in hypnoplasty with a complete absence of anxiety.

However, the ventilation of such material is often accompanied by the abreaction of intense emotion. This is not usually accompanied by anxiety. It is a matter of the hypnotized patient feeling and expressing the emotion appropriate to the ideas which are being ventilated. It thus comes about that the patient often abreacts intense feelings of love or hate or guilt; but true anxiety is not really a part of it. It has been explained how severe abreaction may reduce the depth of hypnosis. This is the danger. If hypnosis becomes too light, the patient may suddenly become aware of the horrifying thoughts in his mind, and he may wake from hypnosis in a state of really terrible anxiety.

The remedy of the situation is easy enough. While a patient is abreacting, a very close watch must be kept on the depth of hypnosis. A change in his pattern of doing things, and a better contact with his environment, may indicate that the patient is becoming too light. Immediate action is necessary. The first step is for the therapist to move back into the picture, as it were. During the abreaction, the patient talks spontaneously, and as long as the abreaction continues, the patient will continue to talk. This means that the therapist is in an inactive role, merely listening to the expression of the repressed material. This in itself may be one of the factors which allows the hypnosis to become lighter. It has the effect that the therapist is temporarily in less close contact with the patient. The therapist must now move to regain closer hypnotic rapport with the patient. He can commence by expressing the same emotion as the patient by means of unverbalized phonation. This allows the therapist to re-enter the situation without disturbing the patient. Once this manoeuvre has been completed, there is a choice of ways to proceed according to circumstances.

The therapist may simply reassure the patient. In dealing with an abreacting patient who is becoming lighter in hypnosis, the therapist must first be sure that he has adequate emotional contact with the patient before he proceeds to verbal reassurance. This pre-requisite emotional contact is assured by letting the patient know that the therapist feels with him. This cannot be done with the hypnotized patient by any logical use of words. The idea must be communicated by non-verbal means by what we do with the patient. If necessary we can take his hand, or put our hand on his shoulder. We communicate our feeling by appropriate *"Um's"* and *"Ah's,"* and grunts. Then a transition is made to verbal reassurance. *"Easy, easy, and it is calm, calm, you let yourself relax, all your body relaxes. It is calm and easy";* etc.

Instead of proceeding to avoid the anxiety reaction by reassurance, another method is to lead the patient to another subject which is less charged emotionally. This can be effected in numerous ways according to circumstances. If the patient is abreacting his emotion concerning some incident, he can be asked where it took place; and then led on to talking about the place rather than the incident. There are countless moves of similar nature. The reader must not be alarmed at the obvious transparency of such manoeuvres. The abreacting patient, when he is hypnotized, is much easier to handle in this way than is a patient abreacting in the waking state.

Another way to avoid an impending attack of anxiety is to take immediate steps to deepen hypnosis. It may be possible to ignore the patient's abreaction, and simply take his arm and initiate repetitive movement. *"Your arm goes back and forth, back and forth. It goes back and forth automatically";* etc. If this can be done, the abreaction ceases, and the danger of acute anxiety has passed.

As regards these acute anxiety reactions, there is a pitfall which may be a real danger to the student. The abreaction may be of extreme violence. It may be quite terrifying to witness such an attack. An inexperienced student might feel that the situation is getting out of hand. He wants to stop it. He may do what might appear to be the obvious thing. He wakens the patient. This of course is the worst possible thing to do. The flood of repressed material now surges into his full consciousness, and hyper-acute anxiety results.

If this should happen, or if the patient should wake himself spontaneously, he must be immediately rehypnotized. This may require not only prompt action by the therapist, but also a good deal of firmness. The patient is extremely distressed. He may be weeping in an uncontrolled fashion, or his anxiety may show itself in acute, distracted restlessness of body and mind. On the other hand, collapse may be the prominent clinical feature, and the patient flops down in a cold sweat with a rapid thready pulse. Whatever the prevailing clinical picture, the patient is too distressed to co-operate in any further hypnosis. The situation is aggravated by the fact that the patient associates hypnosis with his present acute distress. The therapist's first move is to try to re-establish contact with the patient. It may be that he can be helped to a bed or a couch. It may be that the patient has to be lifted to the couch, or firmly manhandled. Powerful suggestions of ease and calm are given, together with all the non-verbal aids to suggestion. One hand is on the patient's forehead and the other takes his hand. If these manoeuvres are successful in establishing a relationship with the patient, the suggestions are changed to relaxation, drowsiness and rest; and the patient is put into an hypnotic sleep.

If this approach fails, the therapist must fall back on authority. This must not be any half-hearted masquerade. It is a matter of a medical emergency requiring effective action. The therapist must suddenly make a complete change in his traditional attitude to the patient. He does everything in his power to muster authority. He talks loudly and in a commanding fashion. He may physically push the patient about. He ignores his protestations, and forcefully induces hypnosis by authority. *"You look at me. You look at my eyes. No, you can't turn your head away."* If necessary, the patient is held by the chin. *"You look at my eyes. You look at my eyes. That is good. It is easy. It is all through you. Everything lets go. Your eyelids are heavier and heavier. They cannot stay open. It is all through you. You cannot stay awake. Deep sleep, deep sleep is all through you."*

There are several practical comments about the situation. Acute anxiety reactions of this nature are not common, but they are definitely much more common in hypnoplasty than in verbal hypnoanalysis. A striking feature is the dramatic way in which the patient recovers when he is rehypnotized, and allowed to rest for a short time. It would seem to be essential that any therapist should have the capacity to fall back on an authoritative technique in a case of emergency. The need for it will arise only on very rare occasions, but when it does arise, it is a matter of real urgency.

The patient can be allowed to rest for half an hour in an hypnotic sleep. Whether or not he is given suggestions of amnesia will depend on circumstances such as his physical state, and likely therapeutic value of his retaining consciousness of the matter in question. In any case, if the patient is put to sleep, it is likely that he will develop a spontaneous amnesia of at least the more disturbing elements of the traumatic incident.

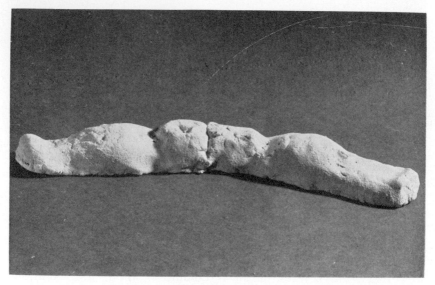

Figure No. 151

Severe anxiety reactions may occur if hypnosis becomes lighter, and the patient becomes aware of the ideas which he is expressing.

This homosexual symbol, which represents the patient made up of a girl baby and a boy baby, was made by a latent invert. It illustrates the type of situation which is likely to produce severe anxiety if hypnosis should become lighter and the patient should become aware of the idea which he is expressing. In this case, the patient made this symbol on several occasions, but adequate hynosis was always maintained, and no anxiety reactions ensued.

FACTORS MODIFYING ANXIETY REACTIONS

The above account of the acute disturbances which may arise from sudden awareness of repressed material should not in any way discourage other therapists from working in hypnoplasty. These alarming incidents are, in fact, the result of incompetent management of the therapeutic situation. As the present study has proceeded, better understanding of the basic psychodynamics has been achieved, and warning signs are more easily read. The result has been that acute anxiety reactions such as those described have not occurred for some time past, and it is now felt that it is unlikely that future patients will be disturbed in this way.

Nevertheless, the danger of anxiety reactions is greater in hypnoplasty than in purely verbal hypnoanalysis. The reason for this would seem to be connected with the relative permanence of plastic expression as compared with the spoken word. If hypnosis becomes too light in verbal hypnoanalysis, and repressed material comes to consciousness, the patient quickly defends himself by amnesia and denial. In hypnoplasty, however, the permanence of the model in front of the patient makes this type of defence much more difficult. The spoken word can be banished from the patient's awareness by these means, but such defences cannot remove the model, which remains the tangible evidence of the awful thought. At best, his unconscious defences can prevent him understanding the model which he has made, but this is obviously a much more difficult form of defence by denial than that which applies to the spoken word. The result is that anxiety reactions are so much the more likely to occur in hypnoplasty.

An important practical consideration is the essentially fluctuant nature of the hypnotic state. The therapist can never afford to feel that he has the patient deeply hypnotized, and therefore has no occasion to worry about anxiety reactions. Variations in depth occur, which appear to be spontaneous. These may actually come in response to inadvertent non-verbal communication from the therapist, or they may arise as a result of the disorganization of the repressive mechanism through hypnosis. It would seem that the partial failure of repression allows some flux and reflux of un-

399

conscious material towards and away from the threshold of awareness, and this in turn has its effect on the depth of hypnosis.

The spontaneous ventilation of unconscious material, which occasionally occurs when a subject has been hypnotized for some other purpose, would point to the operation of some such mechanism as this. The effect in hypnoplasty is that variations in depth represent a constant threat of anxiety reactions.

OTHER CAUSES OF ANXIETY

If a patient who has not attained the necessary critical depth of hypnosis for hypnoplasty is offered the clay, and given suggestions to model, he will wake from hypnosis, and experience an anxiety reaction of greater or lesser severity. This is simply a situation analogous to the giving of too steeply graded suggestions in the ordinary process of induction. The patient rejects the suggestion, and the hypnotic process comes to an end.

Rejection of the suggestion to model is distinct from a defensive refusal to model. In the latter case, the patient remains hypnotized; there is no anxiety; but he uses the hypnotic situation as a defence against the disclosure of disturbing psychic material in modelling. By his actions, he communicates the idea to the therapist that he believes that a hypnotized person cannot do these things.

The rejection of the suggestion to model represents a straight-out failure in technique. An error has been made in the estimation of the patient's depth of hypnosis. Mistakes of this nature usually come about through the fact that the depth of hypnosis can vary in different areas of ego activity. In some respects, the patient may be deeply hypnotized, but in others he may still be comparatively light. Before attempting hypnoplasty, repetitive movement of the arm, with the eyes open, should always be induced first.

An unusual cause of anxiety arises when the actual process of modelling offends the basic personality structure of the patient. Thus a phobic patient, who had a basically obsessive personality, became very disturbed in hypnoplasty by the clay sticking to his fingers. He had obsessive ideas of cleanliness, and he equated the modelling clay with dirt. He experienced a severe and unexpected anxiety reaction. However, hypnosis was maintained, and his hands were washed while he was still hypnotized. He was then allowed to rest in an hypnotic sleep, and he returned to a calm state of mind by the end of the session.

Figure No. 152

The hypnotized patient sometimes behaves in a way which is seemingly contrary to his normal personality. He does things which he certainly would not do in his normal state of consciousness. If the patient should wake from hypnosis, and find that he is doing something which he would ordinarily consider wrong or improper, he is likely to suffer an anxiety reaction. This situation refers to matters which the patient ordinarily considers as socially wrong or improper, rather than morally wrong or improper. There is a good deal of evidence to suggest that even the deeply hypnotized patient will not do anything which in his waking state he considers morally wrong.

Thus a young man was being treated for stuttering. He was rather inhibited and was particularly rigid in matters of propriety. He would never say or do anything which was in any way out of place. Although he was being treated mainly by suggestive hypnosis, he was given one session of hypnoplasty for diagnostic purposes. He makes a likeness of his girl friend's pudenda. This is something which in reality he has never seen or felt, nor would he even talk of such a subject. Yet this lad, who is so proper and reserved in his everyday life, immediately makes the likeness of something which would be absolutely taboo in his ordinary conversation.

Don't know.
Joan's legs.
Up at the top.
I have often thought I would like to see her without any
    clothes on.

While he was making the model, he became intensely preoccupied with it. When he finished the shape, he started to fondle it, caressing it again and again with his fingers.

This serves to illustrate the type of situation which may provoke an anxiety reaction if hypnosis is allowed to become too light. In actual fact, adequate depth of hypnosis was maintained. After the caressing action had continued for some time, it was brought to a stop by appropriate suggestions. The patient was put into a deep hypnotic sleep before being awakened. He subsequently developed a complete spontaneous amnesia for the session.

XXIII

HYPNOPLASTY — EXCERPTS FROM CASE HISTORIES
CASE NO. 1
WRITER'S CRAMP, SEXUAL IMPOTENCE

A business executive in his middle forties seeks treatment on account of increasing difficulty in signing his name. His hand becomes so tense that he loses control of the pen, and is likely to force the nib into the paper. He also complains of sexual impotence of some years duration.

CASE NO. 1

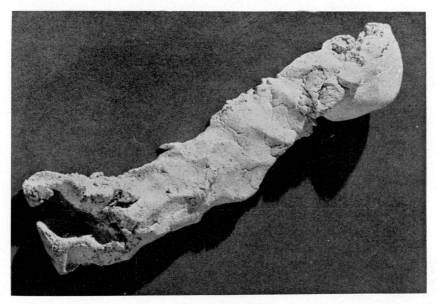

Figure No. 153

The patient is deeply hypnotized. He speaks in a low, mumbling voice.

> *Figure.*
> *Don't know if it's a man or a woman.*
> *Just a figure.*
> *Lying face down.*
> *A figure.*
> *Flat on her face.*
> *Just a figure lying flat on her face.*
> (Mumbles incomprehensibly)
> *Suppose it's a woman.*
> (Inaudible mumbling)
> *Bed, bed, bedroom.*
> *Cannot see the figure in the bedroom.*
> (Pause)
> *Hair.*
> *Looks like B———, she was dark.*
> *Just a girl, not bad though.*

405

There were sheets.
She got married.
(Silent tears)

The model and the associations illustrate the projection of ideas on to unstructured material. His reference to the figure as lying face down, and later his identification of the figure because she is dark, strongly suggest that the patient is hallucinating.

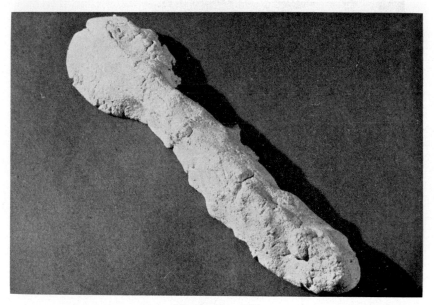

Figure No. 154

The patient is deeply hypnotized. He shakes his head and mumbles. He makes snorting noises which would suggest contempt or derision.

What I haven't got.

Kitten did that.

Not right (loudly) *looks like a penis.*

(Mumbles)

(Loudly) *Does not belong to me.*

Does not belong to me. (The patient pushes the model away)

Not me.

I am not there.

Like to be.

Therapist: *Where?*

There. (Points to model)

In the room with yellow sheets.

Looks like, could be B——— (becomes inaudible)

(Pause)

Somebody else there.

Didn't know him.

I can see him.

The associations show clearly that the patient is having hallucinatory experiences. His varying emotion is expressed by the way in which he mumbles inaudibly, and then suddenly shouts out loudly.

407

CASE NO. 1

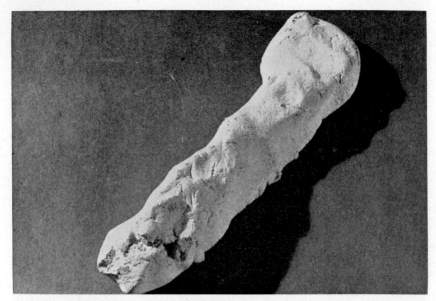

Figure No. 155

Somebody's penis.
Dark.
Don't know.
Dark (mumbles)
Hair.
Seems as if he was in the room with me.
Looks like —
Under the shower.
Dark.
Dark skin.
(With some animation) *That's — just having a shower.*
Talking about how big they all are.
(Laughs and at the same time tears are in his eyes.)
He's got the broadest one, the thickest.
Wouldn't mind one like it.
(His eyes stare fixedly. Tears drop on the table in front
    of him.)
Says he got all the girls (His voice trails off inaudibly.)
They laugh about me.
(With animation) *They are laughing at me.*

The patient's presenting symptom was writer's cramp, but in hypnosis he refers almost exclusively to his impotence, which in his waking
state was mentioned only as a matter of secondary importance.

CASE NO. 1

Figure No. 156

Woman's body.
Dark, so it must be B————.
Can't see her head.
Just see the bottom from here down. (Puts his fingers over her head.)
Woman's body.
Dark skin.
Can't see her head clearly. (He holds his fingers covering her head.)
Beautiful.
Woman's body.
Beautiful breasts. (Eyes moist, his nose dribbles.)
(With emotion) *Headless.* (He still has his fingers over her head.)
Clothes.
Light touches.
Fair hair, prickly.
(His nose dribbles and drops fall on to the table.
I wipe his nose with his handkerchief without it showing any signs of disturbing him.)
Therapist: *What's happening?*
Just there in front of me, standing up.

Just there in front of me, standing waiting for me.

This is a further illustration of active hallucinatory experiences. The way in which the patient held his hand over the head of the model is an example of the hysteroid behaviour which is so frequently seen in hypnosis. The meaning would seem to be that it is only the lower part of her body which concerns him.

CASE NO. 1

Figure No. 157

My wife.
Surrounded by nothing.
Don't know where she is.
Just there.
Surrounded by nothing.
Can't see.
She's standing there.
There on her own. (His nose dribbles.)
Green so it must be grass underfoot.
Nothing, just grass.
Green field surrounded by nothing.
House floating in the air.
House floating in the air.
There's nothing.
Therapist: *What should there be?*
Can't see it except the house.
It's on the ground now. (Tears running down his cheeks.)
Different, not the one I want.
She's surrounded by nothing.
Therapist: *What should she be surrounded by?*
Beautiful clothes.

411

CASE NO. 2

SPASMODIC TORTICOLLIS

The patient is a man in his middle forties who has suffered from spasmodic torticollis for some years. He has undergone various forms of medical and psychological treatment without success. His head is kept turned around to such an extent that his chin rests on his shoulder. All the time the patient supports his head by holding his chin in his hand. This awkward posture seems to relieve some of the tension in the muscles of his neck, although it does not bring his face to the front. If he is persuaded to take his hand away from his chin for a moment, the spasm in the sternocleidomastoid muscle is more violent than ever.

Recently the patient has become very dispirited. If he is confronted with any problem at work, he leaves his office and returns home, without even attending to routine matters. His wife in the past has stood by him, and supported him, but she has now become embittered by his apparent lack of determination.

CASE NO. 2

Figure No. 158

Baby.
Pretty baby.
Pretty girl.
Like a nice baby girl.
Pretty little baby girl.
Not very good at that sort of thing.
Always frightened of having too many children.
Like to have a baby daughter.
Love children.
Did not plan the two boys.
Was sorry they were coming but all right afterwards.

413

CASE NO. 2

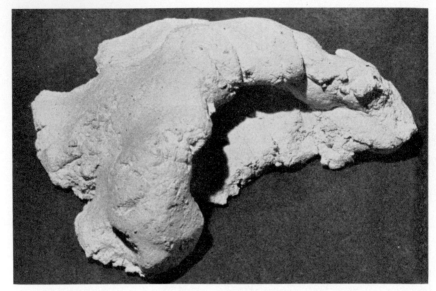

Figure No. 159

Fireplace.
Cave with a fireplace.
Warmth and security.
Warmth and happiness.
Own fire.
Nobody can come and take it from you.
Warmth.
Frightened of losing things.
Security.
Got to keep the family.
Everything to me.
Got to get stronger.
Never given them their own home.
Security, must have security for them.

414

CASE NO. 2

Figure No. 160

My son Bill.
Tried to get rid of him when he was first coming.
Went to a chemist.
No money.
Tried to get rid of him.
Now beautiful boy.
Then with John.
Did not want him either.
Joan did not tell me until three months.
Said I would have another mouth to feed.
At the time we did not want them.
That was a sin.
Make it up to them.
Should not have done that.
Against God's will.
See myself.
Murder.
That's what it is.
But God willed otherwise.

Bill I love you.
Everything to me.
Tried to get rid of him.
Why?
(Pause)
Want the children to admire me.
Strong and well again.
Look after them as I didn't before.
Get their affection.
Not worthy of them.
That's the fear.
This deep in my mind.
(Pause)
Have not even paid for our engagement ring.
They did not want me to marry her.
Never any money.
(Pause)
Make myself look big.
(Pause)
Should not have married her without money.
She stuck to me.
(Pause)
Work.
Practice going.
Do not like that tedious work.
Want to be a big shot that talks to the clients.

CASE NO. 2

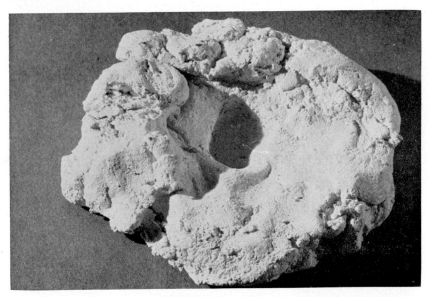

Figure No. 161

Water tank.
Where I proposed to my wife on her father's property.
Sitting on the side.
Gave her a ring.
She can't wear it for two weeks, not twenty-one.
Love her.
No money.
Her father's rich.
He'll help us if I don't get any money.
Keep everything secret.
Then ask if it's all right.
Left things in a bit of a mess.
Brought her to town.
Lived in one room.
She was used to good things.
Go away.
She works on the property.
(Pause)
Silly jealousy.

Silly.
Madly jealous.
Thought Bill not my child.
After John was born.
Came home early.
Joan had man talking to her.
Insurance man.
She accused me of thinking it.
(Pause)
Friends there.
They said they would wash up. (Joan and man friend.)
Said he would take her to the pictures.
Said yes.
Then I would not let them go.
I did not trust her.
(Pause)
Two of them came into the room.
Said they had something to tell me.
Thought they were going to tell me they were in love.
Stomach turned over.
They only came to tell me a joke.
(Pause)
Somebody said, you will never get over it (his neck).
Frightened to go out.
They look at me.
(Pause)
Carry on Jim, forget the neck.
It is just imagination anyway.
Think straight, and your neck will go —
(Pause)
My past sins.
(Pause)
Get better.
Have to get better.
Go back to work for the boys.
(Pause)
Affection.
Love and affection.

Figure No. 162

Son, Bill.
Standing beside the wireless.
Looking at me.
Just standing there beside the wireless.
Saying, don't upset Mum, Dad.
Be quiet.
Try and not argue with her.
He is smiling at me now.
The sun coming in.
Bill is there.
(Pause)
Lounge room.
Bill, Joan and John.
(Pause)
Bill is really my son.
Once I thought Bill was not my son.
Nothing like me to look at.
People say that.
Frightened she might go with somebody else.
(Pause)
I see her father and mother saying she is too good for me.
(Pause)
They can't push me around.
Make them wait for me.

419

CASE NO. 2

Figure No. 163

Bill my son, big and strong.
Every time I see him I feel ashamed.
He hates me. (Weeps)
Haven't provided for his future.
Despises me.
I say to Joan, why don't you love me.
(Pause)
He never was any good, never will be.
Sticks to me for duty not for love.
She says she is like a rat caught in a trap.
(Pause)
Think I put this act on sometimes to embarrass her.
Therapist: *You put this on to embarrass her sometimes.*
Somehow want to hurt her.
She said everyone despises me.
Says I am trying to bring her down to my level.
Might be, too.

420

CASE NO. 2

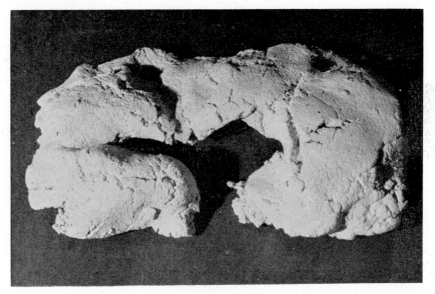

Figure No. 164

Our flat at home.
Represents what I have not been in life.
Stuck in a flat.
No place for the kids.
Come home, and she says if I come home early again she
*   will scream.*
Joan says she is sorry for John as he has nowhere to play.
Failure, I am a failure.

CASE NO. 2

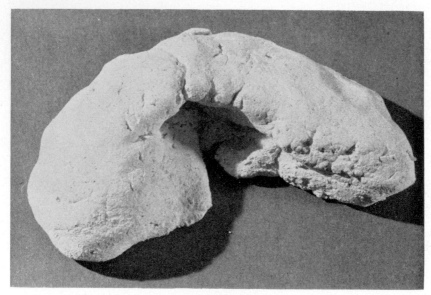

Figure No. 165

A cave.
Cave at —
It's Sunday.
I am with the girl I am engaged to be married to.
Had no money.
Had taken some money.
Had to put it back by Monday.
Borrowed five pounds from the girl I was engaged to.
Had not even paid for the ring.
Was discharged from my job for stealing.
Always my weakness.
Nothing stolen in the last ten years.
Always think of it when I go to —
He said, you have taken some money, you will have to go.
Told my father I had lost my job through the depression.
Stayed home for a year.
Stole my father's watch, sold it for seven shillings.
Always scheming to get money.
Not the fault of society, it's my own fault.

Feeling of guilt, insecurity.
Saw my mother putting money under the carpet.
Took it out when she wanted it.
Halfway through the month and no money.
Gas would be cut off.
Then on the first of the month lollies and biscuits.
(Pause)
Not honest.
See John and Bill looking at me.
Give them a pound a week pocket money.
(Pause)
Walking down the street with Joan.
After we were married pawned engagement ring for one
*   pound.*
Sisters all no-hopers.
Mother — God bless her, she is dead — was weak.
Little boy holding my hands in warm water.
Mother saying, stay home from school you needn't go.

CASE NO. 2

Figure No. 166

A meeting.

A Directors' meeting. (Points to the four figures and names them).

I am the Secretary.

Biggest job I have ever had.

Worth five hundred pounds a year.

Had to work out something to save this man. (Points to one of the figures)

A lot of tax.

Two thousand pounds bad debts.

Discussed what I was doing.

The entries not quite correct.

If they were investigated by the tax people perhaps — perhaps — (voice trails off).

Halfway through the meeting I started to twist and turn and couldn't sit still.

My head turned.

Turning away from that job.

It represented my whole life.

Based on deceit all my life.
Get all jittery at meetings.
Force myself to go.
Helping to avoid taxation.
Business not built on sound lines.
Based on helping defraud taxation.
It is wrong.
See Mr———— every day.
He would not do it.

CASE NO. 3

SPASMODIC TORTICOLLIS

The patient was a married woman in her middle thirties. She had suffered from severe spasmodic torticollis for ten years. During this time, she had been treated by a great number of physicians and psychiatrists, as well as an orthopaedic surgeon. She was hypnotized and treated by hypnoplasty. In spite of the continuance of an extremely unfavourable domestic situation, she made a complete symptomatic recovery, and has remained well for the past six years.

CASE NO. 3

Figure No. 167

Him belting me.

The patient abreacts violently, weeping, sighing and making unverbalized squeaking noises. She starts modelling in feverish haste; and makes the figures quickly, and without pausing. All the time she completely ignores the tears which roll down her cheeks and soil her dress.

CASE NO. 3

Figure No. 168

The girl he used to hang around.

CASE NO. 3

Figure No. 169

Me and my husband — intercourse.

429

CASE NO. 3

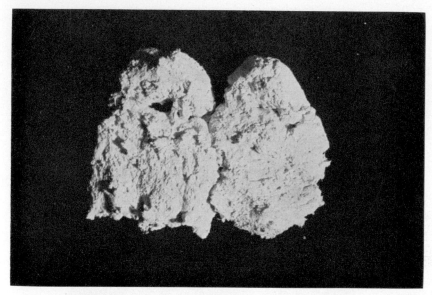

Figure No. 170

The court house.

Her husband had been tried in court for interfering with little girls. The model apparently represents the court house with a twin gabled roof.

CASE NO. 3

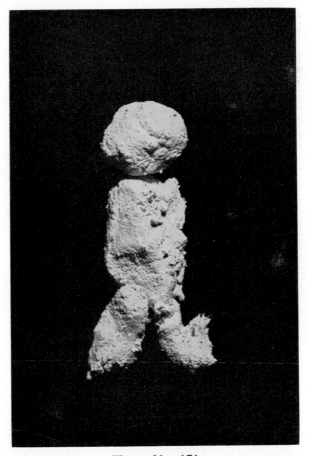

Figure No. 171

The boy.

431

CASE NO. 3

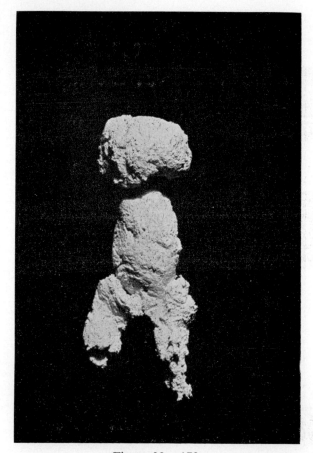

Figure No. 172

The big girl he chased.

The patient gives very little in the way of verbal associations. However, she is extremely disturbed all the time she is making the models. She grunts and groans, and tears roll down her cheeks. This is accompanied by violent movements of her head and neck. It seems that the hypnotic state momentarily relieves the spasm of her neck muscles. Her face comes to the front. Then the muscles suddenly go into spasm, and her head is abruptly jerked around.

CASE NO. 3

Figure No. 173

The little girl he kissed.

CASE NO. 3

Figure No. 174

Me kissing my mother the day of the court case.

CASE NO. 3

Figure No. 175

Me turning my head.

This is the psychogenesis of her torticollis. Ten years previously, during the court case, she had suddenly turned away from her husband. She had not remembered the incident. Since then her head had started to turn spontaneously. The condition had become worse until it was now practically crippling her.

CASE NO. 3

Figure No. 176

My husband and the girl — I can't stand it.

CASE NO. 3

Figure No. 177

Putting me out of the house without any clothes on.
That's my house.
The blob of clay at the bottom is the house.

CASE NO. 3

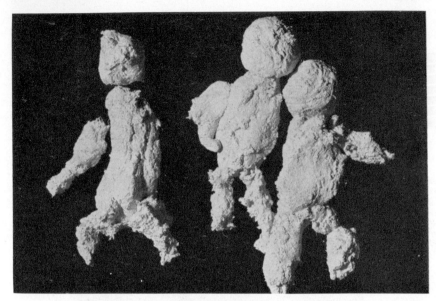

Figure No. 178

It's him showing Bert my pants.
I let him, to get him away from girls.
The husband was a fetishist.

CASE NO. 3

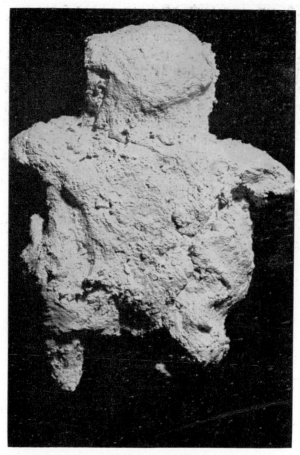

Figure No. 179

I don't want intercourse with my husband.
I am only the scapegoat.
Her husband was rather short and fat. This is how she depicts him.

CASE NO. 4

COMPENSATORY ALCOHOLISM

It was the patient's alcoholism which first caused the relatives to bring her to consultation. She had married during the war; but on his return from service, her husband had shown no capacity to adjust himself to domestic life. There were no children, and she divorced him. Now, still a young woman, she was living in a flat by herself. She had few friends. She was sensitive and lonely, and was compensating for her loneliness with alcohol.

CASE NO. 4

Figure No. 180

Trinket.
Made me promise to look after it.
Asked Tom (brother) *to get it for me.*
My sister took it.
He said, "Don't be childish."
They do not understand.
Tiny little thing with pearls on it.
It was mum's — dad gave it to her.
Sister took it out of my flat.

When she had completed the model, the patient continued to fondle it with her fingers. She became completely preoccupied with it, and the caressing action of her fingers continued in a way which is usually seen only in frankly sexual models or when the patient has made a figure to represent his loved one.

CASE NO. 4

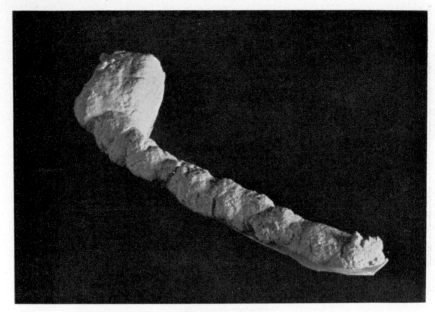

Figure No. 181

Driver.
Bob had his golf sticks.
Hitting up and down, showing me.
Lost his temper, looked stern and hard.
I had beaten him one hole.
He went into the lake.
So cross and hard, I thought he wasn't a sportsman.
I used to play golf every day.
Never play now.

CASE NO. 4

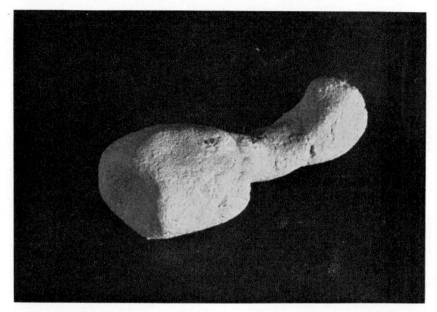

Figure No. 182

The model represents a wineglass. The patient spent some time in trying to get it to stand up, but the clay was not firm enough.

Everyone knows I am here because I was drinking too much.
Did not know, so tired, broken hearted.
No one to talk to, no one.
Sister has husband.
Brothers.
Everyone has friends.
I tried to do everything for mother.

This model represents a projection of her conflicts concerning her drinking. Thus a present-day reality problem finds expression among a series of models which refer to incidents of a few years ago, during the period of her marriage.

CASE NO. 4

Figure No. 183

Everyone says I build a wall about myself.
Get out and get about.
I must go away.
Don't want to be with people all the time.
The wall around myself.

This is typically neurotic symbolism. It is the type of symbol which is very commonly made in the waking state in plastotherapy.

CASE NO. 4

Figure No. 184

Our house.
Flowers.
Where mum should have been all the time she was sick,
*   instead of my pokey little flat.*
I was always going to solicitors about it.
They promised to get out.
Did not go to the war either.

The model has little resemblance to a house, and is far removed from the classical conventional symbolism which characteristically shows a chimney, a door and windows.

CASE NO. 4

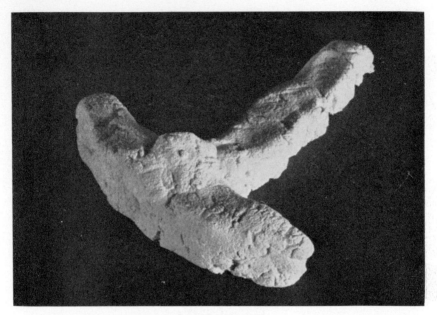

Figure No. 185

I was going away to Commander and Mrs. ————.
Shape of the jetty at Singapore.
Said I would be back there.
Tried to write, but did not tell them I am sick.
I am not sick.

The model illustrates very well the fact that the meaning of a model often becomes clear only from the patient's associations.

CASE NO. 4

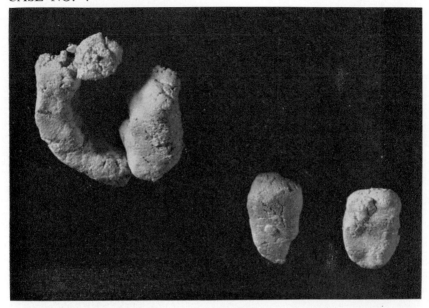

Figure No. 186

I think I would have been all right.
People have been clumsy.
Verandah.
Wanted to die.
How clumsy.
Wanted to go away, and never come back.
Wanted to die, and never wake up again.
At the back door at home.
That's where mother was lying.

In some way the model apparently represents the verandah of her home. The two similar pieces lying side by side close together are the patient and her mother, whom she nursed during her terminal illness.

These models were all made at the patient's first session of hypoplasty. When she was next seen, she said that she had a vague memory of modelling, and of talking about the things she had made.

CASE NO. 4

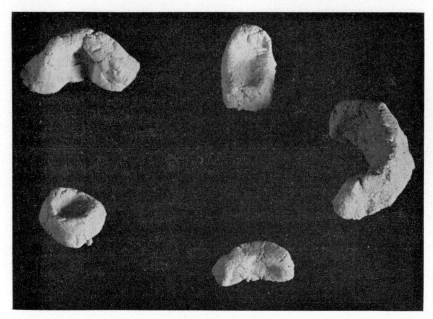

Figure No. 187

My flat.
Got to go back there.
Was away from it all last winter.
Mother was there.
She should have been in her own house.
Horrible little place.
Can't be bothered cooking for myself.
Practise the piano.
So cold when you come in, and no one is there.
Jean is sick now, having another baby.
Bed by the window.
My bed, I can't sleep.
Nothing to live for.
Sometimes wish I would never wake up.

Although deeply hynotized, the patient has made a well organized model. The curve on the right represents the bay window. At the top left is the fireplace, and the other three shapes represent her bed and pieces of furniture.

CASE NO. 4

Figure No. 188

The ship coming home.
Everyone says I can live by myself.
Jim could not live by himself.
Lots of friends, wealth.
Had to have them in his house for company.
Mad on his polo, golf, tennis.
The model is a very crude representation of a ship.

CASE NO. 4

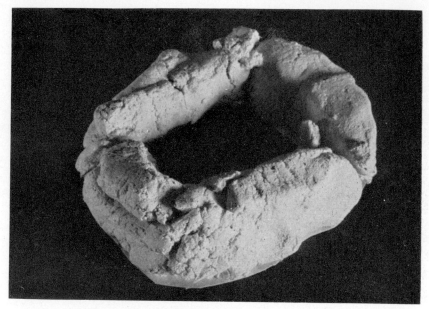

Figure No. 189

Everything will be all right.
It's not home, it's just —
Everything will be all right.
Won't let anyone come near me.
I am going to lock myself in.

From the way in which the patient spoke, it seemed that the model represented two ideas. These are the walls of her flat where she is going to lock herself in physically, and isolate herself from an unkind world. They are also the psychological walls which the schizoid erects around herself to protect herself from emotional contact with her fellows.

PART III
Modelling as an Adjuvant to
PSYCHIATRIC TREATMENT

XXIV

MODELLING AS AN ADJUVANT TO PSYCHIATRIC TREATMENT

MODELLING IN OCCUPATIONAL THERAPY

THE ACTIVE psychodynamic use of modelling in psychotherapy has been discussed. When it is used with the patient in the waking state, it is known as plastotherapy, and as a technique in hypnoanalysis it is called hypnoplasty. In both cases, the modelling becomes an integral part of the psychotherapeutic process. In addition to these techniques, modelling can also be used as an adjunct to psychiatric treatment. When used in this way, the modelling does not enter into the primary psychotherapeutic process, but works to help the patient in a more or less independent secondary capacity. All who are interested in present-day psychiatry are familiar with the concept of helping the patient simultaneously in as many ways as possible. This idea has been popularized as the "Total Push."

Although these adjuvant forms of treatment do not enter into the psychodynamic processes of the basic psychotherapy, nevertheless they are undoubtedly a significant help to the patient. The means by which these adjuvant treatments assist the patient form a secondary set of psychodynamic reactions, which for the most part are independent of the primary psychotherapeutic process.

There is a considerable difference in the patient's reactions to the way in which modelling is used. In plastotherapy, the patient is extremely concerned and thoughtful about the modelling. As it brings to light unpleasant conflicts, he becomes anxious about it. He is inclined to anticipate the next session with a certain amount of apprehension. However, with adjuvant therapy, the reverse is the case. There is a general increase in the effectiveness of the repressive mechanisms. It evokes a pleasant emotional response in the patient, and he characteristically looks forward with pleasure to the next session.

When modelling is used in occupational therapy, it does not help the patient by bringing about the ventilation of suppressed or repressed material, as is the case in plastotherapy and hypnoplasty. It is effective in helping the patient through other mechanisms.

A feature of modelling in occupational therapy is that the occupational therapist shows the patient how to do it. This is essential. If the patient is simply left to his own devices with the clay, then the procedure is no longer occupational therapy, but should be properly classed as recreational therapy. The occupational therapist gets the patient to do the modelling. This process of getting the patient to do it involves a number of factors. She must explain it to the patient; but before she can start to explain it, she must have some degree of emotional contact with him. In other words, she must first establish rapport with him.

We must examine for a moment the basic psychological condition of the patient. In the first place, he is inclined to be depressed as a result of the reality situation of his illness. If he is in hospital, there is the loss of emotional support of those normally close to the patient, of wife or husband or family. This in itself makes it likely that the patient's dependent needs are not fully satisfied. In addition to these factors, there is another very important matter. Any patient is likely to experience vague feelings of guilt. This applies not only to the psychiatric patient, but also to the patient suffering from organic illness. He asks himself, "Why should this have happened to me?" He ponders the question. The answer that keeps coming to him is that this illness must have come as a result of something he has done. He examines his past life. He thinks of his childhood masturbation, or other sexual experiences. He regrets it; and in a vague way it somehow comes to be associated in his mind with his present illness. Ill-defined thoughts of this nature are very common in patients with any type of illness. There are also the practical considerations. The patient thinks of home. He is not there to help. There is the loss of his wages. He feels he has let his family down. If the patient is the wife, she is inclined to think that her husband is not being cared for properly, or that her being away means that the children are neglected. These ideas add to the patient's vague feeling of guilt. In addition to this, illness and hospitalization are associated in his mind as the forerunners of death. There may also be pain, either organically determined pain, or the pain of mental distress. These factors operate to some degree with most patients. When asked directly about them, the patient almost invariably denies them; and they become known only through the indirect processes of psychotherapy. They contribute, in greater or less degree, to the psychological background of the patient's illness.

The occupational therapist establishes rapport with the patient, and starts him modelling. She has to show him how to do it. She gives him her time and her attention. This has meaning. To the patient in whom the above psychological factors are operating, it has very significant meaning. Her presence, her helping him, her being nice to him, are a symbolic expression of love. The patient does not consciously interpret the situation in this way. She is only the girl who helps him with the modelling. Nevertheless, the symbolic meaning of the behaviour of the occupational therapist has a deep effect on him. Through the means of the modelling, she offers symbolic love, and helps to fulfill his dependent needs. This, it would seem, is the principal means by which occupational therapy is effective in helping the patient.

In occupational therapy, modelling thus becomes a means by which symbolic love is offered to the patient. The student might easily raise the question, "Why have the modelling or the craft work? Would it not be easier for the girl to come and just talk with the patient?" This would seem simple enough, but psychological barriers arise which make it so difficult as to be impracticable. Either party may become inhibited in such a situation. Even if the therapist is able to maintain a conversation for conversation's sake, it is unlikely that the patient is equally gifted. The patient becomes tense and awkward, and soon the visit develops into an anxiety-producing situation which is the opposite of what is desired. This state of affairs does not arise in modelling, as there is an ever ready subject of conversation, and the fact that both parties use their hands means that pauses in the conversation pass unnoticed, and without embarrassment. In fact, the therapeutic value of occupational therapy increases as the therapist talks less and less, and relies more and more on doing the modelling with the patient. By this means, she allows full play of non-verbal communication and its unconscious symbolic influence on the patient.

Many institutions have hospital visitors who would help the patient by visiting him and talking with him. However, as a therapeutic weapon, these hospital visits are ineffective as compared with occupational therapy. It would seem that the absence of modelling, or craft work, or some activity with the patient, makes the operation of these symbolic mechanisms more difficult.

Modelling or craft work is also some protection against an overt erotic relationship developing between patient and occupational therapist. This, of course, would bring anxiety, and reality complications. It must be stressed that in occupational therapy it is the unconscious giving and acceptance of symbolic love which is effective, and not any overt erotic involvement with the patient. Modelling, with the opportunity for doing things together, gives full scope for these unconscious mechanisms.

MODELLING AS INTEGRATIVE THERAPY

We have seen how modelling is used in plastotherapy and hypnoplasty as a means of uncovering the patient's hidden conflicts. These conflicts are resolved in psychotherapy. There now comes a time when the search for unconscious material is at an end, and treatment enters the phase of reintegration of the patient's psychic processes. This comes as a stage in the treatment of any psychiatric illness, but it is particularly important with the patient who is recovering from schizophrenia, and with the introvert whose breakdown has been halted at the pre-psychotic stage.

The patient has been confusing the real and the unreal. He has been subject to uncontrolled thinking in which his phantasy runs wild, in which illusionary and hallucinatory perceptions mingle with reality. Recovery necessitates the re-establishment of order and control of the processes of thought. Modelling can be used toward this end.

At first the models are poorly controlled. They are badly executed. One idea may contaminate another. It may be that the patient is now fairly logical and controlled in his speech, but the modelling may still show the bizarre features characteristic of schizophrenia. The modelling is now used to help the patient to better control of his disorganized thought processes. The therapist comments about the model at a reality level. It may be that the patient has made a model of a human figure. "I think we can make it better. We must make both arms the same size. I think we can alter this leg to make it look more lifelike." This is a vastly different approach to the modelling from that which might have been used earlier in the patient's illness. The model of a human figure undoubtedly represents some person who is psychologically significant to the patient. In fact, from our previous work with the patient, it is likely that we can make a very good guess as to who it is. But now we do not question the patient about it. At this stage we are using the modelling solely for reintegration. Our whole attention is now focussed on control, logic and reality. We can proceed, and discuss ways of representing the human figure. In doing so, we deal with the problem of making a good likeness. In this way, we help the patient in his contact with reality. We avoid any discussion of the artistic qualities of the modelling, and we likewise avoid anything to do with the expression of abstract ideas. These matters pertain to a different use of modelling.

The therapist should always have a clear idea in his own mind as to the exact purpose for which he proposes to use modelling. It should not be allowed just to drift along, so that the form which the modelling takes is really determined by the patient.

In integrative therapy, the aim is to have the patient produce work of good craftsmanship. This requires controlled thinking, and good contact with the environment. The patient is encouraged to do work of better and better quality. This, of course, is the directly opposite approach to that used in plastotherapy, in which the expression of unconscious material is the important factor, and craftsmanship is of no consequence at all. Integrative therapy represents the coming out of a psychosis, and the return to reality.

Figure No. 190

When modelling is used as integrative therapy, the emphasis is on control and reality.

This plaque was made by a woman at the time when she was recovering from a severe psychosis, in which she had been quite out of touch with reality.

MODELLING AS RECREATIONAL THERAPY

There is quite another way in which modelling can be used to help the sick in mind. This is in recreational therapy. Modelling used as recreation has none of the drama and excitement of its use in the uncovering of psychological conflicts. Nevertheless, this kind of activity can do much to alleviate the suffering brought about by incarceration in mental institutions. Modelling, as recreational activity, can be used to divert the patient from the tedium of endless days of mental hospital existence. In this field, it helps the patient by filling in his time, and does something towards retarding the disintegrating effect of isolation. In this form of therapy, the meaning of the models is of no consequence. They can be ornamental or utilitarian; vases or ashtrays. It does not matter if they are mere copies. The only significant factor is the diversion of the patient.

This form of therapy is particularly suitable for patients who are likely to remain in hospital for some length of time, and who are having little or no active treatment. It is suitable for those whose illness has robbed them of drive and intellectual discrimination. They may fail to perceive the imperfections of the articles which they make; but for them the making of some simple object brings a sense of achievement which helps to restore their waning self-esteem.

Figure No. 191

A patient recovering from a long illness, fills in the time by making a comic figure of a sailor. The modelling in such a case has no direct therapeutic effect, other than providing a pleasant way of spending the day, and so offsetting the destructive effect of boredom from a long period of hospitalization.

MODELLING AS ART THERAPY

The present study is primarily concerned with the use of modelling as an aid in psychotherapy. Little consideration has been given to the artistic merits of the particular shapes created. However, there is a tendency among authors to describe the graphic and plastic projections of those disturbed in mind as art. Naumburg speaks of Schizophrenic Art and Psychoneurotic Art; Dax of Psychiatric Art; Reitman of Psychotic Art. Malraux refers to Lunatic Art; but he makes it quite clear that, in his opinion, it is not art at all. This interesting question, as to whether or not such projections should be known as art, must eventually be determined by the meaning which the individual gives to the word. It seems that some would regard any spontaneous expression of the unconscious as art, provided that it is expressed in a medium commonly used by artists. This would apply not only to the graphic and plastic arts, but would also bring the schizophrenic verbal expression of unconscious material into line with some modern poetry. Others, on the other hand, would maintain that to be known as art, these projections must have other qualities as well as being an expression of the unconscious mind.

Among the illustrations, the reader will find those which are intriguing because they are bizarre, but which have no line or form, or any aesthetic qualities which would lead one to consider them as art in the ordinarily accepted meaning of the term. But other models are shown that have qualities of form which are distinctly aesthetic. These aesthetic forms were often produced by persons who were equally disturbed in their minds, as those who produced bizarre and poorly integrated forms. From this point of view, schizophrenics may produce two classes of models. One type has aesthetic qualities of line and form, and has a close resemblance to modern surrealistic art. The other type arrests our attention only because it is bizarre. It lacks unity and cohesion. It looks like the work one would expect from a lunatic.

It seems strange that these bizarre, poorly integrated, lunatic productions should have such a capacity to demand the attention of both layman and psychiatrist. To say that such a model is interesting because it is bizarre is too superficial an explanation. There is something in the bizarre quality of these productions which compels our attention. This of course is occasioned by the fact that this type of model is a production of the unconscious. Without his being aware of it, the symbolism is perceived by the observer. It activates similar elements in his own unconscious. The outward manifestation of this process is simply that the observer finds the model intriguing because it is bizarre.

In these days of general sophistication and half-enlightenment in matters of psychological theory, many people critically examine any unusual shape, and make conscious efforts to interpret the different elements in terms of their own concept of symbolism. This again makes a model intriguing; but it is clearly quite a different process from the former, in which the symbolic appeal is completely outside the observer's awareness.

In view of these confusing factors, it would seem wise that the term "Art Therapy," should be used only when the artistic or aesthetic elements of plastic or graphic expression are the important factors in the therapeutic process.

When modelling is used as a form of art therapy, the whole emphasis is on the aesthetic qualities of the model. Meaning is ignored. Craftsmanship is stressed only in so far as it relates to the artistic merits of the production. The work can be orientated toward either reality or the abstract. The matter is discussed, not so much in cold logic, but rather in a way which will bring to the fore the patient's artistic feeling.

It is not altogether uncommon to find in the process of psychotherapy that the patient has an unsuspected sensitivity; that he has a potentiality to sensitive feeling which he himself never suspected. By judicious use of modelling, such a patient may be led to new values. The expression of artistic feeling in modelling may awake dormant elements of his personality. It may not only bring him to a wider interest in art, but may indirectly lead him to a fuller way of life.

By the use of modelling as art therapy, certain intelligent extroverts can be led to greater subjectivity; and so also others who have habitually denied their subjectivity as an unconscious defence against hurt.

With other patients, modelling can be used to fulfill a creative need. With some persons, this need to create is very real and very compelling. Many intelligent psychoneurotics and introvert personalities, who have little opportunity for sublimating this creative drive in their occupational and social life, can give direct expression of their creative need in modelling. This, with a little supportive psychotherapy, may stave off the feelings of restless nihilism with which these patients are so frequently beset.

INDEX

Index

muso mea